This book is full of pro
and teachers to facilitate children's learning

✪ How to handle temper tantrums, antisocial behaviour and aggression

✪ How to use Sound Therapy to overcome learning difficulties

✪ A simple, effective, affordable program for parents to use at home

✪ Help your children to settle down, sleep well and be calm and focussed

✪ Stimulate brain connections so listening and learning become easier

✪ Set your child up for good language skills and improve reading, writing and spelling

✪ Improve integration between the right and left brain hemispheres to achieve clear auditory laterality

✪ Learn of drug free, non-invasive methods to help children concentrate and learn

✪ Discover ways to make study and homework easy and fun

✪ How to create a nurturing, gentle sound-environment for your babies and children

✪ How to use sensory integration therapies

✪ How to assist development and integration of the senses including auditory, visual, tactile, movement and balance

✪ How to use movement and balance activities to improve proprioceptive and vestibular function

WHY AREN'T I LEARNING?

Listening is the key to overcoming learning difficulties

Rafaele Joudry

Cartoons: Allan Mackay

An essential guide for parents and professionals

Published in 2004 by
Sound Therapy International
92 Maloney St Rosebery
NSW 2018
Australia

National Library of Australia Cataloguing-in-Publication data:

Joudry, Rafaele, 1957
Why aren't I learning? : listening is the key to overcoming learning difficulties.
Bibliography.
Includes index.
ISBN 0 9579246 2 3.
1. Sound - Therapeutic use. 2. Learning.
3. Learning disabilities - Treatment.
4. Hyperactive children - Education. I. Title.
370.1523

Cartoons: Allan Mackay
Design and layout: Kathleen James
Cover design: Michelle Rajcany, M Design www.mdesign.net.au
Index: Jessica McGowan and Kathleen James
Printed by Ligare, Sydney

Contents

A mother's love; Fathers care too; A note on language; Why this
book?; Educational tools and Sound Therapy; Who this book is
for; Research partnership; Does my child need therapy?; Which
chapters should I read?; Living with a 'different' child; You
are not alone; Common behaviours; The sensory integration
premise; The behavioural view; The mechanistic view; The
integrative/organic view; Make up your own mind; Practical
action tips.

The ear; When does the foetus hear?; What does it sound like
in the womb?; Sonic Birth; High frequencies; Sing to your
baby; A mother who sings to her child; How is it that we speak?;
Practical action tips.

But my child is not deaf; Closing the ear; Listening; The
Tomatis effect; Speech; Ear; Hearing loss; Understanding; High
frequencies; Left brain Right brain; The elements of listening;
Practical action tips.

Introduction

Why aren't children learning?

Learning is the most important activity our children undertake in preparation for their lives as adults, when we hope they will be able to contribute to the community in ways which fulfil their potential. Yet today it seems that more and more children are beset by learning difficulties, which means they struggle and fail, where they should be progressing with natural ease. Teachers are dismayed at how to teach a class when several children with ADHD are making it impossible for anyone to concentrate.

Parents are anxious to see if their children perform to the required standards, and when they don't, are thrown into the desperate hunt for solutions, hoping they will find a way that their child can catch up to the normal level.

How is it affecting our children and their future?

When children cannot keep up with their peers, cannot handle the curriculum, cannot learn to read and write fluently, what future do they have? Even trades and manual careers today require the 'three R's. Not only are illiterate young people faced with bleak employment prospects, but their self-esteem suffers throughout their schooling and a vicious cycle is created which often leads to drug use, crime or psychological problems.

Recent decades have seen significant increases in neurodevelopmental disabilities, such as ADHD, autism and other problems which affect children's ability to learn. In the United States, three to five percent of children have ADHD, and youth visits to physicians for the disorder have increased ninety percent from 1989 to 1996 .[1] While these conditions are often blamed on genetic causes, a growing body of evidence points to environmental and chemical contributors to the changing patterns of childhood disease.[2] Thousands of synthetic chemicals are now part of our daily lives, and most of these have only been invented in the past fifty years. Over 85,000 synthetic chemical compounds are now registered for commercial use in EPA's Toxic Substances Control Act.[3] We are also seeing increasing rates of asthma, childhood cancers, and disorders of endocrine function and reproduction.

If, as a result, more and more children are finding it harder to think, concentrate and learn, what does this mean for the future capacity of our race? As more and more people have reduced brainpower, surely scholarly institutions, and then professional bodies and government policy, will be affected. This is a very grave problem for society!

How can it be resolved?

While it is essential that we, as a society, address the causes of the problem, parents meanwhile need support to deal with the enormous struggles of daily life with a learning-disabled child. Every possible remedial therapy and support system should be made available to parents to ease their burden, and to help their children regain their natural ability to learn with ease. We need to look to methods which are harmless and will not lead to further health problems or possible drug addiction. Parents need to be alerted to early signs of learning problems, to be aware of the resources they can access, and to know how they may be able to prevent learning problems from occurring in the first place. We need treatments which are easy and cost-effective to implement. These families are under enough strain without also having to pay out thousands of dollars for remedial programs. Government budgets are becoming more and more restricted, so solutions must be cost-effective. We need to look to prevention, which is always cheaper than cure. Then our social resources can be directed, instead, towards improving our overall standard of education.

What must be done to find solutions?

Throughout recent history a number of inspired doctors and other practitioners have made links between various fields of endeavour, and have come up with methods which restore natural function and ability to the parts of the brain and the senses where they are needed. One of the methods which most effectively addresses the issues of integration and function to assist learning is Sound Therapy, based on the work of Dr Alfred Tomatis.

Brilliant in his time, Tomatis did not fully understand how his method worked. Only now, with more advanced neurological knowledge, are we truly beginning to understand the mysteries of the inner ear system and how integral it is to our ability to learn. As we follow this path, mysteries are revealed which explain many areas of functioning — perception, expression, thinking and being. Sound Therapy opens the curtain which other approaches to learning leave drawn.

This book is about the rich and intricate connection between the ear and learning. In it we explore the different functions of the ear including:

- Hearing, balance, spatial orientation and the ear's role in sensory integration.
- The ear's ability to transform the vibrations we call 'sound' into meaningful and beneficial stimuli.
- The role of the ear in prenatal, developmental neurology.

- The role of the ear in relation to language, evolving consciousness, the sense of the 'other', and the early budding of our desire to communicate.

All our senses — sight, touch, smell, taste, balance, movement, internal body-awareness and hearing — play an essential role in learning. We will look at how ear function is interlocked with, and fundamental to, our other senses and the whole, marvellous learning process.

Addressing the correct development and integration of the senses is a natural and supportive way to improve functioning and learning capacity for all children. Bringing this awareness into our child-care and education systems could serve to prevent a great many problems from developing in the first place. Therefore I hope that this information will be used, for prevention, by all families who wish to help their children be the best they can be.

On a practical day-to-day level, the book gives easy action tips and an understanding of many resources which parents or practitioners will be able to access easily in their community, or apply themselves in homes and practices.

How to get the most out of this book

If you are looking for a thorough understanding of the learning difficulties field as it relates to sensory integration, then reading the whole book will give you that in-depth appreciation. If, on the other hand, you are a busy practitioner or a parent with no time for yourself, you may want to use the book more as a reference guide. The index at the back, or the table of contents at the front, will guide you to the pages which relate specifically to your child's condition. Chapter 4 'Sound Therapy,' explains how Sound Therapy may benefit each type of learning or developmental difficulty. Chapter 7 'Not another label,' has more general background information on each condition. The checklist table on page 9 in Chapter 1 will help you work out which conditions may be relevant to your child. If you are feeling despair that nothing will help your child, dip into the inspiring 'real life' experiences in Chapter 8. Learn how other families, with problems ranging from mild to severe, have been delighted by rapid and unexpected improvements. Also, check out the boxes at the end of each chapter for practical ideas which you can start applying today to help your child adjust and to make life easier.

See references overleaf

References

1 Goldman LS, Genel M, Bezman RJ, Slanetz PJ. 'Diagnosis and treatment of attention-deficit/hyperactivity disorder in children and adolescents.' Council on Scientific Affairs, American Medical Association. *JAMA* 1998; 279:1100-7.

LeFever GB, Dawson KV, Morrow AL. 'The extent of drug therapy for Attention Deficit-Hyperactivity Disorder among children in public schools'. *Am J Pub Health*. 1999; 89:1359-1364.

Elia J, Ambrosini PJ, Rapoport JL. Treatment of attention-deficit-hyperactivity disorder. *NEJM* 1999; 340:780-788.

2 Needleman HL, Gunnoe C, Leviton A, Peresie H, Maher C, Barret P. 'Deficits in psychological and classroom performance of children with elevated dentine lead levels.' *N Engl J Med*. 1979; 300:689-695.

Patandin S, Lanting CI, Mulder PG, Boersma ER, Sauer PJ, Weisglas-Kuperus N. 'Effects of environmental exposure to polychlorinated biphenyls and dioxins on cognitive abilities in Dutch children at 42 months of age'. *J Pediatr* 1999; 134:33-41.

Prevalence of Autism in Brick Township, New Jersey, 1998: Community Report. CDC: April 2000.

Hilary, E. *Children of a Toxic Harvest*. Melbourne: Lothian, 1997.

3 Goldman L.R, and Koduru S.H. 'Chemicals in the environment and developmental toxicity to children: A public health and policy perspective.' *Environ Health Research;* 2000 108 (Suppl 3): 443-448.

Acknowledgements

In writing this book, more than ever before, I have had a sense of the enormous support of the team behind me. Without them, the work would be not only impossible but also of no relevance. The team extends from my business partner and general manager, through the rest of the head office staff at Sound Therapy International, to our network of several hundred independent distributors — and all the parents and practitioners who use Sound Therapy in their practices and families. And finally, to the actual production team for the book. In particular I wish to thank Janine Mason for coming up with the title, Catherine Bull for assisting with interviews and distributor listings, and all those who shared their personal stories in letters or interviews; and those who shared their professional perspectives, including Tara Ellis, Dominique Oyston, Julia Dive, Helen Milbourne, Daniel Danusa, Sue Larter, Jeanette Mackay, Hilary Peart, Ian Patterson and Miguel Olmos Sanchez. I am grateful to the distributors who read the manuscript and gave me feedback on its professional integrity — in particular Justus Lewis, for her insightful comments. I am also greatly indebted to my editor, Amanda Moriarty, whose meticulous passion for perfection, and willingness to work around the clock to fit my tight deadline have made the book so much more readable. I wish to thank Jessica McGowan for her meticulous final proofreading and indexing and my graphic artists — Michelle Rajcany, for the enchanting cover design; Kathy James for the handsome page layout, and Allan Mackay, for the delightful cartoons — all done to incredibly tight deadlines.
My printer, Ligare, my publicist, Reyna Matthes and my distributor, Gary Allen, also deserve a mention, for they are all crucial links in the chain for getting a book from my desk into the reader's hands. Finally, I express my heartfelt gratitude to my business partner, Helen Walden, who managed everything else in my life and my business for two months while I worked seven days straight, and who also read the manuscript and gave perceptive and essential pointers for improvement throughout.

About the author

Rafaele Joudry was educated in England and Canada where she completed a Bachelor of Social Work before emigrating to Australia. A strong interest in learning and child development fuelled her work in preschool education and family services before she founded Sound Therapy International in 1989. She has since dedicated herself to research and public education on the subject of child development, environmental health and ear/brain function. As a leading Australian speaker and author she pioneered the groundbreaking technology of Sound Therapy, which she has brought to thousands of families around the world.

Since the release of her first two books: *Sound Therapy: Music to Recharge your Brain* (1999) and *Triumph Over Tinnitus* (2001) and her booklet *Listening Helps Learning,* her speaking engagements to self-help groups and conferences have numbered well over 500. She has been featured on the ABC, Channel 9 TV and dozens of radio programs nationally. She also co-ordinates a team of clinically-based researchers to further advance knowledge of how Sound Therapy benefits brain function and learning.

This latest book, focussing on easy, practical, non-invasive treatments, responds to a growing need from families to address an array of learning and developmental disorders. Rafaele has created a new compilation of cutting edge resources which can help restore children's learning abilities by enhancing sensory integration.

Chapter I

NOT ANOTHER TANTRUM !

Sometimes, being a mother is like skating on ice while you juggle eggs and blow bubbles — all at the same time. You need to have the patience of a saint, the organising skills of a CEO, the negotiating skills of an ambassador and the ability to selflessly put your own needs to one side for twenty years — or at least until they get their driver's licence. And that's just for mums with average children. What about the mums whose children have special needs, such as those with autism, Asperger's, ADHD, Down syndrome, dyslexia or other learning or developmental difficulties?

Mums make great jugglers

A mother's love

The joyous truth about mothers is that in spite of all these trying moments, no matter what struggles the child may have through life, the mother nearly always sees beyond them and loves the essence of that child. This gift of unconditional love is the most precious thing any child can receive.

Mums give unconditional love

Having been a foster parent, a preschool teacher, a community organiser and then a health educator working with parents for many years, I have the greatest respect for mothers, whose work is drastically under-recognised by our society.

Fathers care too

Kids need a Dad too Many fathers are now starting to take on more parenting responsibility, a move which is to be applauded for its benefits to the mother, the child and the father himself. The love of a father is also crucial to a child's well-being, and all children throughout life continue to need their father's love and approval. A father who can demonstrate these, gives his child a key to self-fulfilment for which there is no substitute.

Throughout this book, I usually refer to the mother as the primary caregiver. I am aware that there are exceptions to this norm, particularly in the case of single fathers. For all those 'Mr Mums' who are reading this book, please take for yourselves this acknowledgement of the 'mother's role.'

A note on language

To avoid clumsiness of language, I have in some examples, referred to the child either as 'he' or 'she' interchangeably. Please know that each example is meant to refer equally to either sex.

Why this book?

Babies arrive helpless When children enter this world they have no say in shaping the environment they come into. The values, food, family customs, education, entertainment, advertising and health care they receive, are all decided by those of us who came before. A child is a clean slate on which we write our successes or our failures. We adults who have created the social order thereby become one hundred percent responsible for the well-being of the new arrivals, until they can fend for themselves and begin to cast their votes and influence society. When I see some of the things that children have to deal with today, I feel compelled to pitch my effort into helping to create a more welcoming environment for them.

Let's give each baby a fair go The human brain is a miracle of complex wiring for sensory appreciation, intelligence, emotion and creative endeavour. Each newborn baby is an amazing gift — a whole new human life, who might dream and search, become and achieve so much. How can we ensure that each child does have the opportunity to reach his true potential?

A special education

My own educational background is unusual, for my parents chose to educate me, and my sisters, at home. They did this because they valued education so much that they did not want our opportunities spoiled by the rigid structure and possible insensitivity of the school system. Their own experiences of school had not been positive, and they did not want to risk sending us into an environment that could destroy our love of learning. Hence, my childhood was extremely unstructured. We were given no curriculum, no exams, and no expectations, except that we be creative and happy. The absence of not only school but also television, and the provision of many miles of countryside in which to roam free, certainly made this easier.

My parents hated school

I had a great deal of time to think about what I wanted to learn, how I wanted to learn it, and to organise that learning for myself. I created my own structure when I was fifteen. I spent the mornings teaching my younger sister and the afternoons studying French, history, maths and English with my parents, who I had organised into a roster that suited my day. What was important was that I learned how to seek out information that truly interested me.

I organised my own school

This lead me, in my later teens, to attend a college based on principles of humanistic education, where it was expected that in any learning endeavour, the emotions must be involved for the interest to be fully engaged. Many of the students rebelled against this, thinking it was all too contrived and precious. They just wanted to be given a course to study! I thrived, as it was a natural continuance of my early experience, only this time I had two hundred other teenagers to share it with.

How children learn

I became fascinated by open questions about how learning happens: what goes on with attention, desire, memory and lateral thinking to allow us to learn best? I studied the work of the educational radical, John Holt, author of *How Children Learn* and *Freedom and Beyond?*[1] I loved his work because he looks at the world from the point of view of the child, and shares very thought provoking views on what really helps children to learn. I worked in early childhood education for a few years to test out my ideas, and was rewarded with the delightful ability of four-year-olds to

I asked, 'How do children really learn?'

3

digest vast amounts of information — and then demand more with their insatiable 'why?'

The differences in my pre-school group were fascinating, and it has taken another two decades to understand what was going on for some of these children. There was one little boy who could not mix in or socialise, but would tease and taunt and act the fool. The other parents asked me to say something to his mother, which I fumblingly tried to do. I remember her saying how he would sleep for twelve or fourteen hours if they let him. I don't know what difficulties he was struggling with. Today he would probably be labelled ADHD, but I suspect he had a problem with sensory integration. Then there was the little girl who hated to touch anything that might get her dirty, who cried if anything got on her hands or her dress. Yet when I set up water play she loved it so much she went home soaking wet every week, until her mother insisted that we get rid of the water tub. She may have had an over-sensitivity to tactile stimulation, or a vestibular disorder, which no one picked up. This would hold her apart from her classmates throughout her schooling, making her feel separate, afraid, and somewhat limited in life. I am glad that, at least for a few weeks, she had the chance to get physically involved in a stimulating sensory activity that may have helped boost her neural development at the age of three.

Some kids are not comfortable in the world

Perhaps because I had such wide ranging opportunities in my childhood, my passion has always been to give people a chance to explore more of who they are, to broach new learning frontiers, so that they might become unique and whole.

Why Sound Therapy?

Later, I chose to pursue community development and health education; and finally, Sound Therapy, as I found this offered the best way for me to make a difference to the most people.

Sound Therapy made my mother's life easier

Our family story, how my mother Patricia Joudry and I became in-volved in Sound Therapy, is told in more detail in our other two books: *Sound Therapy: Music to Recharge your Brain* and *Triumph Over Tinnitus*. I introduced my mother to Sound Therapy when we were living in Canada, because she had a peculiar problem where she could not concentrate on conversation in a noisy room. I heard of

Sound Therapy, a treatment program being used in Paris, which improved ear function and auditory discrimination. She was able to get the treatment in Montreal and it fixed her hearing problems as well as her chronic insomnia, exhaustion, techno-phobia and writer's block. This recovery made an enormous difference to her creative output, her social life and her general coping skills. She continued to use and benefit from Sound Therapy for the rest of her life. Wishing to share the great benefits she had received, she enlisted the help of some Canadian Benedictine monks who helped her to develop the portable Sound Therapy program which is now known as the 'Joudry method.' Fifteen years later we conceived of an international service network which became Sound Therapy International, and which I have continued to develop and operate from Sydney, Australia. With several hundred practitioners now recommending the method, it is on its way to becoming a mainstream treatment to assist children to learn.

A powerful tool for change

Sound Therapy uses music, that has been filtered in a special way, to stimulate the ear and brain. It is a powerful tool, going far beyond music therapy, for it can restore brain function and enhance learning at any stage of life. However, because of the way brain pathways are built, it is a fundamental fact that the earlier an intervention is given, the greater will be its effect. The mother listening prenatally will perhaps help the child more than anything. A child listening in the first weeks or months will have more impact than listening at age three; but listening at four is again so much more powerful than listening at eight or ten or twelve. Yet, because of the amazing resilience and plasticity of the brain, this is doesn't mean that the seventeen-year-old or the thirty-year-old will not profit. In fact even the ninety-year-old usually notices a significant advantage from the therapy. Just like education, Sound Therapy is beneficial at any stage of life.

A baby's brain is more flexible

When a child is growing and learning, each year, month and day are momentous opportunities for a foundation of joy and knowledge to be laid down. My aim in this book is to give life-enhancing tips to parents to help make the journey easier and more rewarding for themselves and the child. All children have a tremendous capacity to

All children learn better with help

5

learn, whether they are gifted children, of average ability, or specially challenged. The tools in this book are life-enhancing and beneficial to all children, not just those with learning disabilities. I believe that all parents will find ideas and techniques in these pages to enrich the learning and joy in their families.

Educational tools and Sound Therapy

Sound is the best way to help learning

This book is largely an in-depth exploration of adding sound, as an educational and therapeutic tool, to the smorgasbord of treatments offered today to enhance learning. This range includes private tutoring, remedial education, sensory motor (movement) activities, speech therapy, behaviour management, diet, supplementation and medication. Sound Therapy is the least known and least explored therapy to be added to this list, and is currently only included in a small number of multi-treatment clinics and referral networks. It is however a vital part of assisting learning and brain development.

Sound Therapy is a listening program that was researched and developed by the pioneering French ear specialist, Dr Alfred Tomatis. It uses specially filtered classical music to stimulate the ear and enhance brain development. It is an easy and highly effective way to improve auditory processing, language development, learning and behaviour. It has been found effective in speeding and enhancing language skills for all children. It has also frequently proved beneficial for children with special needs such as ADHD, Down syndrome, autism spectrum disorders and speech problems.

The particular benefits of sound therapy:

- It provides direct brain stimulation through the auditory sense
- It can correct many language problems early, before schooling becomes a problem
- It enhances and builds brain connections
- It improves sensory integration by activating the cerebellum
- It improves language skills by stimulating the auditory cortex
- It improves ear function and reduces ear infections

- It enhances other forms of remedial learning and sensory treatment
- It is simple and easy to use
- It is cost effective
- It can be used at home or in schools
- It is beneficial for all children, whether of average ability, specially gifted, or learning disabled

Who this book is for

Bright children and slow children need help

This book is meant for parents, teachers and child care workers, and specialists in learning difficulties who are endeavouring to help children develop their full potential. It is meant for those working with troubled, developmentally challenged children. However, it is not exclusively about children with special needs. It will also be of relevance and interest to those working with average children, or children with exceptional talents and abilities. Some parents reading this book may have children who are showing just noticeable signs that something may be a little amiss with their development. In this book I hope you will find the clues to what may be affecting your children, and how you can help them.

It is about how you as parents, and we as a society, can provide the best opportunities and support for the development of our children's brains.

As a parent, this book will give you practical, easy to use tools which will make your life easier; and your children happier, more focussed, more intelligent and easier to manage — preferably without using medication.

Research partnership

We support research to help more families

At Sound Therapy International, in our years of public education and provision of therapeutic programs to families, the one thing that has become increasingly clear is that prevention is better than cure. One of the aims of our program is to help families identify problems early; to identify possible contributors to children's developmental difficulties, and avoid or remove them from our environment. We also aim to bring affordable, family-based solutions to as many children as possible.

All this work needs to be backed up by evidence-based scientific research and information. To help us provide the necessary knowledge background to achieve these aims, we have formed a partnership with the Shining Star Research Foundation. The aims of the foundation are to support research to identify important early intervention to assist sensory integration. This is with the ultimate goal of enabling each child to become a brilliant, unique and fulfilled individual—a 'shining star'. A percentage of profits from the sale of this book goes to Shining Star Research Foundation.

Does my child need therapy?

The sooner your child gets help, the better

As parents, it is hard to face the thought that our children may have some kind of developmental disorder. More than anything, we want our children to be healthy, talented and brilliant reflections of ourselves. However, the fact is that many children today are dealing with new environmental challenges, and many do have special needs. The sooner those needs are identified and catered for, the more likely it is that our children will reach their true potential.

Which chapters should I read?

If you are pressed for time and do not want to read through the whole book, the following table is a quick guide to help you find out which chapters may be most relevant to your child. Check which 'descriptive traits' apply to your child, to help you locate the relevant sections more quickly. Bear in mind that many of these symptoms will overlap between different conditions. This is just a rough guide to direct you to further reading. At the end of most chapters you will find practical action tips, as a quick reference to some of the ideas in the chapter that you can use with your family.

Terminology	Descriptive traits	More back-ground info	Treatment options
Auditory processing disorder Listening problem CAPD (central auditory processing disorder) Dyslexia	• History of ear infections • Difficulty in using language and explaining herself/himself in words • Poor at following or remembering instructions • Slow to develop intelligible speech • Difficulty in reading aloud • Lacks response to human speech, yet responds to environmental sounds • Letter and word reversals—'d' for 'b', 'tip' for 'pit' • Difficulty pronouncing words, i.e., 'busgetti' for 'spaghetti', • Difficulty with rhyming • Slow to learn the connection between letters and sounds. • May have difficulty telling and/or retelling a story in the correct sequence. • Lack of clear laterality (hand preference) by the age of four or five.	**Chapter 4** Sound Therapy **Chapter7** Not another label	**Chapter 4** Sound Therapy
Visual processing disorder Dyslexia	Eyesight is normal but seems to have trouble with: • Reading and writing • Focusing or eye tracking • Blurred or fluctuating vision • Eye turn or lazy eye • Double vision • Eyestrain or fatigue • Reduced peripheral vision • Glare or light sensitivity • Night vision problems	**Chapter 6** We move with our ears	**Chapter 4** Sound Therapy **Chapter 6** We move with our ears
ADHD Attention Deficit and Hyperactivity Disorder: Inattentive (ADD) Hyperactive/ Impulsive (ADHD)	• Daydreams a lot • Has difficulty paying attention • Seems not to listen • Fails to finish schoolwork or tasks • Avoids tasks which require attention, such as schoolwork • Is easily distracted and forgetful • Fidgets, squirms, can't sit still • Runs about or climbs excessively • Is 'on the go' or acts as if 'driven by a motor' • Talks excessively • Plays the class clown • Blurts out answers • Has difficulty awaiting turn • Interrupts others	**Chapter 7** Not another label	**Chapter 4** Sound Therapy
	Continued overleaf		

Autism spectrum disorders Autism Asperger's Childhood disintegrative disorder Retts disorder	• Insistence on sameness; resistance to change • Uses gestures or pointing instead of words • Repeating words or phrases in place of normal, responsive language • Prefers to be alone; aloof manner • Difficulty in mixing with others • May not want to cuddle or be cuddled • Little or no eye contact • Unresponsive to normal teaching methods • Sustained odd play such as spinning, rocking • Inappropriate attachments to objects • Apparent over-sensitivity or under-sensitivity to pain • No real fears of danger • Uneven gross/fine motor skills • Not responsive to verbal cues; acts as if deaf, although hearing tests in normal range	**Chapter 7** Not another label	**Chapter 4** Sound Therapy
Sensory integration disorder Tactile Vestibular Proprioceptive	• Avoids touching and being touched • Overreacts to light stimulation, being accidentally brushed against or contact of clothing • Or seeks out physical contact, constantly touching, chewing or rubbing up against things • Avoids moving and overreacts to being moved unexpectedly • Extreme sensitivity to losing balance or becoming dizzy • Avoids running, climbing, swinging • Gets travelsick in cars or lifts • Seems rigid, uncoordinated • Has a strong dislike and intolerance of certain food textures such as lumpy foods or slimy foods • Has a strong reaction to certain odours or may constantly sniff people, food and objects • Slumps a lot and has very poor posture • Poor muscle tone: very loose and floppy or tense and rigid • Poor eye-hand co-ordination • Hates chewing	**Chapter 6** We move with our ears	**Chapter 4** Sound Therapy **Chapter 6** We move with our ears
Food intolerance Allergies Chemical sensitivity	• Sugar craving or other cravings • Sometimes 'vagues out', can't concentrate • Hyperactive • Emotional reactivity • Recurrent illness, sinus/ear infections	**Chapter 9** What's this on my plate?	**Chapter 9** What's this on my plate?

Weakened immunity Viral infections Toxic overload Brain damage	• Shows signs of distress, fretfulness, after vaccination • Increased ear or sinus infections • Does not babble or coo by 12 months • Does not gesture (point, wave, grasp) by 12 months • Does not say single words by 16 months • Does not say two-word phrases by 24 months • Loses any already acquired language or social skill at any age.	Chapter 9 What's this on my plate?	Chapter 9 What's this on my plate?
Other specific conditions: Cerebral palsy Down syndrome Fragile X syndrome Epilepsy	Traits are specific to each condition. See **Chapter 7**	Chapter 7 Not another label	Chapter 4 Sound Therapy Chapter 6 We move with our ears Chapter 9 What's this on my plate?

Living with a 'different' child

Whether you have a child who is diagnosed with ADHD or learning difficulties or sensory integration disorder or autism, all of these conditions lead to behavioural problems. Do you recognise any moments from this real account of one mum's day with two challenging children?

'When one day bleeds into another and you haven't been to sleep 'til 2 am, you get up feeling like a walking zombie. You were up four times in the night to screaming nightmares or bedwetting. Then the kids are up again at 7 am and you stagger out, bleary-eyed, to start making their breakfast, grabbing the tea towel off Jared before he pulls all the glasses onto the floor.

Half asleep, you have to feed them and wrestle their clothes on, while trying to stop them trashing the house, then make sure they don't kill each other before you get them into the car.

Even going to the toilet gives no respite with the little one hanging onto your knees and the eldest wanting a hug when you'd like a quiet moment.

You come back to the kitchen and Jared is pulling things out of the cupboards—any that don't have a safety catch are fair game. He pulls everything out just for fun. Then while you're putting those things back in, he pulls a chair over to get up to the high cupboards and drops the picnic basket on his brother's head. More screaming.

You put him out in the yard so you can think to get their breakfast organised. He finds some sticks in the yard and starts playing at being Buzz Lightyear or some knight in shining armour swinging a stick around pretending it's his sword. When you open the door to let him in, he pokes you in the eye with it. As you sit down to feed the baby with a damp cloth on your eye, the baby throws his spoon at Jared so Jared whacks him and he cries. Then you tell Jared off for hurting the baby and he starts crying too, so you can't hear yourself think. Not much breakfast is being eaten!

You finally get all their bags organised, bundle them into the car, drive to Day Care, do the shopping, and it's 2 pm before you get anything to eat. Today was the first time in six months that you have taken him to Day Care because he's been behaving better and you think that surely now he'll fit in OK. You sure need a break! Doing the shopping was a breeze with only the baby. You are finally sitting down to a cup of tea when the phone rings. It's Day Care! The supervisor says, through loud howling in the background, "Could you please come and get your son. He is uncontrollable and we simply cannot cope with his violence towards the other children."

You choke back the tears of exhaustion and frustration. Gritting your teeth you say, "I'll be there soon," thinking to yourself, "how is it — I manage him twenty four hours a day; these are trained professionals and they cannot handle him even for two hours!" You have seen before how, in any conflict, your son gets blamed and the other children are always assumed to be perfect angels. A child with ADHD has special needs, but he isn't given a fighting chance.

Wherever you go you see lots of people looking and thinking what a bad parent you are. When you turn up at Day Care you hear two different kids say, "There's that naughty little boy". "All he needs is a good smack". Labelled naughty before he goes in the door, what chance has he got of forming good relationships?

Finally Dad gets home and you sit down for dinner, hoping for a few peaceful minutes to eat. Next thing, the baby pulls a hot pot of curry over himself. He was sitting on Dad's lap next to the counter and grabbed the cord to the electric frying pan, dragged it towards him in one gesture and the curry went all over him. So it's off to the hospital instead of sitting down to dinner, both blaming yourselves, "why weren't we more careful?" But it's impossible to be careful enough with octopus arms everywhere and that insatiable impulse to reach and grab, far beyond the level of the average child.

The only break you get is on a Saturday, when once Dad thinks he can take Jared to the shops. But that doesn't last long. While Dad is reading the list and trying to find the items, Jared grabs a packet of chips and runs out of the store and up the street. Dad follows in hot pursuit. Jared crawls under a parked car so he can't be caught and calls out "na-na, na-na-na you ca-an't get me!" Dad arrives home cranky and hands Jared over ranting, "Take him would you I've had enough!" he carries on, "We *have* to do something — this is *ridiculous!*" Dad does not take Jared to the shops any more.

You know very well how hard it is shopping with Jared. One day you lost him in the supermarket for forty minutes. You were pulling your hair out, frantic with every story going through your head about how it only takes two seconds for a child to be abducted, not daring to wonder, has he been picked up by a paedophile? Finally, after forty minutes of desperate searching, you found him sleeping in somebody else's pram! Then there was the day he put the dog in the drier, set the kitchen alight, drove the car out into the street, threw the cat into the fan, and drove his bike headlong into a stone wall.

If you can get them to sleep before 12 pm you're doing well. And then it starts all over again. But still you love them more then anything.'

For more detail on children with a range of special needs and how to help them, see Chapter 7: *Not another label!*

You are not alone

Many mothers have confessed that they have come very close to 'losing it' with their learning-disabled children. Sleep deprivation, combined with the need to be constantly vigilant (often into the late evening), the difficulty of getting breaks because baby sitters and child-care centres can't cope, constant trouble at school — all add up to an overwhelmingly stressful life. Motherhood is not a job

It's hard not to 'lose it' when you have a wild child

13

you can just resign from! If the mother is at home with the children it is usually impossible to achieve anything around the house, so her partner frequently comes home to chaos, the cooking and shopping not done, and a wife desperately needing a break. These stresses can, and often do, lead to conflict in marital relationships.

If you identify with these scenarios, be assured that there is help available. Thousands of other parents daily face the same challenges, and a broad network of specialist practitioners and researchers is devoted to finding solutions. In the chapters that follow, you will find many answers to explain why children behave like this and what can be done to help them.

Common behaviours

Some of the common difficult behaviours in children with ADHD and other learning and developmental disorders are:
- irritability
- poor concentration
- impulsivity
- unreasonableness
- restlessness
- argumentativeness
- tantrums
- uncontrollability
- aggression
- excitability
- unhappiness
- short attention span
- lack of perseverance
- unwillingness to co-operate
- restless sleep and trouble settling to sleep
- disruptiveness and hyperactivity

as well as poor school work including:
- reversal of letters
- poor reading ability, spelling and maths
- fear of school
- inability to make friends

These are often accompanied by health problems such as:
- sore throats
- tonsillitis
- bronchitis

- colds
- bed-wetting
- urinary tract infections
- constipation and diarrhoea
- stomach pain
- leg pain and joint pain
- ear infections
- twitching
- eczema and rashes

How can all this be addressed?

For parents overwhelmed with the daily rigours of just coping, it is hard to find help. When help is offered, parents often accept what they are told and are willing to try anything, but very mixed advice may be given by different sectors of the community. How can you decipher which is the most relevant, supportive and useful avenue to follow? I will now explore the different philosophies which underpin various views on the causes and treatments of learning difficulties. I hope this will assist you, the parent, in choosing which methods are best for you.

Whose advice should you take?

The sensory integration premise

The premise of this book is that almost all learning and developmental problems can be most effectively addressed with sensory integration therapies. These may include Sound Therapy, vision therapy, and tactile, movement and balance activities. Probably the most fundamental and intrinsic of the sense organs to sensory integration is the ear, housing as it does the organs of both hearing and balance.

A healthy brain needs all the senses to work together

However, this view is relatively new and unfamiliar to many parents and practitioners. The rest of this book will examine the evidence to support this premise, and how it differs to the conventional views.

I will explore three different viewpoints which I will call 'Behavioural', 'Mechanistic' and 'Integrative.'

The basic premise of the Behavioural approach is that the problem is caused by poor parenting or the wrong sort of education. The child is not learning simply because he needs a different sort of instruction. The solution offered is: remedial instruction programs, parenting classes and more intensive study hours for the child.

The Mechanistic approach is a reductionist view that seeks to identify the specific fault in the way the brain functions, and then supply the missing element to compensate for that fault. If certain neurotransmitters are not being produced, a drug is administered to replace those chemicals. Specific measurement is taken only of the identified problem and how the intervention affects it. Little attention is paid to side effects or larger social impacts.

Then there is the Integrative approach. This is based on a philosophy of wholism which sees the brain as a self-healing, regenerating system that can effect its own repair if given the right sensory stimulation. Rather than isolating one specific problem or deficit, this approach looks for all the linkages between different areas which need improvement, and heals by increasing interconnections in the nervous system.

Let us look now in a little more depth at the assumptions and implications of each of these views.

The behavioural view

Some people say the kids are just badly behaved

This view says the child would do well if he or she tried harder, the educational system needs to change, and that reward and punishment behaviour modification techniques work best. We need to measure and improve teacher effectiveness and provide special instruction to those children who can't learn in the classroom.

'It's just poor parenting'

Parents do what they have to do to cope

The behavioural perspective tends to focus on mistakes made by parents and teachers. If you see a lot of bad parents trying to manage ADHD children it is easy to assume that the parents are the problem, that if only they didn't give in to the child, or if they gave him more love or firmer boundaries or more stimulation, he would behave differently. Poor parenting certainly can exacerbate ADHD, but it is not the cause. Because ADHD children are so stressful to manage, many parents, finding after some years that they cannot solve the problem through discipline, back off and choose a more peaceful path. It is easy, then, for an unfamiliar observer to jump to the conclusion that the lack of discipline is the cause of the problem, when what they are seeing is just the coping mechanism of the parent.

The very best, most patient, most aware parents in the world may find they have an ADHD child, and some of the worst parents have children who do not suffer from the problem. So, to blame the condition on poor parenting is a superficial and unsatisfactory response. Even if there is a statistical correlation between poor parenting and ADHD, this does not prove that the one caused the other.

In fact, a study done by researchers Dr Barkley and Dr Cunningham in 1980 showed that, rather than poor parenting causing ADHD, the hyperactive behaviour prompts poor parenting habits. When the child's behaviour improved with drug treatment, the mother's responses changed for the better.[2, 3]

'They need different ways of teaching'

ADHD children learn differently. They do not conform well, or respond well to traditional curricula. They are often bright, get bored easily, rebel and do their own thing, and may turn out to be quite brilliant and talented later in life. Fortunately, educational experts are finding ways to teach ADHD children more effectively by using multi-sensory stimulation, letting the learner play a more active role in her education and by following her interests rather than a set curriculum. These innovations are excellent and it would be wonderful if they were applied to the whole educational system. However, they are more labour intensive, so this is unlikely.

Should schools change so ADHD kids can learn?

It is advantageous for ADHD children to be seen as different, rather than disabled, and this attitude comes from a position of truly wishing to help and facilitate the growth of the individual. However, we are fooling ourselves when we suggest that ADHD is not a disorder. Although we can accommodate these children with better resources and special tutoring, the fact is that life is more difficult for them, and they are limited in some of their capacities to plan, organise and enact their will in an orderly way upon the world. These approaches are effective coping strategies, but they do not address or remedy the underlying problem, which is that these children are not able to focus their attention the way they should.

The mechanistic view

Some people say the cause is genetic

This view says that the child is not learning due to a genetic disorder which causes the brain to malfunction unless given certain drugs. Malfunctions can be isolated and compensated for. Until we can fix the gene problem, the best course is to use chemical stimulants to help the brain to function better. There is no viable alternative and this is an easy and effective treatment. Parents have a right to a peaceful home life, and the child has a right to be given a substance that will allow him to concentrate and learn.

'It can be easily fixed with a drug'

Drugs are the easiest treatment

Drugs give an apparently quick fix, but parents choosing this option may not have anticipated the possible dangers of drug therapy. Because drugs are in most cases wholly geared towards treating the symptoms, by suppressing the symptoms in this way we make it less likely that we will ever identify and treat the underlying causes of the problem.[4]

Drug treatments are popular with many consumers today because they want a 'quick fix'. We are used to an 'instant' culture where anything can be fixed with a machine or a pill. Overstressed parents are particularly in need of quick, effective solutions when dealing with overactive, exhausting kids. Hence, they are receptive to, and willing to accept, the medical approach of stamping out the symptoms with drugs. The trouble with this type of 'quick fix', though, is that in the long term it usually makes the problem worse. The generation that is growing up on drugs now, for example, will be even less able to provide their children with healthy immune systems, or an environment to support them.

'There is nothing wrong with giving kids psych drugs'

In short term drug use there is noticeable improvement in about 80% of cases.[5] What is alarming is the rate of increase at which medication is being given to our children. An article in the *Journal of the American Academy of Child and Adolescent Psychology* quotes the incidence of ADHD at 3%. The rate of medication has doubled every two years since 1971.[6]

Abuses have been revealed which include incidents of children snorting Ritalin, teachers and pharmacists stealing it, and parents selling it. An expert from the Ohio State Pharmacy Board, Tim Benedick, said on an ABC 20/20 show, 'Ritalin is highly addictive. It is speed.'[7] While these examples are from the US, other countries generally follow the same trends to a lesser degree.

Ritalin has been nicknamed 'paediatric cocaine.' It is very similar to cocaine in its chemical make-up, and both drugs use the same receptor site in the brain. They create the same 'high' and are used interchangeably in medical research. We are prescribing drugs very similar to cocaine to children as young as three.[8] Is it any wonder we have a drug problem? Are we teaching our children that drugs are the answer to any problem? It is seen as acceptable because a doctor is involved. But who is to say that doctors have infallible judgement on these matters, especially when their training and ongoing professional pressure teaches them, too, to solve so many problems with a drug prescription?

Do we want to give the message that drugs solve problems?

The integrative/organic view
Learning disabilities are increasing due to environmental toxins

ADHD and other neurological functioning disorders are growing in epidemic proportions. While there has not been a lot of research funding directed to this field, there is sufficient evidence for us to be extremely concerned.

In the past sixty years, thousands of new chemicals have been invented and we know very little about their combined effect on our, or our children's, health. For example, in the US over 85,000 synthetic chemical compounds are now registered for commercial use in EPA's Toxic Substances Control Act, and 2,800 high-production-volume (HPV) chemicals are currently produced in quantities of 1 million lbs, or more, per year.[9]

There are thousands of new chemicals

Australia is known to have a worse record than most western countries in its regulation and control of the use of toxic chemicals.[10] Many hundreds of these chemicals, which are widely used in foods and other consumer products, have never been tested for their potential toxicity to humans; fewer still have been tested for their possible developmental toxicity to children.[11]

Moreover, toxicity tests are often completely inadequate to measure long term effects; nor do they address the

We don't know if they're safe

impact of ingesting wide combinations of chemicals. Therefore, the hazards that these chemicals may pose to children's health and development are still largely unknown.[12]

However, we are seeing increasing evidence that this uncontrolled mix of new chemicals is contributing to changing patterns of disease in children: the wide prevalence of neurodevelopmental disabilities such as ADHD and autism, increasing rates of asthma and childhood cancers, and hormonal abnormalities which effect endocrine function and reproduction.[13]

Chemicals prevent concentration Certain toxins have been found to disrupt attention span, as in ADHD. The most studied of these is lead, which is known to decrease IQ, reduce the ability to pay attention, and increase disruptive behaviour in the classroom.[14]

Another class of toxic chemicals which has been shown to interfere with children's cognitive development is Polychlorinated biphenyls (PCBs).[15]

Chemicals can get into the womb PCBs are especially problematic because of their long persistence in the environment — and in human tissue. Children may be exposed to PCBs in utero (as they can cross the placenta), through breast milk, or from dietary sources such as fish and shellfish, and from certain other fatty foods, which contain high concentrations of PCBs. These chemicals have been associated with poorer neurodevelopmental function in infants.[16]

Other studies in Holland and Michigan found that such exposures could result in lower IQ scores and poorer verbal abilities.[17]

Less research has been done on environmental causes of autism spectrum disorders, but several studies have shown connections between thalidomide and autism.[18]

Other research indicates an interaction between genetics and industrial contaminants in the environment.[19]

Chemicals cause behaviour problems For those who look, there is plenty of evidence (despite limited funding to this field of research) that there are real, increasing, environmentally caused problems affecting our children. This is creating increased learning and behaviour problems, which are taxing parents, child care centres and schools to their limit as they attempt to cope.

Supporting development versus covering symptoms

While prevention is a pressing issue for environmental policy makers, parents and teachers are faced with helping those children who have already suffered damage. The new wave of sensory integration therapies offers the most palatable solution to addressing these problems, after the fact. Numerous inventive, pioneering clinicians have found ways to repair chemically caused damage, using only supportive, harmless means. The philosophy of sensory integration therapies is to access the nervous system via its sensory receptors, using the portals that nature designed, to bring about learning and neural development.

The idea is that the brain never stops learning and rebuilding itself. Interruptions at a crucial stage of development can leave the child lacking in certain brain structures, but a remarkable degree of repair is sometimes possible when an approach is used that works with, not against, the nervous system. The right stimulation will increase the plasticity of the brain, enabling it to regenerate more effectively. Because the human body works in a highly complex, integrated way, a weakness at any point has multiple impacts on function. Conversely, when one sensory pathway is restored, there may be exponential benefits as other, linked systems spring back into operation.[20]

The brain is always improving itself

Make up your own mind

Let me now, for the rest of this book, take you on a journey that will highlight these new concepts in more depth, so that by the end you can reach your own, well-informed conclusions as to which of these viewpoints will serve you best.

Decide your own beliefs

In Chapter 2, I will explore the work of Dr Tomatis, the brilliant French ear doctor who discovered how to light up new brain pathways by stimulating the ear, and who taught us of the primary importance of the hearing sense for healthy neurological functioning. In Chapter 3, I will explore how Tomatis found the links between listening and learning, and how these can be developed to full advantage in the early months and years of a child's life. In Chapter 4, I will follow this story through the

An overview of the Chapters

development of Sound Therapy as a portable program for home use, all the situations where it can be applied and the array of benefits which may result. Chapter 5 looks at learning, how it happens best, and how to create and foster an environment and family activities that best support happy, creative learning. Then, in Chapter 6, we will delve into the use of physical therapy and movement activities to activate sensory integration, focussing in particular on the vestibular (balance), proprioceptive (position), and tactile (touch) senses. Chapter 7 looks in detail at each of the most prevalent learning and developmental disorders, to give specific information on what to expect and how each difficulty might be treated from a sensory integration perspective. In Chapter 8, you will read letters and interviews with many Sound Therapy users who share how they have benefited in a great variety of ways from the listening program. Chapter 9 looks into the impact of environmental and biochemical substances on learning, and how to address these challenges with either dietary changes or drugs. Chapter 10 goes into greater depth on the research background to Sound Therapy, and the ear's role in sensory integration and remedial education. Finally, Chapter 11 offers my conclusions, which are based on all of this information.

Or go for the quick read   Join me on this journey of exploration, if you will, or alternatively, if you wish to simply get a quick glimpse into what might be most useful for your child, follow the suggestions in the checklist table a few pages back, and read only those chapters or sections which are most relevant to your family's needs.

PRACTICAL ACTION TIPS

Dealing with everyday temper tantrums

✪ Give small rewards often. Each time you go into a new shop, stop before going in and promise a small reward on leaving — only if your rules are met. This will give you some leverage to stop them going ratty.

✪ Keep to regular schedules and routines.

✪ When the child has temper tantrums, hold him, look him in the eyes, tell him you love him and remind him to keep breathing, in through the mouth — out through the mouth.

✪ Distract your child with something interesting to take energy away from the conflict.

✪ Try to avoid places that are too stimulating like shopping malls

✪ Go to places where they can let off steam like the beach or the park.

✪ Identify what may trigger bad behaviour, late nights, parties, and plan how to avoid or manage those situations.

✪ Avoid reacting to impulsive rages. Keep calm and casually downplay what is happening.

✪ Don't humiliate or blame the child, but find an alternative that allows him or her to cooperate and still save face.

✪ See practical tips at the end of Chapter 7 for more detail.

References

1 Holt, John, *How Children Learn.* New York: Dutton, 1970.

Holt, John, *Freedom and Beyond.* New York: Dutton, 1972.

2 Dengate, Sue. *Different Kids: Growing up with Attention Deficit Disorder.* Sydney: Random House. 1994.

3 Green, C. and Chee, K. *Understanding ADHD.* Sydney: Doubleday, 2001.

4 Block, M.A. *No More Ritalin.* New York: Kensington Books, 1996, 24.

5 Vinson, D. 'Therapy for attention deficit hyperactivity disorder;' *Archives of Family Medicine,* Vol 3, May 1994, pp. 445-451, cited in Block, *Ibid* 27.

6 Jacobvitz, D. et al 'Treatment of attentional and hyperactivity problems in children with sympathomimetic drugs: A comprehensive review article,' *Journal of the American Academy of Child and Adolescent Psychiatry,* Vol. 29, No. 5, (Sept. 1990), cited in Block, *Ibid.*

7 20/20 Show, ABC television, October 27, 1995, cited in Block, *Ibid.* 30.

8 Volkow, Nora, et al, 'Is Methylphenidate like cocaine?' *Archives of General Psychiatry,* Vol. 52, (June 1995), 445-451, cited in Block, *Ibid.*

9 Goldman L.R, and Koduru S.H. 'Chemicals in the environment and developmental toxicity to children: A public health and policy perspective.' *Environ Health Research;* 2000, 108 (Suppl 3): 443-448.

10 Crumpler, Diana, *Chemical Crisis.* Newham, Australia: Scribe Publications, 1994.

11 National Academy of Sciences, *Toxicity Testing: Needs and Priorities.* Washington, DC: National Academy Press, 1984.

12 Schaffer M. 'Children and toxic substances: confronting a major public health challenge.' *Environ. Health Perspect* 1998; 102 (Suppl - 2): 155-156.

13 Landrigan, PJ. and Slutsky, J. 'Are Learning Disabilities Linked to Environmental Toxins?'

http://ldam.org/ldinformation/resources/O1-04_LDToxins.html

14 Needleman HL, Gunnoe C, Leviton A, Peresie H, Maher C, Barret P. 'Deficits in psychological and classroom performance of children with elevated dentine lead levels.' *N Engl J Med.* 1979; 300: 689-695.

Thomson GO, Raab GM, Hepburn WS, Hunter R, Fulton M, Laxen DP. 'Blood-lead levels and children's behavior-results from the Edinburgh Lead Study'. *J Child Psychol Psychiatry* 1989; 30: 515-528.

Silva PA, Hughes P, Williams S, Faed JM. 'Blood lead, intelligence, reading attainment, and behaviour in eleven year old children in Dunedin, New Zealand.' *J Child Psychol Psychiatry* 1988; 29: 43-52.

15 Lai TJ, Guo YL, Yu ML, Ko HC, Hsu CC. 'Cognitive development in Yucheng children.' *Chemosphere* 1994; 29: 2405-11.

[16] Stewart P, Reihman J, Lonky E, Darvill T, Pagano J. 'Prenatal PCB exposure and neonatal behavioral assessment scale (NBAS) performance.' *Neurotoxicol Teratol* 2000; 22: 21-9.

[17] Jacobson JL, Jacobson SW. 'Intellectual impairment in children exposed to polychlorinated biphenyls *in utero.' NEJM* 1996; 335: 783-789.

Patandin S, Lanting CI, Mulder PG, Boersma ER, Sauer PJ, Weisglas-Kuperus N. 'Effects of environmental exposure to polychlorinated biphenyls and dioxins on cognitive abilities in Dutch children at 42 months of age'. *J Pediatr* 1999; 134: 33-41.

Jacobson JL, Jacobson SW, Humphrey HE. 'Effects of in utero exposure to polychlorinated biphenyls and related contaminants on cognitive functioning in young children.' *J Pediatr* 1990; 116: 38-45.

[18] Goldman L. *Healthy From the Start.* Pew Environmental Health Commission. 1999

Strömland K, Nordin V, Miller M, Akerström B, Gillberg C., 'Autism in thalidomide embryopathy: a population study.' *Developmental Medicine and Child Neurology* 1994; 36: 351-356.

Rodier PM, Ingram JL, Tisdale B, Croog VJ. 'Linking etiologies in humans and animal models: studies of autism.' *Reprod Toxicol* 1997; 11: 417-22.

Rodier PM, Ingram JL, Tisdale B, Nelson S, Romano J. Embryological origin for autism: developmental anomalies of the cranial nerve motor nuclei. *J Comp Neurol* 1996; 370: 247-61.

[19] Goldman, *Ibid.*

Prevalence of Autism in Brick Township, New Jersey, 1998: Community Report. *CDC*: April 2000.

[20] Tomatis, A.A, *The Conscious Ear*, New York: Station Hill Press, 1977.

Kranowitz Carol Stock, *The Out of Synch Child*, New York: Penguin, 1998.

Chapter 2

BABY IN THE WOMB

The miracle of language

Daniel was slow to begin speaking. His mother had been under a lot of stress during her pregnancy and he was born several weeks premature. He suffered from a series of ear infections and allergic-like symptoms in his first two years. By the age of three he was only saying a few words and no one but his mother could understand him, but the doctor said this was within normal range. It was very hard to get him to sleep at night so the whole family's rhythms were disrupted and his parents were exhausted. Then they went to an environmental doctor who suggested mineral supplements, a change in diet and a few other sensory integra-tion therapies. Daniel started seeing a specialist physiotherapist who developed a movement plan to stimulate sensory integration. He also had cranial osteopathy to correct the alignment of his cranial bones which had been affected by his birth, and he started listening to Sound Therapy every night. Within a week his parents were amazed at the change in his speech. He started using words they didn't know he knew, using them in context and putting together much more advanced sentences. After two weeks he was sleeping better, was better co-ordinated and easier to manage all round.

This story is typical of children whose development has been delayed by stress, toxins and illness. Recovery often comes very quickly when the right combination of treatments is given to stimulate integration of the nervous system.

Sensations build brain pathways

A baby's brain begins to develop several months before birth. Millions of brain pathways are created, the foundations for thinking and learning already laid in place at birth. The first years, the first months, the first hours of life have immense importance in the future intelligence of the child. The baby's brain is stimulated by inputs from the senses. Smell, sight, touch, taste—movement, all these sensory inputs build the new being's sense of the world.

The more we learn the more complex our brain grows

Children's author and learning advocate Mem Fox, says 'It's as if the brain were an excited acrobat learning fantastic tricks with every new piece of information.'[1] What the acrobat does with this new information is actually to build new brain connections, creating axons and dendrites, the communication wires that connect the neurons and send messages between them. A child's learning, which grows by leaps and bounds in the first months and years, is built up in layers. First the child learns to appreciate space, movement, the sensations of its body. It learns to recognise faces, to hold its head up, to cry for food and to move its hands. These learnings affect the most basic brain wiring, creating a structure of communication between the neurons on which more complex perceptions can later be hung. By the time she is a year old, the child will probably have learnt all the sounds in her native language. Later she refines her ability to reproduce the sounds, and later still learns the letter symbols that represent them.

Happy children learn better

Each layer of learning lays a foundation on which the next level of understanding can be built. Just as with building a house, the quality of the foundation is of vital importance for the stability of the next level. If the foundation is shaky because it was learned under stressful conditions, if there is an association of pain or fear or humiliation which occurred at the time of certain levels of learning, this will always be restimulated when that learning is accessed. It is for this reason that child psychiatrists advocate the great importance of creating a safe, loving environment for the child in his early hours, days and months.

The first layer of learning is the most crucial, as it determines the wiring structure for everything that hangs off that level. However, the brain's genius is that it learns to adapt by closing off painful memories, going around them, creating new pathways of understanding. Instead of the simple structure of a house which has stumps carrying bearers and joists, then walls, rafters and a roof, the brain is made of millions and millions of complex interweavings which are infinitely adaptable. To an enormous extent, the brain can deal with trauma, setbacks and stress, all the while receiving the stimulation of human language, which eventually takes on meaning. However, it is still true that a happier, more secure child learns more easily and develops greater intelligence because her attention is not being diverted by disturbing emotions which interrupt the chemical and electrical transmissions of the neurons. Trauma may cause a child to set up more complicated pathways which make the efficient conveying of information difficult.[2]

When a child gets upset, learning is disturbed

The ear

The ear is a miraculous organ combining hydraulic pressure pumps and electro-chemical energy systems which are far more complex than any machine used today. The complexity of this organ's contribution to learning and language can perhaps be better understood if we look into its evolutionary origins. The ear evolved from the gills of the fish, and its original purpose in the early vertebrates was for sensing variations in pressure. It was only much later that it became our instrument of hearing.[3] As a hearing organ, its first role was to stand guard against danger. Detecting the direction of sound was of primary importance. Now, it has become our instrument of communication with other people and has been adapted to analyse nuances of sound in incredible detail.[4]

The ear started out as a pressure gauge

Dr Tomatis, who was the first to uncover the miracle of healing the ear with sound, calls the ear 'the Rome of the body' because almost all the cranial nerves lead to the ear. This shows that hearing is not an isolated sense but is integral to all levels of our awareness. Our sense of hearing interacts with our visual and tactile senses, and with our vestibular sense which gives us our orientation in space.

Nerves connect the ear to all our senses

29

Our hearing organ is encased in a series of bony chambers which also house the vestibular system, the organs which inform our sense of balance and movement. This intimate involvement perhaps shows why music has such an influence on the whole body.[5]

The ear feels sound the way the skin feels touch

Hearing is the most developed of the senses before birth. The ear develops alongside the brain, and, as neural connections are formed in the womb, the structures we use for hearing are growing at the same time. Our whole nervous system; the incredible sensory receptor of our skin, are linked, too, in so many ways to the developing ear. In tracing its embryonic development, Tomatis concluded in fact that the skin is differentiated ear.[6] We listen with our whole body, as though our body is a huge extension of our ear.

When does the foetus hear?

Your embryo is listening to your voice

It has been proved that the foetus has hearing at four and a half months, but Dr Tomatis, the pioneer of the work on early human hearing, believed that hearing begins much earlier.[7]

Baby birds learn to sing inside the egg

Tomatis began with the question 'why do we need to speak?' Why this need to be in constant communication? He began to get answers from the literature on the hearing of baby birds inside the egg. When studying to be an ear, nose and throat specialist, he was reading the work of the world renowned English scholar, Negus, *The Mechanisms of the Larynx.* One of the observations in this comprehensive work was that if the eggs of songbirds are hatched under silent foster mothers, the birds, when they are hatched, may be unable to sing.[8]

This triggered Tomatis's curiosity and exploration into the auditory world of the unborn. He realised that the auditory conditioning of the birds must begin in the egg, and asked, therefore, 'is the same true for humans?' Tomatis would have liked to repeat the experiments himself but was unable to, due to a lack of time, money and eggs.[9]

What does it sound like in the womb?

The baby hears high sounds first

The sounds that the foetus hears are predominantly low frequencies due to being filtered through water. At the time of his first experiments, using the technology available in the 1950s, Tomatis incorrectly concluded that the filtering effect of liquid raised the frequencies of the sound, meaning it made the sound higher pitched. In fact, it is the reverse. However, he was correct that the foetus hears high frequency sounds first, because the part of the embryonic ear that develops first is the part that hears high frequencies.

Environmental sounds form a background medley over which the mother's voice dominates, holding the attention of the foetus. These sounds are extremely important, for through them the first emotional and mental bonding is established between child and mother. Much research shows that babies become calmer when exposed to a tape of intra-uterine sounds.[10]

The baby connects with the mother's voice

Tomatis gives a beautiful description of the sounds heard in the womb:

> *'The universe of sound in which the embryo is submerged is remarkably rich in sound qualities of every kind. The foetus experiences internal rumblings, the movement of chyle at the time of digestion, and cardiac rhythms at a sort of gallop. It perceives rhythmic breathing like a distant ebb and flow. And then its mother's voice asserts itself in this context, a little noise superimposed on all the other sounds, a noise in the form of a coded message of exceptional quality.'* [11]

Tomatis suggests that the visceral sounds of the mother — the heartbeat, the intestinal gurgling and respiration — explain our universal love of the sound of surf, which reflects these rhythms and perhaps gives us our own internal sense of rhythm.

The mother's body gives us our sense of rhythm

Our knowledge of embryonic development now confirms what Tomatis first mooted about how early we begin hearing in the womb.

Gestation and the development of the ear

3rd week	ear first appears
16th week	ear is functional and foetus responds to a sound pulse
20th week	the cochlear structures are functioning
24th week	foetus begins actively listening [12]

Being head down helps the baby hear

Position may also make a difference to auditory perceptions. An eight month old foetus in the cephalic (head down) position will experience more sound from bone conduction. Its head is closely wedged against the mother's pelvic bones. This will stimulate sound vibrations in the tiny bones of the foetus's middle ear, already developed to its full size.[13]

Sonic Birth

A newborn has to adapt to hearing through air

Sonic birth is the term Tomatis developed to describe the acoustic experience of the birth transition. A major adjustment is required to adapt from the muffled internal sounds heard in utero to receiving and deciphering sound carried through the medium of air. The amniotic fluid empties out of the baby's ear on the tenth day after birth. Prior to that, she still hears sound as in utero. When the fluid empties, the child is left in auditory darkness and must begin adapting to the air medium.[14]

Here our mother plays a crucial role, if she is available to us, to motivate and communicate, for she is the link between pre-birth and after-birth experience.[15]

Tomatis says that we long

> '...to be cuddled and caressed by a voice that seems to be the same as the already familiar one that spoke to us in the depths of our uterine night. We think we recognise it, even though we cannot put an image to it. This voice approaches us whenever we cry with hunger. As we suck with greed what our mouth has touched, we drink avidly at the same time of the voice that pours its bounty over us. Vocal food is as necessary to our human development as the milk we take in.'[16]

Sound can help the baby to adjust to the airy world

The Sound Therapy program that Tomatis eventually designed is another way of bridging that gap between the heavenly sounds of the womb and the reality of this air filled world. In doing so it also gives us the opportunity, at any age, to bridge the gap in the psyche of the individual who somehow lost or left dormant a part of the self, which never fully transposed itself into the adult world. Part of development, whether sensory, mental or emotional, can be left in limbo when, on some level, there have been insufficient personal resources to achieve maturity. This lack can be bridged by sound when we create a simulation of the birth experience, and, through the process of Sonic Birth, support the individual to successfully make the transition.

High frequencies

One of the most important discoveries Tomatis made in his years of research was the beneficial effect of high frequency sound on the brain. The mother's voice is the first high frequency sound we hear. Its special encoding of detailed meaning, its message of love, gives it an importance no other sound will ever have.

The mother's voice is the best high

High frequencies are high tones, as opposed to low tones. Children's voices contain more high frequencies, and fewer low frequencies than adults' voices. A violin gives out more high frequencies than a cello.

Children's voices are high too

The human ear is designed to respond to, and benefit from, the rich medley of high frequency sounds found in a natural environment. Rain, running water, birds and insects generate an abundance of stimulating, high frequencies. Unfortunately, today children grow up in a world dominated by low frequencies and these have a tiring and dulling impact on the nervous system. They are not the sounds which stimulate, enliven and create interest. Moreover, most of the low frequencies are machine noises, accidentally generated by industrial necessity, not created for the purpose of enjoyment, communication or education. Our willingness to let ourselves and our children suffer this constant bombardment of noise, clearly demonstrates that we do not attribute much importance to the impact of sound upon our health.

Nature is full of high frequencies

The noise level in the womb is thought to be about 30 to 96 decibels. This is around the level of normal conversation. Compared with our normal sound environment, the womb is relatively quiet.[17] However, ultrasound, which is used to give us a visual image of the foetus, is known to cause a much higher level of noise and may be quite disturbing to the foetus.

Ultrasound is very loud for the baby

There is clinical evidence that noise can damage babies. A Japanese study of pregnant women near Osaka airport found they had smaller babies and an increased incidence of premature births. I would have to suggest that air pollution could be a contributing factor in this case. However, chronic noise has also been associated with birth

Noise may cause birth defects

defects.[18] Knowing this, surely it would be wise to protect newborns as much as possible from noise pollution? Yet it is not one of the recommendations given in prenatal training.

Sing to your baby

Sing when you're pregnant

Since the baby's first attunement and first learning of language occurs when still in the womb, mothers can enhance this further by singing to their babies before birth. In her article 'The Maternal Womb: The First Musical School for the Baby', Ruth Fridman describes how she found that both mother and baby benefited when she began teaching music to pregnant women.

Each mother's song is unique

She got the mothers to create their own songs. Once able to set aside their anxieties and fears, they showed great interest and tenderness as they shyly expressed what they would sing to their babies. Each mother found her own personal way of communicating with her baby, using her own rhythms, and communicating things that she may not say in speech, but could say in song.[19] The mothers also benefited from using music at the birth of their babies.

It is vitally important for babies to hear their parents talking to them during gestation. When a pregnant woman sings, her baby responds with movements. These movements are important for the sensory motor development of the baby.[20] The third trimester, when the baby's growth is the most rapid and learning is intensified, is especially important

Newborn babies prefer to hear a song, story, or rhyme that their mother sang to them in utero rather than a new song.[21] One baby at just nine months was singing the song that his mother had regularly sung to him since before his birth.[22] When babies are born prematurely and need to spend time in an incubator it is very valuable to play them recordings of their parent's voices, speaking and singing to the child.[23]

The lullaby is the first language lesson

Sadly, the lullaby has largely become a thing of the past. Young mothers have lost this important folk tradition. Michael Odin MD believes that young mothers have a profound need to sing to their babies, but changes to the birth process and hospitalisation have interfered with this instinctive behaviour. Throughout time, and all over the world, women have sung to their unborn babies. Now we know the significance of this because we understand that the foetus was having its first language lesson in the womb. The inflections of the mother tongue are learned through song as essentially as through speech.

Sound stimulation before birth helps the brain to develop higher levels of organisation. The elements of music — such as tonal pitch, timbre, intensity and rhythm — are also elements of spoken language. This is why listening to music prepares the brain of the foetus to understand and produce the sounds of language.[24] Music is like a pre-linguistic language which stimulates and nourishes the growing baby. Music affects our physical body, emotions, intellect and our sense of beauty. It is a language of its own, which gives us an understanding of that which cannot be expressed in words. Yehudi Menuhin, who was recognised as perhaps the greatest violinist the world has known, partly attributed his musical talent to the fact that his parents were constantly singing and making music before his birth.

Music gets the brain organised

It is beautiful to see the foetus, 'dancing', as it were, in the womb — sometimes as early as the first trimester — as the vestibular system develops.

Giselle Whitwell in her article 'The Importance of Prenatal Sound and Music' says: 'the movements appear as graceful somersaults, flexing of the back and neck, turning the head, waving arms, kicking legs—all self-initiated and expressive in nature.'[25]

Foetuses like to dance

By the second trimester, DeMause describes the actions thus:

'The foetus now floats peacefully, kicks, turns, sighs, grabs its umbilicus, gets excited at sudden noises, calms down when the mother talks quietly and gets rocked back to sleep as she walks about.'[26]

In a London maternity hospital, Michelle Clements observed the response of four to five month old foetuses to different types of music. She noted that they were soothed by Mozart and Vivaldi but became disturbed by loud passages of Beethoven, Brahms or rock music.[27]

Choose gentle music

In summary, research clearly confirms that the preference of newborns is to hear lullabies sung by their mothers, or slow passages of baroque music, Vivaldi, Telemann or Handel, with a tempo resembling the heartbeat at rest.

The heartbeat is the rhythm of life

Infants also prefer music that is consonant (harmonious) rather than dissonant.[28] These composers have continued to be loved for centuries, for their music always communicates peace, order and joy.

A mother who sings to her child

Dominique Oyston is a beautiful young opera singer, with long dark hair, a bright but gentle personality and an extraordinarily powerful singing voice for such a slight form. When I heard her sing in a normal room I could not believe the volume of sound she produced. She explained that it depends on the use of the different muscular diaphragms in the body, not the overall size of the body. I was inspired to take some singing lessons myself, which I found deeply rewarding. In an interview, Dominique shared how she uses singing and ritual every night at bedtime to give her child a sense of deep security and peace.

> 'It's a huge step for the child to go from the experience of what sound is like through fluid to what sound is like through air and bone and accept how different the sounds are. I love this quote about the unborn child experiencing sound in the womb:
>
> "Wrap the child in a protective cocoon of music and imagery; in the womb the child's world of hearing is that of muted watery tones. All sounds become a wash of music through the amniotic fluid."
>
> I realised if I sang my baby to sleep, it would be a way of us connecting. There would be a bond between us and he would feel nurtured as he went to sleep. He was such a shocking sleeper; he woke up all the time and his sleeping was chaotic and erratic. Because it was so stressful, I grew into doing this as a way to try and make some sort of order in the chaos. I remembered all these rhymes and tunes from when I was little that I really valued and loved, so I wanted to do that for him.
>
> Going to sleep is a transition from one world into the next. I think it's good if you can see it as a plan for the first few years. If a child can learn to go into sleep gently, it is a really special experience for the mother and the child. It's something you share; a moment of quiet, because kids can be so noisy and you don't often

have really beautiful quiet moments. The singing is a loving way to draw them into stillness and quiet.

I even sing "Put your socks on", or other instructions, in little sing-song, rhythmic ways. He seems to hear the singing better than speaking almost. I sing the same two songs every night. One is actually a lullaby from Chitty Chitty Bang Bang. *I really loved that movie when I was little. Then an Irish lullaby. So I do those two first and then whatever comes to mind.*

We have other rituals, too, that are part of putting him to sleep. We do bath time, stories, supper, brushing teeth, and in bed we do a little Steiner prayer. (Rudolf Steiner is an educational philosopher who believes in bringing a sense of spirituality and wonder into the everyday lives of children.)

"As I go to sleep each night a beautiful angel watches over me and fills my soul with flooding light and guides me to the stars so bright and blesses me each morning."

You can add in any adjective you want about the angel. It's in the book called The Incarnating Child *by the late Joan Salter, a Melbourne nurse who worked with Steiner teachings.*

So we do that, and then we say, "Dear Angels, Dear God, Dear Great Spirit, Dear Heavenly Light, Dear Mother Goddess", whatever I feel like. I say quite a range of things so he has a sense that people have a lot of different ideas about what the God Force is.

And then we say: Please bless Liam and Mummy and Daddy and all our friends and family and all the people we love. And then I go through a list of thankyous. Thank you for taking care of us, thank you for our safety and the safety of our loved ones, thank you for whatever else has happened that day. We do lots of thankyous and then we do a prayer for the planet Earth: Please shine love into the hearts of people all over the world so that we all can take care of one another and take care of this beautiful planet and all the creatures and all animals, etc. Then Liam adds a few thankyous. It's sort of spontaneous and a nice way of recapping the day.

Then I sing. And sometimes I tell him a little story, if he's not very tired. I'll just make something up like: There was a little red sparkly dragon (because red's his favourite colour), called Liam—it always has to be called Liam—and he really wanted a friend and he lived in a cave in the forest and found a friend. Or anything... about a cat who has kittens, something cute and little and sweet, with fuzzy endings, and really short. Then I sing a couple of songs and by then he's asleep. This procedure always works because it's long enough to wind him down and then he's a goner!

Altogether, this takes anything from 2 minutes to 1/2 an hour at the most. These sound-and-story pictures are the last thing he will take with him from the day. I stay with him just because I like staying with him. I like the idea that he feels safe and that he goes to sleep feeling safe in the world. Because I think there's so much fear out there, and he's a fairly cautious child. So I feel one of the things I need to do is to remind him to look at the world as a beautiful place. Okay, keep away from the strangers down the road – but there's a balance. So that's our ritual and it's about making him feel safe, us being connected and saying, let's do something great with our lives, being human. And it says we're connected to everyone and everything.

I have done the same thing every single night for the last three years. It's easy to do the same thing, because you don't have to think! And usually by that time of night I'm so zonked! And he likes it the same way every time. This is another Steiner idea. Ritual and the repetition of ritual actually builds in a structure that gives children a real sense of safety, so then you don't have to fight so hard to establish boundaries. You just repeat and repeat and gradually they surrender to those boundaries. Liam doesn't fight going to sleep now. To him, going to sleep is just what you do. Occasionally he whines, and I say "no, it's story time". That's it! Because it's so inevitable and so much the same, he can't fight it. And obviously it's not a scary experience. I think a lot of kids are frightened to go to bed or to go to sleep. Bedtime is special for us because it's quiet and it's just Liam and me (and Dad) and it's a really beautiful moment when the world is good.

Rudolf Steiner believed that the mother's voice is very important for the child. When the child comes out of you, it doesn't realise it's an *individual yet. It has no concept of "I"; it thinks it's the mother. There are doctors who say that sleeping with your baby is incredibly good for a child because it reminds them to breathe. Sometimes really little babies forget to breathe when they're asleep. The whole pulmonary system can just stop. Whereas when they sleep with the mother, then they entrain with the whole breathing rhythm of the mother. You breathe and your baby breathes with you.*

The separation at birth can be traumatic. For the mother to sing to the child strengthens that bond Steiner talks about. For the first three years it's like the whole energy field of the mother wraps the child up and encircles them as in a mantle or cloak. It can protect them from the world, because they're such open little beings. They don't have the defences that adults have. As an adult you can shut down your hearing; you can shut down your thinking about something. You can tell yourself, "I'm not going to think about that" and you don't think about it, or you can say "I'm not looking at that" and not look at it. Babies and children can't do that; they don't have that kind of consciousness of use of their intellect and their will to filter impressions. So they're like sponges. Everything goes in. Steiner talks of the mother role as protecting the child from too many sense impressions from the world.

And part of that is the singing and the working in with "I'm here, tune yourself to my rhythms and my songs and get a feeling for what it's like to be in a body." Young children need those strong rhythms. So the whole bedtime process becomes a musical event through the rhythm and repeated action and the songs themselves and the stories, then the silence. Once you start singing and talking to your baby, they feel what it's like perhaps to produce sound as a human. Singing and music can be a big part of that.'

Dominique has a passion to share these gentle processes with other mums, and to do that she has produced some wonderful CDs, made from original analogue recordings, of songs and stories for children based on Steiner principles.[29]

How is it that we speak?

Speech is a miracle Tomatis says that the miracle of speech is taken for granted by all of us, only because we are totally surrounded and steeped in it from the moment of birth and before. If we take a step back and look more deeply at the phenomenon of language, we realise just how extraordinary it is.

We have no organ of speech A question Tomatis asks is 'how is it that we are able to speak; to produce these complex verbal sounds?' We assume that the body is designed with a special device intended for this function. But this is not so. In fact we have to bring into service two parts of our anatomy intended for quite different purposes, that of the respiratory system (diaphragm, nasal passages, larynx, lungs and rib cage) and the digestive system (mouth, lips, soft palate, tongue and teeth), complex structures intended originally for quite another purpose. There is no specific organ for speaking.[30]

We speak with our ears This is all without discussing the role of the ear, which is also essential for speech. Try listening to a deaf person who has never heard speech. They have little chance of producing anything but a muffled jumble of almost incomprehensible sound, with no rhythm, meter, musicality or high frequencies.

Therefore, says Tomatis, we speak with our ears.[31] So in order to speak, our ear and larynx must be engaged together, while being diverted from their original functions.

Tomatis describes beautifully how the infant discovers speech. As the baby first learns that it has control over breath and the making of sound

'...The nascent awareness of our emission and our own audition is of all human phenomena one of the most constant, most precious and most worthy of protection.'[32]

'The dialogue takes hold rapidly and without mediator; to the adult who leans over the cradle, it may sound incoherent, but it is highly significant to the infant who awakens to his own sensations. This endless game of sonic interchange, this bath in a tub of noise that we can run and take without anybody's help, constitutes our first awakening to life, our first declaration of independence, our first awareness of the complex mastery of co-ordination we will achieve as we develop.'[33]

The first word emitted by babies in all cultures is the same. As the tongue and palate move apart and then together again, the resulting sound is 'Mamamama' This sound, made accidentally, quickly takes on significance as the adults interpret it as the baby's first word...language has been spoken. This word immediately brings joy and smiles to the face that the baby sees in front of him and he begins to understand that the utterance of this sound produces the most desired response of bringing his mother to him. Thus the meaning and purpose of language is known with the first word. With this first word, all the baby's fundamental needs are met. Anything beyond that is just play.

'Mama' is always the first word

The ability to summon mother is everything. With her comforting, familiar presence the baby knows that all his needs are met. As the most human of our acts—the development of language—occurs, any illness, sorrow or worry can have a profound effect in interrupting this development. If, on the other hand, the baby's verbal calls go unanswered, for mother is absent, then vocal language loses its meaning and the game loses its attraction. Instead, it recalls the painful memory of abandonment, and absence of that pleasant and delicious sound, the familiar voice of the mother.

Mother's presence gives meaning to language

It is extraordinary in workshops, when we ask participants to speak of a memory of their mother's voice, the depth of sharing that follows. This question always takes us right to the core of the relationship with the mother. Before reading further, you might like to close your eyes and think of your own memories of your mother's voice, and see what feeling this evokes.

Mother's voice touches our deepest chord

If, in contrast, we simply said 'tell us a memory of your mother', we would no doubt hear of more superficial things like the embroidery, the clean house, the flowers she picked. But memories of the voice elicit deeper and more personal stories: the song with which she sang me to sleep, or the tone when she said my name when she was displeased with me. The memories shared are both joyful and painful, and invariably this exercise brings the participants closer together in an intimacy of trust created by the depth of sharing.

Myself, I remember how my mother always sounded so young on the phone. She sounded twenty-five even when she was seventy, and whenever I called her, though she was suffering with her health in her later years, she would always convey to me a sense of acceptance, of optimism and deep spiritual peace. This was her essential nature, which she always protected and maintained despite anything that life might throw at her.

I was fortunate that my mother learned from some wise doctors who, even in the 1950s, were aware of the importance of the baby's sense of security in its first hours and days.

Sleeping in with the parents is now recommended by enlightened experts, as it is safer and more reassuring for the child and easier for Mum, (or Dad if he's the one who is going to get up in the night.) However, it was not common practice in the 1950s when I was born. In fact, my mother was the first person ever to have her baby rooming in with her at the London Clinic in 1957, and that baby was me. The nurses were appalled, during her stay, that she actually had the baby sleeping in her bed. They were constantly trying to get her to conform to the norm and send the baby to the nursery. Even at the last minute, as my parents were leaving the hospital, the matron followed them to the lift prattling on with, 'You know, one day Mrs Steele is going to roll over on one of her babies.' As my parents stepped into the lift, just before the doors closed, my father replied seriously, 'Oh she does it all the time. That's why she has to have so many of them.' In fact none of us ever was suffocated by our mother, but we certainly benefited greatly from the extra love and security we felt from her constant presence in those early months.

PRACTICAL ACTION TIPS

Nurturing sound for your baby

✪ Protect your young children from loud noise. Create a sound nurturing environment with gentle music and Sound Therapy.

✪ Sing to your baby in the womb, in the bassinet, and sing with your toddler. Your child will be the greatest fan of your voice.

✪ Sing the lullabies, songs and rhymes that you remember from childhood.

✪ Play classical music in your home so the child's brain is stimulated by its intricate harmonic structure during its most formative weeks and months.

✪ When nursing your baby, listen to calming music to help you feel peaceful and centred. The calmer you are, the calmer your baby will be.

✪ Nurse your baby in a rocking chair or swing seat. The rocking motion will help to soothe and calm her.

✪ If your child is fretful, try holding him in your arms while you do a regular slow dance to a soothing tune. Hum quietly along with the music. The vibration of your voice will add to his comfort.

✪ Have a regular bedtime ritual that brings you close to your child each night.

✪ Respond when your baby cries. Babies cry because they are lonely, scared, hungry, in pain, or bored. They do not cry because they are naughty and want to get their own way. Controlled crying (leaving the baby for longer and longer periods until it stops crying), advocated by certain experts for many years, causes abandonment issues and will not lead to an easy adolescence.

References

[1] Fox, Mem. *Reading Magic*. Australia: Pan Macmillan, 2001. 12.

[2] Joseph, R. 'Emotional Trauma & Childhood Amnesia'. *Journal of Consciousness & Emotion*, 4 (2), 151-178, 2003.

[3] Tomatis, Dr A. A. *The Ear and Language*. Phoenix: Moulin, 1996. 47.

[4] *Ibid,* 51-54.

[5] Madaule, Paul, 'The Dyslexified World', in *About the Tomatis Method*, edited by Gilmour, T. M., Madaule, P. and Thompson, B. Toronto: The Listening Centre Press, 1989.

[6] Tomatis, Dr A. A. *The Conscious Ear*, New York: Station Hill Press, 1977. 106.

[7] *Ibid.* 145.

[8] *Ibid.* 126.

[9] *Ibid.*

[10] Murooka et. al. 1976: DeCasper 1983: Rossner 1979. Cited in Whitwell, Giselle. 'The Importance of Prenatal Sound and Music'. http://www.birthpsychology.com/lifebefore/sound1.html , 2004, found on http://www.birthpsychology.com/index.html

[11] Tomatis, *Ibid,* 128.

[12] Shahidullah, S. and Hepper, P. 'Hearing in the fetus: Prenatal detection of deafness'. *Int. J. Prenatal and Perinatal Studies, 4 (3 and 4)*, (1992), 235-240, cited in Whitwell, *Ibid.*

Pujol, R., Lavigne-Rebillard, M., and Uziel, A.. Development of the human cochlea. *Acta Otolaryngologica*, , 7-12. (1991) 482, cited in Whitwell, *Ibid.*

[13] Federico, Gabreil F. 'Music Aids Development in the Womb', page: http://www.birthpsychology.com/lifebefore/sound5.html , 2004, site address: http://www.birthpsychology.com/index.html

[14] Spirig, E. 'Dyslexia, Mental Deficiency and the Electronic Ear', IVth International Congress of Audio-Psycho-Phonology, Madrid, May 1974, translated by Jacques J Waters, Child Study Centre, University of Ottawa. 29.

[15] Thompson, B. M. 'Listening, the Basic, Basic We've Been Seeking', in *About the Tomatis Method*. edited by Gilmour, T. M., Madaule, P. and Thompson, B. Toronto: The Listening Centre Press, 1989. 113.

[16] Tomatis, A. A. *The Ear and Language*. Phoenix: Moulin, 1996. 58.

[17] Deliege and Sloboda, 1996, cited in Whitwell, Giselle. 'The Importance of Prenatal Sound and Music'. http://www.birthpsychology.com/lifebefore/sound1.html, 2004, found on http://www.birthpsychology.com/index.html

[18] Szmeja et al. 1979, cited in Whitwell, Giselle. 'The Importance of Prenatal Sound and Music'. http://www.birthpsychology.com/lifebefore/sound1.html, 2004, found on http://www.birthpsychology.com/index.html

[19] Fridman, Ruth. 'The Maternal Womb: The First Musical School for the Baby' http://www.birthpsychology.com/lifebefore/sound2.html 2004, found on http://www.birthpsychology.com/index.html

[20] Fridman, *Ibid.*

[21] Satt, B. J. *An investigation into the acoustical induction of intra-uterine learning.* Ph.D Dissertation, Californian School of Professional Psychology, Los Angeles, (1984), cited in Whitwell, *Ibid.*

[22] Fridman, *Ibid.*

[23] Fridman, *Ibid.*

[24] Whitwell, *Ibid.*

[25] Whitwell, *Ibid.*

[26] De Mause, L. Foundations of psychohistory. New York: *Creative Roots*, (1982), cited in Whitwell, *Ibid.*

[27] Clements, Michele (1977. *'Observations on certain aspects of neonatal behavior in response to auditory stimuli'.* Paper presented to the 5th Internat. Congress of Psychosomatic Obstetrics and Gynecology, Rome, cited in Whitwell, *Ibid.*

[28] Zentner, M. R. and Kagan, J. 'Infant's perception of consonance and dissonance in music'. *Infant Behavior and Development 21(3),* (1998), 483-492, cited in Whitwell, *Ibid.*

[29] www.dominiqueoyston.com

[30] Tomatis, A. A. *The Conscious Ear.* 125.

[31] Tomatis, *Ibid* 125.

[32] Tomatis, A. A. *The Ear and Language.* Phoenix: Moulin, 1996. 58.

[33] *Ibid.* 59.

Chapter 3

LISTENING IS
THE ROAD TO LEARNING

James, who had long-term learning difficulties with reading and spelling, had been using Sound Therapy for just a few weeks when he said to his teacher 'I can learn this now! I don't understand why it was so difficult before.'

Emily could never grasp the concept of the clock face, but suddenly learned to tell the time after a few days of Sound Therapy. She also found she had a whole new group of friends because she was participating and communicating better.

Another nine-year-old girl said, 'It doesn't sound like I'm under water all the time any more.'

Brain stimulation helps children learn more easily

Many students find that when they use Sound Therapy their study is easier, their grades are higher, they can pay attention in class and learning is not so stressful.

Children and teenagers sleep more soundly, wake refreshed and can focus their brain on learning. Children who are delayed several years behind their grade level in language and reading skills, catch up in just a few months after they start Sound Therapy.

Dr Tomatis said, 'Listening is the road to learning', for he had seen, first hand, the dramatic shift that takes place in learning ability once the listening function has been corrected.

We have to listen well before we can read and write

Listening is the most basic element of communication and is a pre-requisite for other skills such as speaking, reading, and writing. It is through the ear and our capacity to interpret sound that we develop a relationship with our environment and with those around us. Interruption in the development of the listening function at an early age can result in emotional withdrawal or maladjustment and may produce severe learning or behavioural problems.

> *'A human being's journey to maturity begins with a dialogue between the embryo and the womb. It finally achieves its goal when the individual becomes part of the social framework. An ideal sonic pathway exists which must be followed in order to reach maturity. When the foetus and mother establish communication, the foetus desires to pursue this further. After birth, the infant wants to extend this communication, first with the mother, then with the father, and then with society in general.'* Dr Tomatis.[1]

Listening is hearing plus motivation

Listening depends on desire and good brain pathways

Listening is a *voluntary* act which requires the desire to use the ear in order to focus on selected sounds.[2] To do this, the child must have both the psychological willingness to hear and the physical ability to use the ear efficiently. Then she must have a high level of efficient brain integration so that the sounds received by the ear can be processed in an effective way. A dysfunction in any of these areas can produce severe impediments to a child's development.

But my child is not deaf

Listening is different to hearing

Apparent deafness is a typical symptom of learning difficulties. If you have taken your child for hearing tests only to be told that his hearing is fine, and you are now at a loss as to the cause of the problems, it may mean the problem lies not with hearing, but with auditory processing.

Ear infections can cause learning delays

Temporary hearing loss, however, affects many children of primary school age through middle ear infections (otitis media). These infections reduce the responsiveness of the middle ear and cause temporary hearing loss, which can affect the child's learning ability during those times.

This temporary sensory deficit is significant at stages of growth where brain development and the laying down of fundamental learning strategies are occurring rapidly. A sensory deficit at such a crucial stage can cause a delay which may affect the child for years to come. There are now excellent educational resources to assist families and teachers in reducing the impact of such temporary hearing deficits.[3] However, it is more useful still to prevent the problem from occurring in the first place. Regular use of Sound Therapy is a simple, harmless and effective way which has been found to reduce the incidence of middle ear infections in children. For examples of this, see Chapter 8, *Listeners' Experiences with Sound Therapy.*

Closing the ear

Why would the ear close down? Tomatis said that children may withdraw from communication because of early emotional trauma, repeated ear infections or other unknown causes. They close down part of the listening capacity of the ear, or involuntarily choose longer, indirect brain circuits, which make their processing of sound inefficient. The ears do not have lids the way the eyes do, but they have ways of closing off internally to protect the child from disturbing input or loud noise. The immature psyche may shut down as a defence mechanism, which then becomes habitual and retards normal development.[4]

The ear can close psychologically

Listening

Much more basic to learning than reading and writing, is listening.[5] Listening is the foundation for learning. Before speaking, reading, writing or other more academic skills can be gained, good listening is essential. This obvious fact is often missed because listening is so automatic, so close to our being that we take it for granted. We do not measure listening, to make sure the listening faculty is operating well, before endeavouring to teach the child more complex skills. Then, when there is a listening disorder, we have to work backwards from the apparent lacks in school performance until we come to the root of the problem.

Listening comes before learning

However, parents of learning disabled children, when asked, will always express their exasperation that the child seems not to be able to listen. Yet he can hear. He can hear when he chooses to, his hearing has been tested and is fine.

Listening and hearing are different

49

Unfortunately there is no recognition in most professions that listening and hearing are in fact two different functions, though one is dependent on the other.

Listening means focussing the ear

When Tomatis speaks of listening he means much more than is normally associated with that word. He made a clear distinction between hearing and listening. Hearing is the passive perception of sound, while listening is a voluntary act which requires desire. The listener must choose at some level of consciousness to focus the ear on selected sounds. In other words, listening is the ability to select the sound information which one wants to hear, in order to perceive it in a clear and organised fashion. Further than that, listening includes the ability to relay the sound clearly and quickly to the appropriate parts of the brain, without distortion. It then includes the ability of the brain to receive, decipher and interpret that sound in a meaningful way. The listening function is therefore very closely related to attention span, vigilance, short-term memory and concentration.[6]

Dr Spirig, a psychologist who used the Tomatis method extensively and is a great proponent of the work, says

> *'We are capable of tuning our listening or of focussing it on a subject that interests us. There is an enormous psychological component in listening.'* [7]

The ear and the brain need to focus together

More recent research also indicates the necessity for different parts of the brain to be well integrated before learning can happen easily.[8] A lack of well integrated neuronal wiring may result in the apparent psychological state of disinterest or obstinacy, for the child will lack the ability to focus. The key to better learning then, is to find a way to stimulate and further develop the brain's wiring.[9]

Tomatis found a way to improve listening and stimulate brain connections through sound. The implication of this is enormous, when we stop to fully contemplate the effect of good listening, not only on learning, but on emotional and intellectual development, on personal relationships, social and work relationships and even on international relations.

The Tomatis effect

We can only speak what we can hear

In his early clinical research, Tomatis discovered that people do not produce sounds they cannot hear. His first law is that 'the larynx emits only those harmonics that the ear hears.'[10] He therefore was able to deduce that speaking or singing is entirely dependent on our ability to listen.[11]

Listening is the key to the development and enhancement of language and learning skills, as without it, no linguistic ability is possible.[12] Moreover, listening is the basis of communication and therefore shapes the child's social development, self-image and confidence as well.[13]

Speech

Tomatis showed that we can only voice what we can hear. What comes out of the larynx is essentially under the control of the ear via the neuronal connections. In other words, speech is controlled by the ear.[14] This discovery, originally made in his work with singers, he later applied to his great interest in children with learning difficulties.

The ear controls the voice

He found that difficulties in reading, writing, remembering instructions, concentration, ease of oral communication and the ability to listen to oneself and express thoughts in words, were all functions of the basic ability to listen and process sound.[15]

Auditory control of speech

So in speaking, we use only those harmonics which we can control through our auditory sense. If we can't control them it means we do not use them for self monitoring when we are speaking.[16] The treatment method which Tomatis developed was designed to give back and to broaden this audio-vocal control.

Ear

Let us take a journey into the inner chambers of the ear and see what remarkable structures are there to support the miracle of hearing. There are different chambers inside the ear (see diagram overleaf), each of which plays vital roles in our hearing and our sense of balance, movement and space.

The middle ear

The middle ear is a small cavity between the eardrum and the inner ear. It contains a chain of three tiny bones called ossicles. These bones link the eardrum to the inner ear. The ossicles have names that describe their shapes. The hammer bone is joined to the eardrum. Its other end is attached to the anvil, which is delicately linked to the next bone, called

Muscles move the bones in the middle ear

51

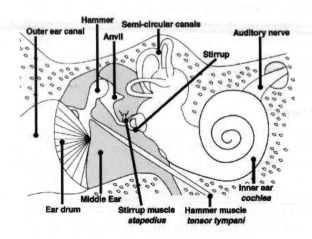

Hammer
Semi-circular canals
Outer ear canal
Anvil
Stirrup
Auditory nerve
Inner ear
cochlea
Middle Ear
Ear drum
Stirrup muscle
stapedius
Hammer muscle
tensor tympani

Diagram of the Ear

the stirrup. The base of the stirrup fills the oval window, which leads to the inner ear.

The middle ear is cut off from the outside by the eardrum, but it is not completely airtight; a ventilation passage, called the Eustachian tube, runs forwards and downwards into the back of the nose. The Eustachian tube is normally closed, but opens by muscular contraction when we yawn or swallow.

The inner ear

We hear in a spiral shaped chamber The inner ear is an extremely delicate series of structures contained deep within the bones of the skull. It consists of a maze of winding passages, collectively known as the labyrinth. The front part, called the cochlea, is a tube resembling a snail's shell and is the organ of hearing.

The vestibular system

Little hairs sense our balance and movement The rear part of the labyrinth, known as the vestibular system, and consisting of two chambers and three semi-circular canals, is concerned with balance. The canals contain hair-like cells and are filled with fluid. The hair cells in the cochlea deal with sound vibrations. Those in the semi-circular canals are sensitive to gravity and acceleration or the movements of the head, (nodding 'yes', shaking 'no' or tilting to the side). The information concerning posture or direction is registered by the relevant cells and conveyed by nerve fibres to the brain.

The active ear

Dr Tomatis' radical breakthrough in treating the ear, came as he began to see the ear as an active organ directed by either voluntary or unconscious messages from the brain. The role of the middle ear is to provide the ear with the best possible conditions so that perfectly analysed sounds reach the cochlea. It does this through the fine-tuning and delicate operation of its two muscles — the muscle of the hammer, which adjusts the tension and quality of the eardrum; and the muscle of the stirrup which regulates the pressure of the stirrup, on the oval window, thereby altering the pressure in the inner ear chamber which is filled with fluid. This muscle, which controls access to the inner ear, never rests — from some months before birth until the moment of death.[17]

The stirrup muscle never rests

The correct tonality of these muscles is absolutely essential for good listening. A hypotonic (reduced tension) condition of the musculature will produce confused hearing, so the person will not understand what is said.[18]

As these muscles are activated by Sound Therapy, the middle ear comes into balance and the inner ear is then trained to become open and receptive to high frequency sounds, such as the baby heard when it was first developing in the womb. This assists children who may have missed out on a crucial stage of their auditory development, to complete the necessary stages.

Active muscles help us hear

Another significant aspect of rehabilitating these muscles is that problems such as glue ear, ear infections, earaches and sinus are usually relieved. Children are very prone to ear problems because in children the Eustachian tube is more horizontal than in adults, so it doesn't drain so easily. Add to this a poorly functioning hammer muscle and you will have problems. A branch of the hammer muscle causes the Eustachian tube to close, so unless that muscle can release when needed, chronic ear blockages will result.

A blocked Eustachian tube means a blocked ear

Hearing loss

It is traditionally believed that the auditory curve cannot be modified, meaning that hearing cannot improve once it has

Hearing can be improved

been damaged. Tomatis found there were many exceptions to this rule, especially among children. Dr Spirig, who used the Tomatis method extensively in clinical practice, said: 'We often find in treating deaf adults and children that their listening and audiometric curve improve, even though they have been told this was impossible.'[19]

By approaching hearing from the point of view of improving listening, Tomatis was able to make a difference to the individual's ability to receive and interpret sound. He found that the ear fully rediscovers its role as an instrument of communication when distortions of the listening curve are overcome.[20]

Understanding

Listening is more than just hearing

A child may have adequate hearing but be unable to analyse the sounds she hears — because listening depends not just on the function of the ear, but the entire auditory pathway in the brain.[21] Even if the effort to attend is made, the child may have difficulty understanding unless the message is repeated or expressed in a different way. This is often not possible in a classroom situation. Inadequate listening, in the full sense of its audio and cognitive components, may affect the child's ability to remember what is said, or may lead to misunderstanding.[22] When one is trying to learn and the second piece of information is based on a misunderstanding of the first piece, there is little hope of gaining clarity.

High frequencies

High frequencies carry lots of information

Poor listening is usually involved in a lack of perception of high frequencies. As we learned in the previous chapter, the perception of high frequencies, heard first in the mother's voice, gives the ear its incredibly delicate ability to interpret complex sound. Tomatis said that frequencies above 8,000 hertz are recharging for the brain. Much more complexity is possible in the high frequencies as these sounds are so much more compact, and therefore contain much more information.

High frequencies carry not only more detailed information, but they also carry the emotion in the message. When a voice becomes monotone, without variation of expression, it is lacking in high frequencies, and it seems to carry no emotion.

Tomatis also discovered that, as he treated his subjects for ear related and communication disorders, the high frequency sounds he was exposing them to had an unexpected beneficial effect. His clients reported feeling more energised, mentally alert, with an overall sense of well-being. Thus he discovered that high frequency sound not only activates the ear, but is also of neurological benefit as it stimulates the firing of brain cells.[23]

High frequencies give us energy

Left brain, Right brain

When speech begins, the baby repeats a single syllable as in the words 'Ma-ma', 'Pa-pa', 'Da-da'. Tomatis' theory is that the right and left brain hemispheres each produce one of the syllables. They are then reproduced vocally at different moments because of an asymmetry of the nerve path to the speech organs. The two branches of the vagus nerve (10th cranial pair), which links the brain to the speech organs, reach the larynx by different routes. The distance to be covered is longer on the left side. Therefore sound from the right ear reaches the brain a fraction of a second faster than sound from the left ear.[24]

Babies make double sounds because they have two ears

The two sides of the brain and the two ears play different roles in the processing of sound. The left hemisphere is served directly by the right ear and, to fulfil its role as the primary supplier of linguistic information, the right ear takes the role of deciphering high frequency sounds.

Sorting out laterality

High frequencies are the sounds which give meaning to language, both because they are the definers of consonants and because the higher harmonics carry the emotional message of the sound. For this reason, the right ear must be the dominant ear for a person to listen effectively. The process of one side of the brain becoming dominant in certain activities, such as right-handedness, is called laterality. This is particularly important in the case of the ears.

The right ear works faster

If the left ear is dominant two problems may arise. One, there will be a fraction of a second's delay in sound reaching the language centre in the brain, causing auditory confusion and possible stuttering or dyslexia. Two, the person will be predominantly oriented to low frequency sounds and will feel distanced from others — since the low frequencies are long wavelengths, covering distances of 35 to 140 metres. The result is that this listener feels distanced from the source of the sound and consequently is isolated from the people with whom she, or he, tries to communicate. One listener who described herself as a dyslexic adult wrote:

> *'I already knew I was "locked in" for that is how I have experienced the world, as though I lived at a distance; which makes sense because the eyes are the furthest away sense. Being a dyslexic adult, with switched off ears, has caused terrible suffering, as you will understand. I am in my mid-50's and it has taken all these years to wait, and work only with body and eyes, cut off from true sound.*
>
> *I am "switching on", Patricia, with a calming effect. I can hear the anger in my voice. My speech has become softer; I am so amazed by this listening ability. I keep on thinking it will stop. If it does, I'll go mad.*
>
> *Now my experience of Sound Therapy has humbled me. I am in awe of sound. I can actively focus on sound sources. It's incredible, as though I have been given a new instrument, calming my mind and soul.'* [25]

Left-ear-dominant people who have used the Tomatis Sound Therapy, have described living with a sense of being shut off from sound and from other people. This has changed as their laterality shifted to the right ear.

The elements of listening

Listening is the foundation for learning

All these elements — the tone of the ear muscles, the psychological receptivity, the efficiency of brain pathways — are crucial to successful listening. If any are affected, the whole system breaks down. So we cannot afford to ignore listening. If we attempt to improve a child's learning ability without first addressing any deficit in listening, we are building on shaky ground. Therefore, listening must be the first port of call for addressing how your child learns, for listening is the key to learning.

PRACTICAL ACTION TIPS

Encouraging good language development

✪ Listen well to your children, so they will learn to listen.

✪ Turn off the TV so your family can have conversations.

✪ Have your child's hearing checked regularly.

✪ To prevent ear infections, keep the child's ears warm, avoid too much dairy and wheat products, and use Sound Therapy.

✪ If learning problems begin to appear, start by addressing the listening problems first.

✪ If there is any sign of language delay, act right away. See Chapters 4, 6 and 7 for more explanation.

References

1 Tomatis, A. A. *The Conscious Ear,* New York: Station Hill Press, 1977. 106.

2 Madaule, P. 'Listening Problems and the Young Child', in *About the Tomatis Method,* Ed. Gilmour, T. M., Madaule, P. and Thompson, B. Toronto: The Listening Centre Press, 1989. 146.

3 Howard, Damien. *The Ear Troubles Kit,* http://www.eartroubles.com/ 2004.

4 Madaule, P. 'The Tomatis Method for Singers and Musicians', in *About the Tomatis Method,* Ed. Gilmour et al. 80.

5 Thompson, B. M. 'Listening, the Basic, Basic We've Been Seeking' in *About the Tomatis Method.* Ed. Gilmour et al. 115.

6 Madaule, P. 'Music: An Invitation to Listening, Language and Learning', in *About the Tomatis Method,* Ed. Gilmour, et al. 69.

7 Spirig, E. 'Dyslexia, Mental Deficiency and the Electronic Ear', IVth International Congress of Audio-Psycho-Phonology, Madrid, May 1974, translated by Jacques J Waters, Child Study Centre, University of Ottawa. 3.

8 Kranowitz, Carol Stock. *The Out of Synch Child.* New York: Penguin.1998.

9 Greenfield, Susan. *The Human Brain.* London: Phoenix. 1997.

10 Tomatis, A. A. *The Conscious Ear.* 86.

11 Thompson, *Ibid.* 118.

12 Gilmour, Timothy M. 'School Listening Training Programs,' in *About the Tomatis Method,* Ed. Gilmour, et al. 106.

13 *Ibid.* 106-107.

14 Sidlauskas A E. 'Language: the Ideas of Dr Alfred Tomatis', *Revue Internationale D'audio-physcho-phonologie.* No 5 Special – April-May (1974). 31.

15 Gilmour, Timothy M. 'School Listening Training Programs', in *About the Tomatis Method,* Ed. Gilmour, et al.106.

16 Spirig, *Ibid.* 7.

17 Spirig, *Ibid.* 19.

18 *Ibid.*

19 Spirig, *Ibid.* 27.

20 Tomatis, *Ibid.* 164.

21 Spirig, *Ibid.* 20.

22 Gilmour, *Ibid.*

23 Weeks, B. S. 'The Therapeutic Effect of High Frequency Audition and its Role in Sacred Music', in *About the Tomatis Method,* Ed. Gilmour, et al. 182.

24 Tomatis, *Ibid.* 155.

Gilmour, P. 'Overview of the Tomatis Method', in *About the Tomatis Method*, Ed. Gilmour, et al. 18-21.

[25] Joudry, P. and Joudry, R. Sound Therapy: *Music to Recharge Your Brain*. Sydney: Sound Therapy International, 2000. 127-129.

Chapter 4

SOUND THERAPY

A home-based listening program for children

Frances was a bright, friendly child who everyone liked when they met her. Her parents were very attentive and wanted the best for her, but Frances wasn't learning. She just couldn't retain what was covered in school, she couldn't remember the letter sounds, she was always losing things and forgetting what her mother told her. Because she saw the difference between her abilities and those of her friends, Frances was starting to feel bad about herself. Her parents decided to try Sound Therapy to see if it could help her with reading and spelling. Frances went to bed with the headphones on every night, listening to the Sound Therapy music or stories. After three days she told her mother she was feeling much better. Her head felt clearer, she wasn't having nightmares and she was paying attention better in class. Her school report card said it all: 'Frances is focussing much better this term and has jumped ahead in leaps and bounds'. Frances also found her athletic abilities improved and she was being chosen first for teams at netball. She felt much happier and was making new friends as well.

Sound heals, like the mother's voice in the womb

Children build their sense of the world, contact, meaning and love from listening to their mother's voice in the womb. Through the miracle of life, the baby's brain is formed out of neurons, axons and dendrites; patterns and meanings are created as the mother's voice lays down an imprint of order. No wonder, then, that sound has such a powerful capacity to heal, to affect mood, mental function, brain development and learning ability as we grow. Dr Tomatis drew on the remarkable power of sound to heal when he made the unique discoveries which launched the field of Sound Therapy.

What it does

Helps learning co-ordination, behaviour and self-esteem

Sound Therapy works on the whole being by retraining the ear — activating and building brain pathways, as well as affecting thinking, emotions and physical co-ordination. As the whole auditory pathway is stimulated and opened, the child's ability to learn is dramatically enhanced. Connections between the two hemispheres of the brain are strengthened so that thinking and co-ordination improves in many areas. The child's equilibrium, sense of self-control and self-esteem develop, so naturally, behaviour improves.

Building brain pathways

Neurons talk to other neurons

The brain is made up of specialised cells called neurons. These build up electrical energy until there is enough to fire off a signal to another neuron. Each time a neuron fires, it is helping to build and strengthen brain connections.

Our neurons are connected by tiny branching filaments called dendrites, and longer ones called axons, which link more distant parts of the brain. These connections use both electrical and chemical energy. Once the electrical charge is sufficient and the neuron fires, a signal heads off along the axon or dendrite. The electrical charge causes the release of a naturally occurring chemical from a nerve. Thousands of different chemicals, called neurotransmitters, act to carry messages between the neurons in the brain. Once the message arrives at another neuron, it needs to be transformed back into an electrical impulse to be received. This will only be successful if the destination neuron has the right receptors — that means the right sort of neurotransmitters, or brain chemicals. One of the differences between a brain and a computer is that a computer uses only electrical energy, whereas the brain uses chemical energy as well, making it infinitely more complex.[1]

A child's brain is unbelievably active, as learning happens much faster in childhood than in later life. Therefore, the firing of neurons and activation of neurotransmitters is occurring at a great rate. Sound Therapy can support and speed this process by helping to activate the neurons even more. Where there are developmental problems, the structured activation caused by the rhythmic, harmonious patterns in the filtered classical music, assists in healing and connecting the brain.

Children learn even faster with music

Activating the ear

The ear is obviously the organ of receptive language, on which so much of learning depends. Dr Tomatis says that the ear is the gateway to the brain. It is the sensory organ which has the most direct and complex interconnections with many different parts of the brain. The ear is linked to all three levels of the brain: the automatic, or so-called reptilian brain; the emotional brain, which first developed in mammals; and the cerebral cortex, which is unique to humans.

The ear is connected to most parts of the brain

The ear is active even when we are asleep, monitoring our environment in case of danger. The complex, intricate connections of nerve endings in the inner ear convey extraordinary detail about the outside world to our brain. Sound quality also gives us immediate information about emotion. Danger, excitement and love are all conveyed by sound, so the limbic system, our emotional brain, is highly attuned to what the ear tells us. Information, knowledge, language, most of the learning we do in school is brought in by the ear - so the cortex, our thinking brain, is constantly wired in to what the ear is telling it. All this makes the ear a natural portal by which we can gain tremendous access to many parts of the brain. Sound is an encoding system by which we can reprogram brain pathways.

Sound affects emotions and knowledge

Much evidence points to the fact that learning difficulties are in some way linked to ear function. Therefore, a therapy which directly and naturally improves the ear's performance is a direct and easy way to assist with learning. Sound Therapy is different from music therapy because it uses specially treated sound, intended to physically improve the way the ear works, as opposed to just using music for an emotional impact.

Addressing the cause

Sound Therapy works at the deepest level

Parents sometimes think, 'Why should my child need Sound Therapy, he can hear perfectly well?' With Sound Therapy we are going deeper than simply improving hearing. We are also going to a deeper level than is addressed with most remedial education programs. Unlike other programs, which attempt to assist a child to adapt to or compensate for a learning difficulty, Sound Therapy attempts to 'effect a repair'. We are implying, then, that with most learning difficulties the root of the problem is in some way involved with the ear. There is substantial evidence for this, detailed in Chapter 10, *Research: the Brain and Sound Therapy.*

Sound Therapy for general developmental issues

Are the sounds coming in jumbled?

If there is a delay in your child's auditory development, the sooner it is addressed the less likely it is that the child will fall behind in school. Listening is the foundation for learning. Your child may be receiving sounds into his brain in such a way that they are jumbled and incomprehensible.

It may not be obvious that listening is the cause of your child's problems, but remember that listening is the foundation for most of our communication skills.

Poor listening can lead to:

- poor concentration
- bad behaviour
- delayed reading and writing skills
- poor performance at school
- social isolation
- the child not achieving up to his potential

How to identify a potential listening problem

If several of the points on this list apply to your child, then it is very likely that he would benefit from Sound Therapy.

❑ Difficult family history

❑ History of ear infections

❑ Difficulty in using language and explaining himself in words

❑ Short attention span, easily distracted

❑ A tendency to misinterpret messages or to ask for them to be repeated

❑ Poor at following instructions

❑ Slow to develop intelligible speech

❑ Does not get along well with peers

❑ A lack of enthusiasm and initiative

❑ A reluctance to communicate

❑ Difficulty in reading aloud

❑ Poor social skills, which may result in withdrawal, hyperactive or aggressive behaviour

❑ Difficulty in reading and writing which manifests as reversal of letter forms, sound confusion, slowness or messy work

❑ There may seem to be a higher aptitude in maths than in English

❑ Child lacks response to human speech yet seems to respond to environmental sounds

Changes to expect

With the support of Sound Therapy, your child may soon find that listening is easier, concentration happens without effort, and short term memory improves — so learning becomes enjoyable instead of being an impossible task. Sound Therapy also repairs the parts of the brain

Sound Therapy restores control

responsible for controlling mood, aggression, impulsiveness and hyperactivity. A child who was out of control can now gain control of himself. Self-esteem improves quickly when children realise they are overcoming their difficulties, and they soon become much more pleasant at home and in the classroom.

Fast and easy

An easy, home based, self-help program

Because Sound Therapy is so much easier to apply than many of the other elements of a remedial program, it is a great way for parents and children to give themselves a breather and some early success. The program is done in your own home, at any suitable time of day, and no travelling is required. It requires no time for supervision, as listening can be done during other activities. There is nothing wrong with beginning Sound Therapy while you are organising other aspects of your program, which may include tutoring, speech therapy, diet and sensory motor (movement) activities.

History
Dr Tomatis 1919-2001

Dr Alfred Tomatis was a French ear, nose and throat doctor who began his own branch of research in 1946. He had the kind of enquiring mind that always goes beyond what it has been taught — the mind of a true scientist, who sees a phenomenon and asks 'why could this be?'

Tomatis searched for answers

A great source of inspiration to Tomatis, was a doctor who was called to treat him during one of his many childhood illnesses. At the time he was suffering from three fevers which he had contracted simultaneously — typhoid, Maltese fever and typhus murin. A parade of doctors had failed to diagnose his condition, so finally the well-respected Dr Carpocino was called. After examining Tomatis, he pronounced, 'I don't know what is the matter with him. I must search for the answer.' He persisted in his search until he was able to successfully diagnose and treat the boy and bring him back to health. It was his statement 'I must search' which had the most profound effect on Tomatis' development and career choice, for from that moment on he decided to do the same. He would become a doctor so that he could search for answers to what he did not know. To find out totally new information one must go outside of the parameters of existing disciplines, and this is what Tomatis did. He worked in his research clinic with hearing impaired retirees, with singers and then with learning disabled children.

The Electronic Ear

As Tomatis experimented and studied his subjects, he gradually developed a device for filtering sound so that it retrained the ear to proper functioning. He called his device the Electronic Ear. He described it as a replica of the natural ear, for it had the ability to adjust its responses to different frequencies of sound and control the type of sound that travelled on to the recipient's natural ear. By making the adjustable functions of the ear external to his patient, Tomatis could manipulate them, and begin to enforce the type of natural, open hearing which his patients may have lost. The Electronic Ear was the basis of what became known as the Tomatis Method. Tomatis found that playing filtered classical music through the Electronic Ear was a highly effective way to retrain the listener, and that its benefits included greater learning ability and better brain function as well as better co-ordination, listening, energy, emotional health and intellectual power. He also used classic stories for children, which develop imagination, lateral thinking and deeper wisdom at the same time as strengthening ear-brain pathways.

The Electronic Ear trains the natural ear

Patricia Joudry

Patricia Joudry was my mother, and it is thanks to her that Sound Therapy became accessible to the general public at an affordable price. While the Tomatis clinics gave, and continue to give, a very valuable service with structured supervised programs, the cost and time commitment they involve made them beyond the reach of many families.

My mother underwent the clinical treatment in Montreal. Her reason for having the therapy was to help with a problem she had hearing in a noisy room. She was not deaf — she simply could not separate a single conversation from the background noise. I was astonished to hear that there was a treatment for this, and recommended that she try the Tomatis therapy. She did so, willingly, and we were all amazed at the results. Not only did it fix her 'background noise' problem and her extreme sound sensitivity — it also cured her chronic insomnia, perpetual exhaustion, and her writer's block! Her full story is told in our book, *Sound Therapy: Music to Recharge your Brain.*

Students can listen in class

She was like a missionary on fire, after her Sound Therapy breakthrough, wanting to share her discovery with the entire world. She found a way to do that when she was able to enlist the monks of St Peter's Abbey in Saskatchewan, in Western Canada, to assist her in putting out the portable Sound Therapy program. The monks were using Sound Therapy at their vocational school at the abbey, which ran a program for learning-disabled teenagers. The therapy was much more effective when they were able to make it portable, with Patricia's cassette tapes, as the students could listen in class. They listened on Walkmans™, the volume was kept low, and rather than distracting them from hearing the teacher, they found it helped them to concentrate and pay attention.

Sound Therapy International

The side effects are good too!

I became involved in Sound Therapy after reading my mother's book, as I wanted to benefit from the 'side effects' of better sleep and more energy. I started distributing her book and tapes in Australia and was soon receiving letters reporting remarkable experiences. People were overcoming chronic stress, depression, self-confidence problems, and hearing disabilities — and children were learning to read, speaking better, feeling happier and achieving much better at school. The enthusiasm of my listeners led me to produce more tapes for children, make educational videos, write new materials and begin training practitioners. I was in demand to speak to groups of mothers, teachers, retirees and varied practitioners.

Advantages of the Self-Help Program

Portable, affordable, accessible and easy

The program which my mother developed is a self-help program. It is portable, affordable, accessible and easy to use. It takes very little time, fits in with your daily activities and is simple to administer. This means that any family, parent, teacher or individual can use the program after simply reading one of our books.

However, this doesn't mean you have to do it without help. We now have an army of several hundred practitioners using and recommending our method. If you purchase through one of our independent distributors, they will be available to give you follow-up support. Sometimes families have special needs and questions, and prefer to have the support of a therapist working alongside them.

While we pride ourselves on running a professional organisation with quality customer service, our commitment is to always keep the therapy affordable. There are no high clinic fees to pay, and no exorbitant costs for unnecessary tests. It is still a portable, self-administered method which any family can afford to purchase and have as an ongoing resource to use at home.

Conditions Sound Therapy may help

This chapter gives specific information on how Sound Therapy is likely to help a range of learning and developmental challenges. These include auditory processing, achieving right ear dominance, ADHD, dyslexia, speech problems, autism and Down syndrome. It covers listening for parents and the benefits of prenatal Sound Therapy listening. Then there is a detailed section on how to use the Sound Therapy listening program and the Sound Therapy Converter. A summary of the information in this chapter is also covered in our booklet, *Listening Helps Learning*, which is available from our head office or our independent distributors.

Which conditions are relevant for you?

The booklet contains a full catalogue of our children's products, which you can also find on our website: www.soundtherapyinternational.com

Auditory processing

Successful listening and learning depends on good auditory processing. Auditory processing means the ability to translate the stream of vocal speech sounds into words and meaning, and then recreate those sounds as speech.

Hearing, understanding and making sense of sound

Effective auditory processing depends first on accurate hearing. Children must be able to see the printed letter, hear the sound of the letter, say the sound, relate the sound to the written symbol for the letter, and then register it and store it in the auditory cortex. Then they need to be able to retrieve the memory and relate the letter symbol to the sound again, and recreate it vocally. In addition, they need to be able to blend the letter and its sound with all the other letters which form a word. Therefore, there is a great deal more than hearing required for successful use of language.

A fractional delay, at any stage of this perception and vocalisation, can lead to great difficulties when it comes to learning the complex literary skills of reading, writing and spelling. While difficulties in speech may go unnoticed in the early years, they become magnified under the pressure to perform at school, and to translate spoken into written skills.

A tiny delay causes problems Timing is a crucial aspect of auditory processing, because a slight delay can mean the sounds are heard, or perceived or reproduced, in the wrong order. Such difficulties, called 'linear sequential processing problems', make it extremely difficult for the student to accomplish note taking and writing. Poor auditory memory may be part of the problem, and a person who is otherwise quite intelligent may have enormous difficulties performing academically when these functions are impaired.

Establishing right-ear dominance

The right ear must always be louder Sound Therapy recordings are made so that the sound is louder in the right ear. This improves the efficiency of the brain in processing language because the right ear connects to the left side of the brain, which is the language centre. This makes linguistic pathways more efficient and the result is an improvement in reading and vocal skills.

Sound Therapy stimulates the brain pathways which enable very fast transmission of information from ear to brain and from brain to vocal apparatus. When the processing speed is increased, it is easier for the student to keep up. He or she will not be constantly struggling with information which is jumbled and mixed up because of being received in the wrong order.

ADHD

Affects more boys than girls Attention Deficit Disorder or Attention Deficit and Hyperactivity Disorder is an increasing, and very demanding problem. While it has been observed to run in families, the fact that the condition is on the increase indicates that there are probably environmental factors involved as well. It appears to affect 20% of boys and 8% of girls. However, some researchers think that a lot of girls are missed in the statistics because they are more likely to have dreamy symptoms than hyperactive ones. They are less difficult to manage, so may miss out on diagnosis and treatment.

ADHD and the brain

ADHD is believed to be caused by a deficiency in the transmission system, which relays messages between cells in various parts of the brain. Our new abilities to see the brain through MRI scanning give us greater insight into certain brain disorders. In ADHD the limbic system, which is the emotional and impulsive brain, is working full throttle — but the cortical areas which focus attention, control impulses and control stimuli are not fully active and engaged.[2]

The brain can't control impulses

MRI scans of ADHD children show a lack of brain activity in several right hemisphere regions.[3] These include the anterior cingulate cortex, an area which focuses attention on a particular stimulus; and the prefrontal cortex, which is key in controlling impulses and planning actions. An area in the upper auditory cortex which integrates stimuli has also proved underactive. This may cause the child to be unable to grasp the big picture. They experience the world as fragmented, with one stimuli after another vying for their attention. Poor functioning of the frontal lobe means the child cannot think quickly enough to put the brakes on and control the impulse to act. This impulsiveness and hyperactivity also leads to behavioural problems and poor social skills. The same is true for adults with ADHD.

Sound Therapy stimulates these underactive areas by increasing the energy in the neurons, which in turn is thought to raise the level of excitatory neuro-transmitters. The increased cortical activity allows the person to get a grasp of the whole situation, inhibits the limbic system and results in more controlled and focussed behaviour.

ADHD and auditory processing

The majority of children with ADD/ADHD have auditory reception problems, so they seem not to hear or remember instructions. When their hearing is tested, however, it usually proves to be normal, since the problem is what they do with the information after they hear it. These children are so easily distracted by environmental stimuli that they

Sound Therapy helps them remember instructions

cannot retain a list of instructions in their minds. They also cannot tune out unwanted input and focus on selected sounds. It is this indiscriminate reception of auditory input which leads to the inability to concentrate their attention on a selected topic for any length of time.[4]

Improved inhibition and attention

The ear can tune in and pay attention

By stimulating the frontal lobe, Sound Therapy may restore the child's ability to think quickly and put the brakes on before acting. In a sense, Sound Therapy has the same effect as stimulant drugs such as Ritalin. Brain function is speeded up and the child becomes more efficient in dealing with environmental stimuli. Sound Therapy also retrains the listening capacity, or the auditory reception process, so that the child can learn to focus on the desired sound and to relay the sound directly to the language centre in the brain. Auditory reception problems are caused, in part, by the shutting down of the ear to certain frequencies of sound. The ear muscles become lazy and unresponsive and must be stimulated in order to regain the capacity to tune in to the desired sound. Sound Therapy has been shown to provide this rehabilitation for the ear as well as helping to reorganise auditory transmission in the brain. This process reduces stress and tension in the whole nervous system as the child, instead of being constantly distracted by every sound in the environment, becomes able to attend to a chosen stimulus.

Hey Mum, watch me learning!

Paying attention in class makes a big difference

Sound Therapy can have widespread benefits for children with ADHD. If the child is hyperactive, you may observe a significant decrease in activity; while lethargic, dreamy children may become more energised. As listening discrimination is retrained, memory and concentration improve so that learning can be achieved with a great deal less effort. If the child has had difficulties in learning a particular skill, such as spelling or telling the time, there may be a sudden shift in these areas. Sleep and appetite problems will also be resolved as the whole system becomes calmer and less erratic. The behavioural difficulties, such as impulsiveness and aggression, are now brought down to a manageable level. The child may now be able to pay attention in class, understand and follow instructions and be motivated to communicate and learn. For more background information on ADHD see Chapter 7, *Not another label*, and for examples see Chapters 8, *Listeners' experiences with Sound Therapy.*

How to use Sound Therapy for ADHD

Sound Therapy must be used with headphones, and parents may be concerned that an overactive child will damage the portable player. A solution to this may be to put the music on when the child goes to bed. Use mini earphones and tape them into the ears with surgical tape. Listening is just as effective if done during sleep. A regular program of daily listening should be cultivated. It may also help if you put the Sound Therapy on your child at times when the child is wound up or emotionally reactive. Sound Therapy can also be a great aid to study and concentration.

Its easy to use during sleep

Dyslexia

Dyslexia was a popular term for learning difficulties in the 1950s, and through the 1970s. One of the earliest writers on the subject was Dr Hinshelwood, who was an eye surgeon, which may account for the initial emphasis on visual difficulties. The group of symptoms listed for dyslexia eventually came to include poor co-ordination, lack of sense of time, multiple learning difficulties, poor memory and concentration. This group has a surprising number of overlaps with what is now called ADHD.

Dyslexia means learning difficulties

The role of the ear in dyslexia

Dyslexia is generally thought of as being the tendency to reverse letter forms; hence poor spatial orientation, and problems with linear sequential processing. Dyslexia was a major focus of Dr Tomatis' research, and he was one of the first practitioners to discover the great importance of the ear in the condition of dyslexia.

Laterality and sound confusion

Tomatis focused his theory of treatment for dyslexia largely on laterality, meaning which side of the brain is dominant for particular functions. The left hemisphere of the brain is the main centre for processing language. Sensory information received on the right side of the body generally goes to the left hemisphere of the brain, and vice versa. This is also true for hearing. Because the most direct

The right ear must lead

way of conducting sound to the left hemisphere is via the right ear, for efficient listening the right ear must take the leading role. In addition, to fulfil its role as the primary supplier of linguistic information, the right ear takes the role of deciphering high frequency sounds.

Because high frequencies give definition to consonants and portray the emotional intent of the voice, this gives the right ear a very important role. Tomatis found that to listen effectively, a child must develop right ear dominance. A child who is left ear dominant will normally have much greater difficulty processing language. Longer, less efficient brain pathways must be used. The sounds from the left ear go first to the right hemisphere and must then cross the corpus callosum (the great divide between the right and left hemispheres) to get to the language centre in the left hemisphere. This delays sound reaching the brain by a fraction of a second, causing auditory confusion, and dyslexia or stuttering.

Dr Tomatis argued that children with dyslexia have failed to achieve right ear dominance and that therefore the order in which they hear sounds becomes jumbled. If they sometimes use the left and sometimes the right ear as the directing ear, sounds may reach the brain at different speeds, so letters will be jumbled. This accounts for errors of reversal, such as writing 'was' as 'saw' or pronouncing 'spaghetti' as 'busghetti'.

Correcting linguistic pathways

Tomatis believed that the balance between the two hemispheres of the brain is of fundamental importance in overcoming dyslexia. Both hemispheres play a role in processing language, but the roles they play are different. The eye must combine with the power and the quality of the ear to make sense of the written sounds. This co-ordination happens easily when the left hemisphere deals primarily with audition and the right hemisphere deals primarily with vision.

In dyslexia, the route which allows for phonic analysis has been damaged. Sound Therapy may help to restore the functioning of this route and eliminate the cause of the problem. Tomatis says, 'We read with our ears ... the ear is the organ of language, the pathway to language assimilation, the key that controls it, the receptor regulating its flow.' Sound Therapy stimulates and exercises the ear, encouraging it to receive and interpret sound in an efficient manner. Music is a highly organised series of sounds which the ear has to analyse. Therefore, listening to music is an excellent way for a child to learn how to perceive sounds in an organised fashion, or in other words, to listen. The higher volume of sound to the right ear, which is built into all Sound Therapy recordings, means that the right ear is educated to be the directing ear. When this right ear dominance is achieved, the problem of reversal is often reduced or entirely overcome.

I'm not dumb anymore!

Children with dyslexia often have feelings of inferiority after repeated failure. It is unfair that they must try many times harder than anyone else to achieve only mediocre results. Sound Therapy may offer immediate emotional relief because it is a method of treatment that requires no extra effort from the child. A therapy that does not require the child to struggle with the problem area of language enables him or her to feel let off the hook for once, and enjoy a treatment which is not a constant reminder of his or her own inadequacies. Sound Therapy aims to remedy the basic cause of the language difficulties. Once the child is able to receive and interpret sound accurately and easily, his or her ability and motivation to communicate is greatly increased. Thus the problem learner is transformed into a receptive and motivated learner. For more background information on dyslexia see Chapter 7, *Not another label,* and for examples see Chapter 8, *Listeners' experiences with Sound Therapy.*

How to use Sound Therapy for dyslexia

Children with dyslexia will usually take to Sound Therapy willingly and be relieved to have something that makes their auditory processing easier. Some dyslexic children who have not attained right laterality may initially struggle with the adjustment required. As the brain reorganises its pathways, the child may react with stress or irritation and may, at this point, resist listening to Sound Therapy. It is very important to encourage the child through this stage, so that the reorganisation of brain pathways can be completed. The resistance and irritation will pass once this occurs, and learning and language functions will become much easier.

Speech development
Speech and the brain

Unless there is a deformity in the vocal apparatus, most speech difficulties are caused by some interference or distortion in auditory reception. Although the hearing may be normal, the relaying of verbal information to the brain could be impaired. Hearing our own voice is a source of constant feedback while we are speaking, and if there is any confusion in the sequence of received sounds it will cause confusion in the output of speech. The results can be substitutions of one sound for another, stumbling over words, or a flat and toneless voice.

The great majority of people use the left hemisphere of the brain as the primary integrating centre for language. Some studies have shown that stutterers process language primarily in the right hemisphere, or a mixture of the two. The right hemisphere is less efficient for processing auditory information, so this results in problems in the timing of speech output.

Speech difficulties frequently lead to problems in other areas where language is used, such as reading and writing. The basis for all these skills is the ability to hear and process sound accurately.

Improved vocal control

Dr Tomatis made an important discovery about the relatedness of the ear to the voice. He established that the larynx emits only those harmonics which the ear is able to hear. A lack of tone in the voice indicates a lack of tone in the hearing. Sound Therapy may finetune the hearing and restore the ability to hear missing frequencies by exercising the ear muscles and stimulating the receptor cells in the inner ear. It may also correct reversed or mixed laterality, so that the left hemisphere becomes the processing centre for language. Sound Therapy continually plays more sound into the right ear. The right ear connects to the left hemisphere of the brain, so when the right ear becomes dominant the language function naturally switches to the left hemisphere.

Listen to me talk now!

Dr Tomatis worked with a group of 74 stutterers and discovered that all of them had difficulty hearing from the right ear. When he educated them to use the right ear alone, all of them began to speak correctly. Children with other types of speech difficulties have responded similarly to the treatment. Not only does their speech improve, but their behaviour changes. They become more confident, more dynamic and more eager to talk and communicate. Parents also report improvements in reading and the use of written language. Children with delayed language development or who have difficulty with receptive or expressive language improve spontaneously. Sound Therapy is an excellent adjunct to speech therapy and will generally make the speech pathologist's job a lot easier. For more background information on speech development see Chapter 7, *Not another label,* and for examples see Chapter 8, *Listeners' experiences with Sound Therapy.*

How to use Sound Therapy for speech problems

Simply listening to Sound Therapy normally has a significant impact on linguistic development and speaking ability. The child should listen for at least 30 to 60 minutes a day, or more if desired. More active involvement can be encouraged using the Let's Recite tape in the Family Kit, as it gives children the opportunity to repeat what is said and to integrate their speaking with their new experience of listening. Another good exercise for children with any form of speech difficulty, is speaking into a microphone while monitoring their voice through the right ear. This can be done using a personal cassette player with a microphone, and wearing only the right headphone. The child can speak, sing, read or make any vocal sounds. A similar effect can be achieved without the equipment by simply closing off the right ear with fingers or an ear plug. This increases the volume of the child's own voice in the right ear. This exercise can be done for some time each day, in conjunction with the listening.

Autism spectrum disorders

Autism is a complex developmental disorder which causes children to become emotionally isolated from the world around them. Asperger's syndrome is higher-functioning autism, meaning the symptoms are milder and the child functions well or above average in many areas of life, while still having certain abnormalities in their way of relating to others. A definite cause of autism spectrum disorders is not known, but a fairly consistent trait is believed to be distortion in the reception of sensory information. Many children with autism exhibit extreme sensitivity to noise. Some frequencies are actually painful for them to hear.

Psychological view

Dr Tomatis took a psychological view, suggesting that in order to shut out painful sounds, or other unwanted stimuli, the child closes down the hearing mechanism so that certain sounds cannot penetrate the consciousness. On a physiological level, this closing off of the ear can be achieved by a relaxation of the muscles of the middle ear. Over time, these muscles lose their tonicity. Sounds are then imprecisely perceived and, as a result, incorrectly analysed. Tomatis believed that the reluctance to communicate in children with autism, resulted from the closing off of their being to auditory input. Although they may understand what is said to them, they have tuned out many of the frequencies in the sound and have thus tuned out the emotional content of the message.

Biochemical view

Environmental medicine is now uncovering evidence that autism is related to viruses and toxins which affect the child in its early months, interfering with neurological development. There is now an understanding that there is a physical abnormality in brain structure and function. The inability to deal with language and interaction is now known to be fundamentally due to physiological rather than psychological problems. However, the two systems are so intertwined that neither can be said to operate without the other.

Repairing auditory connections

Sound Therapy offers a child with autism the opportunity to re-open the listening capacity. The fluctuating sounds produced by the Electronic Ear gradually exercise and tone the ear muscles, teaching the ear to respond to and recognise the full range of frequencies. The stimulation given by Sound Therapy builds brain pathways and can, to a degree, make up for missed neurological development at an earlier stage. As this happens, communication takes on new meanings and the child begins to respond where, before, he or she was unreachable.

Tomatis discovered that because of the way the foetal ear develops, the first sounds heard in utero are high frequency sounds. The child hears not only the mother's heartbeat and visceral noises, but also her voice. Re-awakening the child's ability to hear high frequencies re-creates this earliest auditory experience, and enables emotional contact to be made — with the mother first, and then with others. For more background information on autism spectrum disorders see Chapter 7, *Not another label*, and for examples see Chapter 8, *Listeners' experiences with Sound Therapy*.

I love you Mummy!

Children with autism have responded to Sound Therapy by showing a greater interest in making contact and communicating with the people around them. Interactions with their family members have become more affectionate and appropriate. There is often increased eye contact and the children have a longer attention span. They may initiate contact rather than waiting to be approached. For children without language, vocalisation has increased — initially as screams and then as babbling. Children who can speak may develop a more appropriate use of language; for instance, beginning to use more personal pronouns ('I', 'you') or first names, and using words to express their feelings. They may begin to laugh and cry at appropriate times. Once children have begun to emerge from their emotional isolation, they show increasing responsiveness to what they are being taught and to the people who care for them.

How to use Sound Therapy for autism

The child should be encouraged to listen to the filtered music or stories every day for a period of thirty to sixty

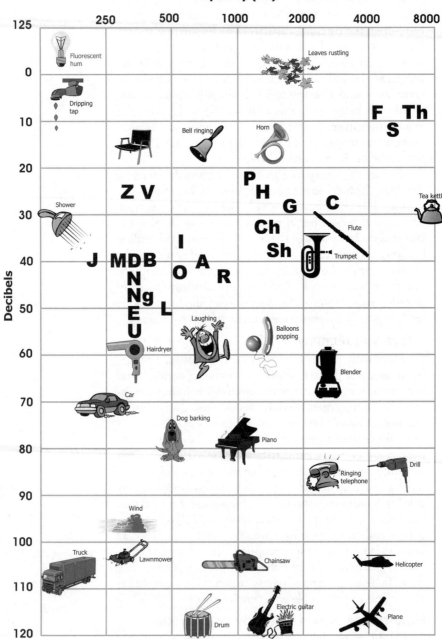

Diagram of Sounds

minutes, or more if desired. Long-term treatment, possibly over many years, is recommended for children with autism. Both the music and the stories are suitable for children with autism and related conditions. For children who can speak, the Let's Recite tape in the *Family Kit* has been a useful addition to the listening program, as it gives the child the opportunity to repeat what is said, encouraging participation, and vocal expression of the new range of frequencies being heard.

In a clinical setting, the Sound Therapy treatment of children with autism includes playing the mother's voice filtered through the Electronic Ear. This can now be achieved in the home with the ***Sonic Brain Activator.***

Down syndrome

Seventy-five percent of children with Down syndrome have a hearing impairment. This is most often due to recurrent middle ear infections and wax impaction. Repeated chronic middle ear infections result in fibrous adhesions which limit the movement of the ossicles, resulting in progressive hearing loss. Children with Down syndrome are significantly affected by sensory deprivation and they need supportive measures if they are to reach their full cognitive potential. A delay in the comprehension of language results in a delay in speaking. The impairment of language abilities delays learning in all areas and makes the tasks of education and socialisation more difficult. This results in behaviour problems, which could be avoided if the language abilities were improved.

Clearer hearing, clearer speech

It is very important for children with Down syndrome to have their hearing treated in the early years to assist with language development. These children respond well to education in the area of social and emotional adjustment, motor skills and visual comprehension. The greatest area of difficulty in learning is in auditory vocal processing. They often have difficulty learning to manipulate the speech system — co-ordinating the tongue, lips, jaw and palate. Because they face much greater obstacles in producing speech sounds, they need particular assistance with their hearing. Dr Tomatis discovered that the voice can only produce what the ear hears. Sound Therapy stimulates the hearing capacity and exercises the ear, training it in particular to receive high frequency sounds that are lost when hearing is damaged. The sounds of consonants, such as b, d, p, g and t, are high frequency sounds, and are of course essential for clear comprehension of speech. See table on page 80 for relative frequencies and loudness (decibels) of different sounds. Before they can begin learning to produce these sounds, children must first be able to hear them. As Sound Therapy may restore hearing in a wider range of frequencies, a greater range of tonality is available to the voice and this is very important for producing intelligible speech.

Better sleep

Sleep disorders are common in people with Down syndrome and this is another area where Sound Therapy can be especially helpful. Sleep apnoea, or short periods of not breathing during sleep, is especially common. People with Down syndrome have small, often 'floppy' airways, which can sometimes be completely or partially blocked during sleep by large tonsils and adenoids, or by floppy walls, or the airway collapsing as air is exhaled. Regardless of the cause of obstruction, the sleeper must awaken briefly to resume breathing. Some patients with sleep apnoea awaken hundreds of times per night.

Symptoms associated with, but not specific to, sleep apnoea include snoring, lots of 'thrashing' about while asleep, excessive daytime sleepiness, mouth breathing, and unusual sleep positions, such as sleeping in a seated or hunched forward position. Sound Therapy may help to restore normal tone to the pharynx and airway walls. It also works on the autonomic nervous system, which is responsible for regulating the control of body functions that are not consciously directed, including breathing during sleep.

How to use Sound Therapy for Down syndrome

Sound Therapy helps tone the pharynx and improves breathing

Parents should ensure that their children's ears are checked regularly and that they receive treatment for ear infections or wax impaction. In some cases the recurrence of these problems will decrease with the use of Sound Therapy. The movement and exercise produced in the ear by Sound

Therapy often results in a spontaneous expulsion of fluid from the ear, and blockages may not recur. It has been helpful for some children with Down syndrome to listen regularly to Sound Therapy on a long-term or permanent basis, in order to protect the ear against its tendency to become easily blocked and to stimulate the full range of hearing. For the first few months of listening, children should listen to Sound Therapy every day for a period of thirty to sixty minutes, or longer if desired. If the child wishes to listen for several hours at a time it will do no harm. The auditory stimulation provided by Sound Therapy has a re-charging effect on the brain and children with Down syndrome generally respond with enthusiasm. It is important to continue language education through the life of a person with Down syndrome. This ongoing learning process may be greatly enhanced for people of any age by listening to Sound Therapy.

My ears are happy now!

Improved hearing leads to a greater interest in the environment and what is happening, more liveliness and more willingness to learn. Language comprehension and speech improve significantly; and because the links between learning language and learning about the world are direct, the child's education and performance in all areas will be enhanced. For more background information on Down syndrome see Chapter 7, *Not another label,* and for examples see Chapter 8, *Listeners' experiences with Sound Therapy.*

Bed-wetting

Bed-wetting is a problem which often accompanies learning difficulties, language problems and sensory integration difficulties. Improvement in this area is often seen as one of the positive side effects of Sound Therapy. There may be an emotional component to bed wetting, but it is also quite possible that it is due to delayed integration in the nervous system. Because hearing is linked to the autonomic nervous system, involuntary processes such as digestion, breathing during sleep, bladder control and circulation are also affected. A recent letter we received even described how a man with long-term, severe haemorrhoids had seen them completely clear up after he started using Sound Therapy.

Other conditions

The conditions described above are those for which there is the greatest demand for Sound Therapy for children. There are many other disabilities and types of developmental delay which will respond positively to Sound Therapy. Different professions may have different ways of describing the same problem, and some problems are multi-faceted. Some of these conditions are covered in Chapter 7, *Not another label* and some are mentioned in Chapter 8, *Listeners' experiences with Sound Therapy*. Others are addressed in Chapter 6, *We move with our ears* and Chapter 9, *What's this on my plate? Living Naturally*. These include:

- Central auditory processing disorder (CAPD)
- Sensory integration disorder
- Intellectual disability
- Hearing loss
- Cerebral palsy
- Brain damage
- Fragile X syndrome
- Epilepsy
- Food intolerances
- Chemical sensitivity

Also check the Index to help find the relevant sections for you.

For Parents

Many parents who learn about Sound Therapy decide to listen themselves as well as giving it to their children. Parents can use Sound Therapy to improve sleep and energy, reduce stress and deal with the daily demands of parenting. Listening along with your child can be fun and rewarding. Adults will need different information in order to benefit fully from the Sound Therapy program. Therefore it is important to read one of the other books: *Sound Therapy: Music to Recharge Your Brain,* or *Triumph Over Tinnitus.*

Prenatal Listening and Sound Therapy

Sound Therapy is most important and beneficial for expectant mothers. In prenatal life, sound is the first sense to develop fully. The foetus' ear is ready to perceive sound at four and a half months. The baby listens to its mother's heartbeat, respiration and digestive sounds. Dr Tomatis believes that the baby can also hear the mother's voice, and becomes familiar with this sound before birth. Tomatis discovered that the first sounds heard in utero are high frequency sounds (above 8,000 Hz) due to the development of the embryonic ear. Birth is often a traumatic event; the baby is pushed from the familiar protection of the womb into a totally unknown world and bombarded with new stimuli — and now it must begin the process of learning to communicate with others.

The Effect of Sound Therapy

Dr Tomatis says the sound of the mother's voice, with its familiar tone and rhythm, is what provides continuity between the prenatal and postnatal worlds. The infant is particularly accustomed to the high frequency sounds of the voice as heard in the womb, and therefore has an immediate response of feeling reassured when presented with high frequency sounds filtered to a similar level. Playing Sound Therapy will have an immediate, soothing effect on the newborn baby.

The effects of listening for the mother are a soothing of her whole system and stimulation to the cortex of the brain from the high frequency sound. Because of its connection with the vital pneumogastric (Vagus) nerve, the ear plays a part in nearly everything we feel — including heartbeat and breathing, or sensations like a tickle in the throat or butterflies in the stomach. The effects of Sound Therapy are therefore passed through the mother's whole body and have an influence on the development of the foetus.

Prenatal listening program

It is recommended that the mother listens regularly to Sound Therapy throughout her pregnancy. To obtain the full benefits of improved sleep, reduced stress and increased energy, the recommended listening time for an adult is three hours a day. This can be done during other activities, however, so does not require that time be set aside for listening alone.

Effects for the infant

When a baby is born to a mother who has been listening regularly to Sound Therapy, and the headphones are placed on the baby's ears straight after birth, it has been observed to immediately stop crying. Babies whose mothers have listened to Sound Therapy during pregnancy show a distinct lack of tension and anxiety as they grow. They have an inner peacefulness about them and are less reactive, making them easy to manage. They feel secure in their relationship with their mother and will go easily to other people. They have a natural appreciation for classical music and can continue to benefit from its healing properties. Studies have shown that children exposed to classical music before birth are more intelligent. See Chapter 2, *Baby in the Womb: The miracle of language,* for more detail on how prenatal development relates to Sound Therapy.

You don't have to have a problem

Your child does not need to have a problem to use Sound Therapy. The program assists in the normal development of the ear and brain for any child. It is just as important for normal development as going to the playground. Today, Sound Therapy is more important than it used to be, since the world is noisier, and all children face chemical challenges growing up; and many children watch more TV, use computers and lack the movement stimulation which earlier generations enjoyed. Computers stimulate the eyes but not the vestibular system, and the rest of the body's musculature is underused.

How to use Sound Therapy

The child listens to Sound Therapy through earphones for at least thirty to sixty minutes per day, depending on the age of the child. This is a minimum time. Many families choose to have their children listen for several hours, even up to eight hours per day. There is no harm in this, and it can produce quicker results.

The children's kits contain both classical music and stories, both of which have been filtered with Tomatis' Electronic Ear. The child will want to pay attention to the stories, so they are best used at bedtime or during quiet times. The music can be played during any activities including travelling, sleeping or watching television.

Children can listen during their regular daily activities such as:

- Doing their homework
- Riding in the car or the bus
- Watching TV, computer video games
- Nap time or going to sleep at night
- Story time, reading
- Drawing or quiet playtime
- Sick days or hospital stays

Selecting the right kit for your family

A range of kits is available to suit the needs of different children and families. See the order form at the back of this book for details. Our booklet, *Listening Helps Learning,* which is available from our head office or our independent distributors, also contains a full catalogue of our children's products. Our trained telephone consultants are happy to discuss your needs and answer your enquiries.

Starting out

The *Starter Kits* for younger and older children are suitable for treating children with mild to moderate problems, or for general hearing maintenance, and will enable you to see how your child responds to the listening program.

Long-term treatment

For children with more severe disorders, which will require longer-term treatment, it is best to obtain the full program in the *Basic Music Kit* or the *Family Kit.* The *Family Kit* is the best value, as it includes the full six-hour music program and a range of classic children's stories for different ages — all at a discounted price. The stories, made with filtered voice, give the program added interest for children, but it can be conducted quite successfully with the music alone.

Parents and Sound Therapy

Listening to Sound Therapy gives you the perfect antidote for sleepless nights, frayed tempers and constant communication challenges.

If your children see you listening too, this may make them want to listen. Encourage all your children to use Sound Therapy, not just the one who needs it most. This way the child with a problem will not feel singled out. Although a family can share a kit, it may be necessary to have a player for each person so you do not have to wait your turn.

Selecting a personal player

To achieve successful results, Sound Therapy should always be listened to through headphones. If a baby is too young to wear headphones the music can be played in the room instead. In this case, it is ideal to arrange the speakers on your stereo so that the right one is on the right of the cot and the left one on the left, so that the right ear emphasis is still achieved.

The music needs to be played on a good quality, portable headphone player which will accurately convey the filtered sounds without distortion. Model numbers and brands are not given here, since they change every few months.

Since it is sometimes difficult to get the correct information from retail stores, and for your convenience, suitable players can be purchased through Sound Therapy International (see order form at back of book), or through your local Sound Therapy distributor.

How do I know which is the Right headphone?

All good headphones are marked 'R' for right and 'L' for left. Always place the right headphone on the right ear, because Sound Therapy is intentionally recorded with greater volume in the right channel in order to encourage the right ear to become the directing ear for listening. This improves the efficiency of the brain in processing sound because the right ear connects to the left side of the brain, which is the language centre. The result is an improvement in reading and vocal skills.

Listening hours and routine

- Most parents are surprised at how easy it is to get children to use Sound Therapy.
- Even hyperactive children usually love it.
- The length of each listening session will depend on the age and concentration span of the child.
- Some children may be willing to listen for only half an hour a day. Others may listen for an hour or more each time.

- The minimum listening time required for most children to receive full benefit from the program is approximately 100 hours.
- Some children will begin to achieve results in the first few days of listening. However, they should still complete 100 hours.
- Children can continue listening after 100 hours to maximize results.
- Many families have their children continue using Sound Therapy for months or years. There are added benefits which come with long-term listening.

Sound Therapy is completely safe and cannot do any harm. The only reason for restricting a child's listening hours would be so that he or she did not become bored with the program, and then not want to listen anymore. See practical tips on how to get your children to listen to Sound Therapy at the end of this chapter.

Headphones

Children rarely object to wearing headphones unless for some reason they are uncomfortable. It is a good idea to have two different types of headphones, in case one becomes uncomfortable for the child. If your child is too hyperactive to wear the headphones you can put them on at night when the child is sleeping. The mini-phones, which sit inside the outer ear, can be taped in with surgical tape to stop them from falling out during sleep. Some children prefer big, soft headphones. Or try Phillips Ear Gear which has an earphone with an attachment that fits around the ear to keep it in place. You do not need expensive headphones, though you may get a better result with a better quality headphone.

How loud should it be?

The volume should never be too loud, as any loud sound could damage the ear. It should be just loud enough for the child to hear comfortably. If the child is listening while going to sleep, the volume can be turned down very low.

Reading aloud exercise

Children who are experiencing difficulty with reading can begin this exercise after the first ten to twenty hours of listening. The child sits in an erect but comfortable posture, and reads aloud, while holding the right hand near the mouth — as though holding an imaginary microphone. This has the psychological effect of 'switching on' the voice. At the same time it encourages right ear dominance, which is necessary for the successful conversion of visual symbols into sound. If desired, the child can listen to Sound Therapy music at the same time. This exercise should be done for fifteen minutes each day, and can be continued until the reading problems are resolved. Encourage the child by making it into a fun game. Give your child positive attention while he or she is reading, and this will create a positive association with reading aloud. Pretend the child is an important speaker giving a very important address to a group of people. Pretend to be a keen member of the audience, hang on every word and applaud frequently, whether your child is reading well or not. This will give your child confidence, will make the activity fun and get more neurons firing.

Long-term listening and other treatment

For children with mild to moderate conditions or wanting to accelerate learning potential

Once the child has completed the 100 hours listening, which may take two to four months of daily routine, the hours can be reduced if you wish. However, it is beneficial to still listen regularly, or as often as the child wants to, as this will help to maintain the benefits. Regular listening will also continue to develop the child's auditory functioning and neural development. While the brain is still growing is the best time to give extra assistance. If your child develops a habit of listening to Sound Therapy during homework, it may have long-term benefits for her academic results.

For children with profound conditions.

It should be noted that for treating children with profound conditions such as autism, ADHD or hearing loss, a long-term listening program is essential, and benefits may continue to accrue for a period of months or years. In these cases, several hundred hours of listening may be required. To conduct an effective listening program, parents will need to make a long-term commitment to supervising their child's listening. Sound Therapy is likely to be even more effective if used in combination with other forms of remedial treatment such as motor sensory exercises, special diet, supplements, tutoring and remedial instruction. In some cases, drug therapy may become unnecessary when these other approaches are used.

The Mother's Voice Technique

Sound Therapy International now offers a miniature Electronic Ear which can be purchased for use in the home. The 'Sonic Brain Activator' can be connected to a tape player or stereo and will convert any music or voice recordings into Sound Therapy. For instructions, see the section on developing a Sonic Birth program, at the end of this chapter. This program enables the child to listen to a tape of his own mother's voice as Sound Therapy, through the Sonic Brain Activator. This technique offers profound healing and is an important part of the Tomatis program, especially for children with serious problems. A Voice Attachment is also available, which allows the child to hear his own voice converted to Sound Therapy as he is speaking. This technique is usually introduced after an initial period of using the basic listening program.

How to use the Sonic Brain Activator

Here are some ideas for what to do with the Sonic Brain Activator, for different conditions or needs your child may have. For voice activities, plug the voice attachment into the Sonic Brain Activator. Connect headphones to the Sonic Brain Activator and place them on your child's ears. When your child speaks into the Voice Attachment, she will hear her own voice converted into Sound Therapy.

For study

Have the child read text books aloud through the Voice Attachment and Sonic Brain Activator. Read any material which needs to be memorised in this way.

For ADHD or learning difficulties

Have a conversation with the child while the child is talking through the Voice Attachment and Sonic Brain Activator. Talk about a subject of great interest so the child will be animated and will want to talk.

Focussing is easier when it is on something the child likes. This will help to improve self-listening and language processing. If the child is relaxed, improved brain function can happen more easily.

For speech difficulties

Have the child read through the voice attachment or have a conversation on topics of interest. Have the child read passages with certain sounds. Use onomatopoeic words (words that sound like what they mean). See Appendix I. Select passages with the sounds the child needs to practice, or passages he enjoys and can read easily.

For hearing loss or scotoma

(A scotoma is a hearing loss in particular frequencies)
Get the child to sing through the Voice Attachment and Sonic Brain Activator. Sing along with the child to give encouragement. Sing easy songs, then songs which are challenging on the difficult bits. Choose songs the child knows. Have fun and enjoy the process. Have a sing-along. Create the atmosphere that existed before TV when families gathered in the evening to sing folk songs. Use a piano, drum or guitar to accompany your singing. Let the child tap along in rhythm.

For depression

Using the voice can help depression, especially when spoken through the Voice Attachment and Sonic Brain Activator. Be a non-judgemental, loving listener while the child talks about whatever he or she needs to. Maintain total faith in your child's goodness and ability to overcome what is troubling him or her. Also have the child read uplifting passages through the Voice Attachment and Sonic Brain Activator. Or, you read your child a story, speaking into the Voice Attachment, and let the child listen through the Sonic Brain Activator with headphones. Singing is also very valuable. Again, you sing along with your child, while the child uses the Voice Attachment. Get a book of good, old songs.

For anxiety

Let the child listen through the Sonic Brain Activator to Mozart or other music she finds calming and reassuring.

Developing a Sonic Birth program for your child

Dr Tomatis identified several phases of treatment, which follow the course of Sonic Birth and linguistic development. The process retraces phases in the child's development in the womb and after birth, and can assist in healing emotional and linguistic traumas which may have occurred at these stages.[5] The following plan can be used to recreate this program at home. Since this program is quite involved, some parents may prefer to undertake it only with the supervision of one of our Qualified Sound Therapy Consultants. If you are uncertain about managing the program yourself, then we recommend that for home listening you simply use the exercises listed above. However, parents who have training in education or therapeutic modalities may wish to undertake the Sonic Birth program with their children themselves.

Phase 1 - Sonic Return

This is the phase which simulates an acoustic return to the environment of the womb. This phase may take about three weeks, but you may wish to continue until you notice an energy shift. This shift could be marked by sudden tiredness, pain in the ears, dizziness, sleeping better or increased irritability.

Activity:

Passive listening – the child listens to the Music Kit and stories suitable for her age.

Phase 2 - Filtered Sounds

This phase simulates the experience of hearing filtered sounds in the womb. It may take about two weeks but can be continued until you observe an energy breakthrough. This will be marked by an increase in energy, which may be mild or extreme; or possibly by a resolution of some of the issues which began in Phase 1.

Activity:

Passive listening to Basic Music Kit and the Mother's Voice tape (alternate).

The Mother's Voice tape is a tape made by the mother on a normal tape recorder and then played to the child through the Sonic Brain Activator. When the mother makes the tape it is important that she is feeling positive and stress free. She should read some of the child's favourite stories or something positive. Alternatively, use the Mother's Voice Affirmation tape from the Deep Peace Kit. Or, if preferred, the mother can read out the script of that tape.

Phase 3 - Sonic Birth

This phase simulates the change to acoustic stimuli at the time of the birth process and immediately after. This stage may take about three weeks or until embodiment occurs. Embodiment will be marked by a possible release of tension, improved posture or co-ordination, voice changes, feeling more grounded and focussed.

Activity:

At this stage a child of six or older could be introduced to the Full Spectrum kit. This is level two of the advanced Sound Therapy listening program. It is important to do body work with the child during this phase. Use any exercises, dancing or physical remedial programs you have available which are age appropriate. Take the child to the playground, or play romping on the bed or the floor. Also use humming through the Voice Attachment and Sonic Brain Activator.

The Humming Technique

Sit in an upright posture with the head inclined slightly forward. Softly pucker the lips as though ready for a kiss. Make a humming sound in the mid range, not too high, not too low, so that it creates the most resonance in the head. Sit and hum in harmony with your child. Play around with making noises and having fun. Try overtone chanting if you know how to do it. Do any kind of chanting you like, letting the child chant through the Voice Attachment and Sonic Brain Activator for maximum brain stimulation.

Phase 4 – Pre-linguistic

This phase resembles the child's first two years, the pre-linguistic period. It may take anywhere from two weeks to two years, depending on the age of the child. This phase continues until the child is beginning to have a solid grasp of language. The pre-linguistic phase represents the development of the child's relationship with the mother, and the feeling of safety and sense of self which occurs in this phase. In older children or adults, the resolution of this phase may be marked by achieving a state of tranquillity, feelings of deep peace, forgiving someone, early memories, or significant dreams.

Activity:

Adults or children from the age of ten can listen at this stage to the Advanced Sound Therapy Kits Level 3 or 4 if desired.

Right ear emphasis vocal exercises.

For young children, read together and talk about an age-appropriate book, with the child listening to her own voice through the Voice Attachment and Sonic Brain Activator. Older children can read simple poetic passages, rhyming and rhythmic words, or read the list of onomatopoeic words (see Appendix I), through the Voice Attachment and Sonic Brain Activator. At this stage they should stick to passages that are easy and below their age level ability. Also recite poems, nursery rhymes, sing rounds or simple, fun songs with interesting words.

Phase 5 - Language Integration

This phase may last from three weeks to three years or until the resolution of some key issue. This phase is about the child's developing awareness of the 'other'. It is characterised by the development of language and a psychological sense of the relationship with the father. There may be another energy shift, a noticeable improvement in language ability, positive changes in behaviour and attitude, or improvement in the child's relationship with a family member.

Activity:

Teenagers or adults at this stage can, if desired, go on to listen to the *Advanced Sound Therapy Kits* Level 5 or 6.

The child can now read more detailed linguistic passages at their age level through the Voice Attachment and Sonic Brain Activator. Have the child speak sounds rich in sibilants (see Appendix II).

Use specifically tailored affirmations to help your child overcome particular fears or confidence issues. To develop these, have a heart-to-heart talk with your child in which she identifies the areas of fear, concern or grief that affect her life. Then develop short statements which are 100% positive and contradict those issues. For example: if your child is afraid of the dark, explore the fear a little — perhaps she is afraid something will jump out at her and no-one will come. Her affirmation might be 'I am safe in my room and mummy is always close' or 'I am full of courage that shines brightly like the sun.'

The father's voice can also be gently introduced at this stage. If the child has any negative reaction to the father's voice, it may indicate that it is too early or that there is a difficult issue with the father, in which case family counselling should be sought to help resolve this in a positive way. In the case of blended families where there is a step-father, this exercise can be attempted to help bring the child closer to the new father. However, this must be done with great sensitivity so as not to traumatise the child. If there is no father in the child's life but the child has a close and positive relationship with another male figure, the exercise could be done with that person, if the child is positive about this. The same is true for the mother's voice, in the pre-linguistic phase, if there is an adoptive mother. The father can read favourite stories onto a tape which the child then listens to.

Support and guidance available

A specialist team at Sound Therapy International can answer any questions or concerns you may have about your child's progress with Sound Therapy. If you bought your program through one of our independent distributors, that person is fully qualified to advise you. We are always pleased to hear from you if you would like to write and tell us of your child's responses to the listening. Your experience can help other people. Some parents find it useful to keep a diary or log book monitoring their child's progress in the program.

Why choose the Joudry Sound Therapy method?

This comprehensive list of advantages is unique to the Joudry program offered by Sound Therapy International

Product

- The most affordable Sound Therapy program in the world
- No appointments, testing, travel time or ongoing fees
- Closely follows the principles developed by Dr Tomatis, the pioneer and original inventor of Sound Therapy
- Offers all key aspects of Tomatis' discoveries, including the Mother's Voice technique
- Basic Kit suits the whole family, you don't need separate programs for each condition
- Selection is straightforward and easy
- Range of children's kits for each age group
- Stories and poetry support language development
- Analogue mastering
- Highest quality music sources, with top-level performers
- Very gradual programs for gentle adjustment
- Recording done with Electronic Ear built according to Tomatis' original principles
- Electronic Ear has been upgraded to incorporate the latest developments in sound recording technology
- Gradual filtering to 10,000 hertz, optimum level for highest brain recharge
- Choice of own music possible with Sonic Brain Activator
- Immediate voice feedback training with Voice Attachment
- Long-term treatment highly accessible and affordable

- Uses real, orchestral classical music, not synthesized substitutes
- Features Mozart, proven in research to be the most beneficial music for the human brain
- Offers a wide range of benefits which continue to develop for years
- Product guarantee – damaged recordings replaced for small handling fee only

Educational tools

- Highly accessible and informative educational materials including books, videos, information tapes and a large range of specific brochures and information sheets
- Delivery through practitioners or direct to client is equally supported by our organisation
- All users read one of our books which are highly motivating, so commitment to the program is high
- The books are both easy to understand, for basic readers, and academic enough to keep the interest of an educated audience

Training and professional support

- Professional practitioner training program
- Training available by distance
- National inquiry line with trained personnel
- Professional team at head office devoted to constant improvement in product and service delivery
- Team of professional lecturers available
- Over 300 clinics offering the product
- Over 1000 practitioners recommending Sound Therapy
- Ongoing professional development for distributors, through conference calls on marketing and research tutorials

Research

- Research program supported by company
- Based on fifty years of research and clinical practice of the Tomatis method
- Numerous clinical studies done around the world

PRACTICAL ACTION TIPS

Tips for Listening

⊘ Start Sound Therapy early — the younger child is, the greater the benefit.

⊘ Be sure that you place the right headphone on the right ear to create right ear dominance. All decent quality headphones are marked 'R' for right and 'L' for left.

⊘ The stories and music are equally effective and can be used interchangeably as the child prefers.

⊘ Have your child use a carry pouch ('bumbag') to prevent dropping the player. If the player is dropped, the warranty will be void.

⊘ Always keep the volume at a low level, so it is audible but not damaging to the child's ears.

⊘ Use the 'hold' or 'lock' button on the player, if available, to avoid accidentally turning up the volume or pressing a wrong button while listening.

⊘ Make sure listening is done regularly, every day for best results.

⊘ Think of Sound Therapy as a 'treat' not a 'treatment.'

⊘ Ideally Sound Therapy should not be forced on a child, as this would cause resistance and be counter-productive to the aim of opening the listening capacity. Present it as an enjoyable activity and explain the benefits in a way that your child can understand.

⊘ Listen yourself, and have the whole family listen, so the child will want to join in. You will benefit too!

⊘ If possible, have a player for each family member so you do not have to wait your turn to listen.

⊘ Children usually love to take their Sound Therapy to bed. It helps them go to sleep easily and gives them happier dreams. (Children often find that Sound Therapy reduces nightmares.)

⊘ Let your children listen when you are travelling in the car. It will help them to sleep, and to be more patient and contented.

⊘ Let your child listen during activities they like such as colouring, story time, TV time or computer games.

⊘ If necessary, use rewards or bribery — ie 'when you have done 100 hours you'll get a new skateboard.'

References

[1] Greenfield, Susan. *The Human Brain.* London: Phoenix, 1997.

[2] Carter, Rita. *Mapping the Mind.* London: Phoenix, 2002.

[3] Carter, *Ibid.*

[4] Purvis, Karen L. 'Phonological Processing, Not Inhibitory Control, Differentiates ADHD and Reading Disability', *Journal of the American Academy of Child and Adolescent Psychiatry,* April 2000. http:www.findarticles.com

[5] Tomatis, Dr A. A. *The Conscious Ear.* New York: Station Hill Press, 1977.

Chapter 5

LEARNING CAN BE FUN

Simon was a very good student. He was so good he usually blurted out the answer before the teacher had time to lead the class along and get them thinking. This annoyed the teacher. He finished his work fifteen minutes before everyone else, and became bored, so he was often caught mucking up in class. At home he was absorbed in his hobbies and his computer. His parents both had busy careers and they did not realise there was a problem until the teacher called them in and said she thought Simon was heading for trouble. They were shocked to hear that he rarely turned in assignments and his grades were dropping. When they talked to him, Simon said school was boring, the teachers were dumb and he hated his life. Simon's parents were very concerned so they organised some sessions with a counsellor who coached them on spending more quality time with Simon. His dad started playing sport with him and his mum took one evening a week to do something special with him. They also started him on Sound Therapy because they thought it might help. Simon's attitude changed enormously. At school, when he had finished his work he went around to see if he could help the other students or the teacher. He and his dad joined a chess club and he and his mum started going to a ceramics class. Simon began putting extra work into his assignments and coming top of the class.

What makes learning fun?

Learning is easier when you're having fun

Learning is fun when it engages the child's interest. This occurs easily when the child feels good about herself because she is interacting with people who give her approval, or when she is deeply interested in the subject matter; when there is laughter, activity, excitement, discovery and a sense of new achievement and mastery. When learning occurs, the brain is active in many parts. The emotions (acting in the limbic system), are engaged in a positive way, focus is clear and strong, lateral thinking is occurring, new pathways and new understandings are being formed. The emotions, the positive sense of self and the intellect are all engaged. Learning is a whole-brain — or whole-person process. The more sense of wholeness a child has in the learning environment, the more learning will take place.

School and achievement

Parents want their children to do well in school

All parents want their children to do well in school. For some, high achievement is paramount — whether to continue a family tradition, or to improve the child's chances in life beyond that which her family achieved.

For others, it is more important simply that their child is happy, but no child can be happy if she is not achieving at least a certain level of competence acceptable within the school system.

This chapter looks at how to help children as they start their schooling to maximise their potential for learning. We will discuss some ways to encourage the whole-self engagement in the learning process. It is not focussed on learning problems, but on the normal basic development stages of the child.

Singing and rhyming

'She started to sing as she tackled the thing that couldn't be done and she did it!'

Singing gets the right-brain to help with learning

Singing is a tremendously important activity, not only in the development of an individual, but also in the development of a culture. Singing is unifying. It unifies the two hemispheres of the brain, combining the left-brain speech function with the right-brain musical and rhythmic perceptions. Those who have suffered brain damage can sometimes sing though they cannot speak.[1]

Stutterers can sometimes sing without stuttering. Singing is a powerful way to learn a new language, as the right-brain rhythmic and melodic engagement assists memory. The development of vocal perception, as one learns to measure and modulate one's own voice, is a powerful aid to developing the listening ability.

Western, English-speaking cultures are sadly devoid of singing. Apart from religious practice for the minority of families who still practice religion, there is no communal singing in Western, English speaking culture. The TV, radio and cinema have replaced communal artistic expression, celebration and ritual. Ask a modern group of English speaking people to sing and most often there is a cacophony of strained and poorly modulated voices barely able to scratch out a melody. Compare this to a Pacific Islander nation, a Welsh village choir or in fact almost any less financially privileged nation. It appears that our wealth and higher standards of living have deprived us of one of the most vital and nurturing parts of human cultural practice.

We don't sing enough in our culture

The Pentatonic Scale

Rudolf Steiner was a German educational philosopher whose ideas have resulted in the largest international network of non-denominational private schools. In Steiner education there is a lot of focus on story-telling, particularly the original Grimm's fairy tales. These stories carry strong archetypes which help the child's psychic development. Folk stories from many traditional cultures also carry important lessons which can help children learn about the world and the dilemmas and choices they may face in life.

Steiner taught about the 'mood of the fifth', which is the best way to introduce music and melody to children. He recommends for younger children that the songs be actually within the style of the mood of the fifth, which is connected to the pentatonic scale. The pentatonic scale consists of five notes (DEGAB), and however you play the notes it always sound harmonious. Special instruments such as xylophones, lyres and flutes can be purchased for children so that they begin making music in the pentatonic scale. Some are beautifully crafted in wood and chosen for their very high tonal quality, craftsmanship and suitability

A scale with five notes is easy for children to learn

as first instruments for young children. This allows the child to experience music in its fullest meaning.

Children need high quality instruments which are easy to play, so they can fully appreciate the tones and have a good start to music appreciation. These instruments lend themselves easily to free flowing, unstructured music, so well suited to young children. Together, parent and child can enjoy listening and making music.

Like 'Twinkle, twinkle, little star'

Many original classic children's songs are written using the pentatonic scale, such as Mozart's 'Twinkle, Twinkle Little Star'. These songs are so popular because they reflect the mood of the fifth. There are no big intervals and the tones make an easy stepping for the child. Some good websites for purchasing instruments and other quality toys and educational products for children are as follows:

www.myriadonline.co.uk

http://www.ecobaby.com

http://bushby.customer.netspace.net.au/

Rudolph Steiner said:

'The right introduction into the musical element is fundamental to a human being's overcoming all hindrances that impede a sound and courage-filled development of the will in later life.'

Singing workshops

Learn to sing so you can sing to your child

The suggestion that people should sing with their children will strike fear into the hearts of many, for how can you teach your children something which you yourself cannot do? One of the best ways in which you could help your child's development would be to learn to sing yourself. Attend singing workshops designed to free the natural voice, join a choir or take singing lessons. Sing nursery rhymes to your child, join your child in singing along with radio or TV programs. Buy tapes of children's songs and sing along with them. Learn the piano, guitar, or rent a pianola or karaoke machine — whatever it takes!

Be a legend in your own lounge room!

Singing to your child is a perfect development opportunity for both of you. Your child will be the most uncritical audience you will ever have. Now is your opportunity to be a legend in your own lounge room! Children's songs are so easy to sing. They are a great way to start because they use simple harmonic intervals, thirds, fifths and octaves. Start with primary notes – like primary colours they give the fundamentals that help the child to gain an understanding of relationships and harmonies.

To get you started, here are a few songs you may know the tunes to. Try singing them with your child of the appropriate age, and see how much they love it! Singing at preschool is one thing, but singing with Mum or Dad is something special.

5 songs for babies

Twinkle, twinkle little star
Rock-a-bye baby
Hush, little baby, don't say a word
Jingle Bells
Hot Cross Buns

5 songs for toddlers

Bah, bah, black sheep
Mary had a little lamb
Hey-Ho, skip to my Lou
Pat-a-cake, Pat-a-cake, baker's man
Playschool

5 songs for pre-schoolers

The wheels of the bus
Now I know my ABC
Ring-a-ring-a-rosie
Head and shoulders, knees and toes
Eency Weency Spider

5 songs for primary children

Doh, a deer
Row, row, row your boat
Hokey Pokey
Waltzing Matilda
Kookaburra sits in the old gum tree

Learning to read

The best preparation for learning to read is lots of exposure to books and language. TV is not a good substitute for interactive language as it doesn't let you talk back. Passively hearing language is not the same as interacting. What Australian author and literacy expert, Mem Fox, advocates so vehemently and so rightly, is that children need attention

The TV doesn't help children learn to talk

and interaction in order to learn language. Someone who has learned a language in school and then finally goes to a country where it is spoken has to start all over again to learn it in a useful way for conversation.

Reading stories to your child is crucial to the child learning to read, and repetition is vital. You didn't learn to drive a car from one day's experience. It was only the repetition of ten or twenty lessons, plus the prior experience of having ridden in a car all your life, which enabled you to pick up this skill. The brain learns through repetition.

Read to your child every day

Mem Fox recommends reading a thousand stories to your child before the child starts school. Reading aloud is one of the easiest ways to have quality time with your child. It brings a structure, an interesting topic, physical closeness, conversation and an educational activity. Reading a story gives a framework for interaction which helps the parent to enter the imaginative world of the child. You don't have to think up silly games you may feel awkward playing; there is a story which moves forwards, has a beginning and an end, and which, if it is a good one, can bring delight to both parent and child.

Story time is a special bonding time for the family

I know Mem is right about the importance of reading aloud because it explains why I am good at English. Because I was educated at home in a very unstructured way, my education was lacking in many areas considered essential to a school curriculum. After the first two years of schooling, in which I learned to read, I had no formal lessons, classroom time or curriculum to follow; nor did we have a television. However, our father read aloud to us every night, without fail. My sisters and I gathered around the bed or in the sitting room, for one, two, or if we were lucky, three chapters of the book of the moment. He read us the entire series of *Doctor Do-Little*, the *Narnia* books, *Winnie the Pooh*, *The Wind in the Willows*, *Watership Down*, *Oliver Twist*, *David Copperfield*, to mention just a few of the favourites. When it came time to go to university and write essays I had no trouble at all, despite my complete lack of formal school education. Syntax, grammar and creative expression in English came as easily as talking or walking. On the other hand, trying to teach these linguistic rules to children who have had no exposure to literature is almost impossible. The brain doesn't learn that way.

I cannot recommend highly enough that you read Mem Fox's book *Reading Magic*.[2] It is short, engaging and a delight to read and it may make the biggest difference to your children's lives, and your lives as parents, of any learning intervention you undertake.

Children love to be read to

Parents inexperienced in reading often wonder, 'will my child sit still enough for me to read to him?' As Mem Fox says, surprisingly, even most hyperactive children find it soothing and delicious to be read to. They love to cuddle up in your arms, to settle into the relaxing rhythm of your voice, to have your attention engaged in an activity with them. Even most children with ADHD will respond very well to being read to, especially if you begin this practice early enough in their lives. Mem says the best time to start reading to your child is the day it is born. After all, the baby has been listening to your voice in the womb, your voice is its favourite sound, there is nothing it would rather do than relax, cuddle up to you and listen to your voice. And you can read anything you want. The baby won't know the difference!

Reading to your child is one of the very best ways to help her to acquire the skill of listening. Listening then comes naturally, because you are not talking at the child, but for the child, in her service, with love. When a child is being read to she naturally learns to concentrate and relax at the same time.

Your child will learn relaxed concentration

Relaxed concentration is the key to rapid, efficient and pleasurable learning. This was the great discovery of the Bulgarian Doctor Lozanov, who pioneered the field of Accelerated Learning. He discovered that you can put the brain into a 'best state' for learning by a combination of specific inputs. The students must undertake a deep relaxation exercise, relaxing all the muscles of the body; breathing is deep and regular, the classroom is filled with a background of slow, baroque music, and the information to be learned is presented in a four-second rhythm with particular intonation and in time with the breathing. Lozanov's discoveries were revealed to the Western world in the fascinating books on SuperLearning by Sheila Ostrander and Lynn Schroeder.[3]

This 'best state' can be achieved through Sound Therapy by simply listening to the music while you study. Reading to your child also prepares the child to easily access this 'best state' in the classroom.

Stories keep children quiet Apart from bedtime stories, reading aloud to your child can provide a solution to many difficult and stressful instances.

Have your favourite books to hand in situations which are boring and where it is difficult to contain the child, such as in waiting rooms, on buses and planes, or waiting for a meeting to finish.

Non-readers

Today, fewer children look to books to entertain them. Children who can't turn to books are very demanding, needing constant entertainment or wanting to watch TV all the time. You will have an easier time of parenting throughout if, early on, you put in the necessary support for your child to become a keen reader. J.K. Rowling, the creator of the Harry Potter books, has given a generation of children an amazing gift by inspiring them to read.

Literature immersion

Have books all around the house No matter which stage of learning your child is at, you can begin a process of increasing his exposure to books, in your home. Borrow a ton of books from the library. Have them everywhere. If you are interested in books, your children will be. Have books in every room of the house. For older boys who have struggled with reading, get picture books with adult themes such as science, technology or environment. This allows them to get genuinely interested in reading something without feeling babied — or having it remind them of their failure by doing yet another school reader!

Foster a love of literature by reading quality books which you love to your children. If you love the books, your children will love them. Choose books which adults can enjoy too, such as *Winnie the Pooh, The Wind in the Willows, Alice in Wonderland, Heidi* or *The Hobbit*. Look for books by the magical Australian children's author, Patricia Wrightson or books by Mem Fox; or find the books you loved as a child.

Liaising with teachers

Sometimes children struggle with a particular teacher. It is always worthwhile to develop the best relationship you can with your child's teacher, as communication between you can only help the child. When you meet with the teacher, go with an assumption that the teacher desires, and has the ability, to do the very best for your child. Approach the teacher with warmth and appreciation. Let the teacher know all that you are doing for your child, that you appreciate what the teacher is doing, and then make any requests you have, coming from an approach of teamwork and problem solving. Keep the lines of communication open. Wonderful creative solutions and an effective team strategy may come from this approach.

Let the teacher know you are on her side

If you feel that the teacher and the school are not the right ones for your child, consider finding out if your child can change grades or change schools. Sometimes this may be the best answer.

Repeating a grade

Children may be asked to repeat a grade due to social immaturity or poor fine motor skills. This is rarely helpful, but is instead likely to lead to boredom and a sense of failure. It is far more desirable to have tutoring, or an understanding teacher who can provide one-on-one support with particular problems. One-on-one tutoring may be available through the school if your child is in a 'special needs' category. Otherwise it may be a good investment for you to organise private tutoring with the right person. To motivate and accelerate your child's progress, there is nothing like personal attention from a skilled and loving individual, where your child is the sole focus. If you are aware that your child is slipping behind, try to address this before the end of the school year.

Get your child extra support to keep up

Television

Television is one of the greatest obstacles to learning. The argument that it includes educational programs would hold water if children watched only educational programs. In the real world this just isn't so. Unfortunately, kids with learning difficulties are usually the ones who would be happy to just sit and watch non-stop television. A good idea for monitoring and reducing TV time, is to get the guide at the beginning of the week and mark off educational programs. Select programs the family can watch together, such as David Attenborough's nature programs, or a history or science series; shows which promote social values and awareness, such as *Star Trek* and *Blue Heelers*, or get quality family videos like *Storm Boy*, *The Karate Kid*, *Shrek*, and other good Disney movies.

Then turn the TV off, except during those pre-selected times, and interact with each other. I know this sounds harsh in our incredibly busy lives, but the rewards are worth it. Remember how disappointing it can be when the lights come back on after an electricity blackout? You've just got comfortable, thought of things to talk about, gathered around the candles — and then the lights come back on and you have to return to the electronic world.

Brain development in Primary Years

Children need lots of exposure to language

Early exposure to language is of crucial importance, as the prime time for language development is before the age of seven. If this time is missed, as happened with the wolf children who were raised by wolves in the wild, it is possible that language will not develop at all. Before the child can make meaningful sounds, the memory of basic sound and language patterns must be laid down, and this happens in the first two years of life. A child first learns to recognise the sound and meaning of a word. Then begins the more difficult process of being able to reproduce those sounds herself. Long vowel sounds are acquired first, in babbling, followed later by the more difficult consonants. By the age of three, integration of the two brain hemispheres has taken place and fine motor skills are sufficiently developed to produce coherent language.[4]

Unless the processes of listening and speaking have happened correctly, creating a foundation of linguistic fluency, the next steps in learning literacy skills will be fraught with difficulty. These difficulties may not actually become apparent to the parents until the child begins to slip behind in school.

Reading depends on understanding letter sounds

We read with our ears

Dr Tomatis says we read with our ears. Whether children are reading silently or aloud, they are mentally forming words in the auditory parts of the brain. Because the first language we learn is spoken language, this is where the brain pathways are laid down. Reading and writing skills are built on top of our pre-existing auditory sense of language. If that auditory map is faulty, the more complex tasks involved in written language become almost impossible. The eye has to combine with the power and qualities of the ear to make sense of written signs. The letter is the symbol which we understand only through mental recognition of the sound. A faulty synchronisation between eye and ear results in dyslexia.[5]

Neural plasticity and wholeness

Development is about wholeness. School curriculum does not and cannot truly reflect the integration necessary for effective learning. It is only within the human brain, woven on the individual's unique history and experience, that the true fabric of learning has its weft and weave. Language is such a fluid, poetic and complex system, reflecting as it does — in its melodic essence and its very structure — the depth of human history. Because of this, the child (the brain in question) is always at the centre of her own learning.

Each child learns in her own way

The effort to force learning into the form of a curriculum is a response to economic constraints which oblige one teacher to teach thirty children the same material in a year — whether or not that material is relevant to the evolution of each child's development of meaning and knowledge. Average children, for whom the curriculum is designed, may do well, but those who are brighter may be easily bored while those with special needs may be lost in a sea of irrelevance. How can you as a parent assist, from the outside, your special child to get benefit from a system limited by such constraints? Only by having input to the child, and maybe some favourable intervention with the school and the teacher.

It may help to have a conceptual understanding of the potential difficulties you are facing in trying to get your child's needs met by a structure which is designed around a curriculum, not an individual narrative. Your child needs most of all to develop a sense of wholeness in the face of whatever challenges he meets in the tough daily world of school. Stimulating the neural network through various sensory integration therapies can support the development of this sense of wholeness.

Not every child fits the mould of school

111

The story of Rebecca

Testing can bring out the worst in a child

The renowned neurologist, Oliver Sacks, beautifully illustrated the brilliance of the brain in creating its own patterns and sense of wholeness when he wrote about Rebecca. His experience with this client helped to make him aware of the way our wholeness helps us to overcome the fragmentation caused by neurological difficulties. When Sacks first met Rebecca, it was in a test situation where he was performing standard neurological tests to detect her impairments. He writes his impression on this occasion: 'When I first saw her – clumsy, uncouth, all-of-a-fumble – I saw her merely as a casualty, a broken creature...'

Children excel in the environment they love

Yet the second time he saw her, in a totally different setting, his impression was entirely different: 'I wandered outside, it was a lovely spring day... and there I saw Rebecca sitting on a bench, gazing at the April foliage quietly, with obvious delight. In this environment she literally "blossomed!" Her posture had none of the clumsiness which had impressed me before. Sitting there in a light dress, her face calm and slightly smiling...'

Rebecca gave a gesture of appreciation accompanied by surprisingly poetic spurts of language using words such as 'spring, birth, growing, stirring, everything in its time.' As his two visions of Rebecca clashed and fused in his mind, Sacks saw how the testing context had coloured the person she was. He graphically describes how such neurological testing is designed 'not merely to uncover, to bring out deficits, but to decompose her into functions and deficits. She had come apart, horribly, in formal testing, but now she was mysteriously 'together' and composed.[6]

Myth, story and narrative

Ritual and art help people to feel whole

This flash of insight led Sacks to the identification of two intrinsically different modes of thought: the isolating, dissecting mode; and the integrative, composing principle, which allowed Rebecca to become a coherent, intelligible and poetic whole. As he followed her life for the next few years these perceptions were heightened. Rebecca was a young woman of deep sentiments, spiritual knowing, passion and poetry. Through the rituals of prayers at the synagogue, and eventually through theatrical performance, she was able to express her inner self with a fluidity and emotional depth of which one would not have had an inkling in the testing laboratory. Of her performances on stage Sacks said, 'one would never guess that she was mentally defective.'[7] Sacks also watched her survive and rise above her deep grief at the death of her grandmother, her primary parent figure, and recover her sense of self and life purpose.

On one occasion, at a point of transition in her life, she said to the doctor as she looked down at the carpet in his office, 'I'm sort of like a living carpet. I need a pattern, a design, like you have on that carpet. I come apart, I unravel unless there's a design.'[8] This metaphor became for Sacks a symbol of the narrative mode, bringing to mind the distinguished physiologist Charles Sherrington's famous image where he compared the mind to an 'enchanted loom' forever weaving new patterns which give life its meaning.[9] It is this meaning which Rebecca needed in order to function, and for her the narrative model allowed in the poetry, the life energy, vigour, magic — whatever you may choose to call it, but certainly, meaning.

Poetry and beauty give meaning to life

Music is a form of narrative which gives rhythm, purpose and sequence to an activity which may be otherwise devoid of value or meaning. Again and again it has been found that those with very low IQs or frontal lobe damage and apraxia (an inability to do things), who cannot perform a simple sequence of movements, say four or five tasks, are able to do so if they work to music.[10]

Music gives purpose to activity

Sacks has explored not just deficits in themselves, but has taken into his research his interest in the human being as a whole functioning entity, and has explored the ability of the individual to adapt, restore or compensate for the effect of the neurological disorder. He therefore approaches his examination of a patient's situation as the patient does himself. The question being 'how can I restore functionality and wholeness and fulfilment to my life, given the difficulties I face?' This is by far the most helpful, supportive and humane approach to helping a person with a neurological dysfunction.

Look at the person, not the problem

How can these ideas be usefully applied to a family situation where you are creating the best environment for your children to learn? The key for Rebecca was to find a pattern, a form and structure in which she could flow and

Asking 'why?' is the key to learning

express herself. To render meaning, that structure must be self-engendered, it cannot be imposed from outside. Meaning comes from a question or need expressed by the student; for example, the natural curiosity of the four-year-old who constantly asks 'why?'

Stories help children to understand complicated ideas

While children have a very limited ability to understand abstract concepts, it is different when these concepts are presented in the form of a story. Because of the symbolic power carried within a story, they understand it easily. This is how they learn about the world. This further explains why hearing lots of stories at the crucial developmental stages of the preschool years will engender many vital foundations for learning.

Building on strengths

Focus on the strengths, not the weaknesses

Learning is most effective if the approach is to build on the child's strengths rather than always harping on her weaknesses. Unfortunately an uneducated approach to teaching means that we often will automatically focus on the area where learning or understanding is lacking. With a high achiever who wants to achieve perfection in all areas, this may be useful. However, with an underachieving student, repeatedly drilling on the difficult areas may have the same effect as spinning your wheels in the sand. As soon as the dreaded subject is brought out, be it reading, spelling or fractions, the brain goes into shutdown. The child is unconsciously repeating messages like 'I can never understand this', 'oh no, not fractions again!', 'I hate spelling', or 'why can I never get this, I must be dumb?' This is not the ideal mental state for learning! Already the personality is fragmented and divided between negative emotions and an effort to force the concentration to perform. Even a bright student couldn't learn under these conditions. Synapses simply do not fire under stress!

Help your child pursue his passions

Unfortunately the demands of school curricula mean that students have to learn things in a certain order, even if they are not interested and the material seems irrelevant to them. Therefore, learning becomes a forced rather than an inspired process. The best you can do as a parent is spend more time on the areas your child loves, build his self-esteem, have fun, get into it, engage with him. As you expand the size of his island of self-confidence, knowledge and joy in learning, these positive experiences will eventually increase the size of the island and build a bridge into the troubled areas.

It is only when the self — and those immediate concerns of the self — are engaged by the material, that true learning occurs. Paolo Freire, the influential educational thinker who taught literacy to peasants in Brazil, was successful in rapidly overcoming huge knowledge gaps because he made the material relevant to the farmers' lives. Freire won international acclaim for his method of teaching literacy based on the day-to-day experiences of his students. [11]

Rather than teaching with tools like 'see Spot run', he started with words and concepts which the farmers needed right then to improve their situations in their everyday lives. They were experiencing threats to their land ownership and livelihood, so terms like 'land, farmer, acreage, cultivation' were immediately meaningful to them and they learned rapidly. Instead of teaching the word 'food', for example, he would teach 'hunger', a word with significance to Brazilian peasants. It was the first step toward creating the social consciousness that could take them out of poverty. They knew that literacy would empower them in their negotiations and because of this the whole self was instantly engaged in the learning process. Likewise, learning disabled children have a greater chance of learning if the material can be made immediately relevant to their daily lives.

Children will learn faster if the subject interests them

This philosophy is also vitally important in the education of Aboriginal children. When children are put in a classroom where the entire curriculum is founded on a civilization which denies and denigrates the value of their identity and cultural values, this does not support a receptive learning state. As soon as a child can look up to an Aboriginal teacher who deeply understands their very different social framework, the whole child can engage, self-esteem is nurtured and learning can take place.

Learning prerequisites

Wholeness and integration are prerequisites for effective brain function.

Learning requires two things:
Firstly, a sense of wholeness and connectedness due to emotional and social meaning, which creates motivation.

It helps if home and school have similar values

This condition existed in the examples of Paolo Freire, and in Aboriginal schools which offer a culturally relevant curriculum. The situation also exists with affluent or well educated families where the type of material offered in the curriculum is reflects the parents' interests and resources available at home. Home schooling is another environment where it may be easier to achieve integration or wholeness, as the curriculum can be entirely tailored and defined by the child's aptitudes and interests.

Music and exercise help learning

Secondly, wholeness of attention achieved by integration of the right and left brain. When part of the brain is not engaged, learning is impossible. The brain is much more likely to be activated if the child is interested, stimulated, happy, physically active, loved and feeling good about himself. This can also be supported by physical exercises which engage both sides of the brain, and by music.

How music supports wholeness

Classical music uses three strong elements: melody, harmony and rhythm

Rebecca's example of the pattern in the carpet is a very graphic one, showing that a meaningful structure and rhythm can engage the brain whereas dry, isolated information loses the thread of attention. Using stories to illustrate a message is a similar process. Another way is with music, which preconditions the brain to use and recognise patterns. Western classical music uses form in intricate ways which have not been so fully developed in any other form of music. It maximises a detailed exploration of three elements, rhythm, melody and harmony. As the brain automatically attunes to this depth of design, a powerful framework for cognitive thought is being laid down.

Simplicity and complexity

Mozart sounds simple, but it isn't

Music, especially the music of Mozart, has a brilliant way of developing complexity of perception in a simple way. Michael Clark, founder and conductor of the Sydney Mozart Players says that Mozart's music has a unique quality, because when you first listen to it you have the impression that it is very simple. However, when you come to play it and to understand it in depth, you find that it is actually very complex. This was the unique genius of Mozart, to present complexity in such a palatable and apparently simple form.[12]

We are blessed to live in a world where simplicity and complexity both manifest the glory of creation. The process of learning can be seen as a journey from the simple to the complex, and through to a deeper understanding of simplicity. I see it as a three-stage process, and this understanding helps to engender a deeper meaning to any process of life.

The child sees everything in very simple terms, for she does not have the perception to look much below the surface. This is the first stage, which is called the state of innocence. As we grow we enter the second stage, and we begin to discover an unbelievably complex web of questions, truths, contradictions and detail in everything. Knowledge can be extremely confusing as we try to unravel all aspects of our reality. This confusion of searching for knowledge is clearly manifest in adolescence and in the journey of scientific discovery. Eventually the search gives way to a deeper understanding, the third stage, which is surprisingly similar to the innocence and simplicity of childhood. In fact there is great wisdom in simplicity, but it is a wisdom which contains all the complexity of knowledge in a truly useful context.

Children see the world simply

Then it gets complicated

Then it gets simple again

A quote by Oliver Wendell Holmes puts this succinctly in one sentence: 'I would not give a fig for the simplicity on this side of complexity, but I would give my life for the simplicity on the other side.' Mozart must have had an innate understanding of this concept, for his music manifests the simplicity on the other side of complexity.

Simplicity with wisdom is worth a great deal

Specialisation

One of the attributes of the stage of complexity is specialisation. A necessary part of gaining knowledge is specialisation which, however, insists on breaking everything apart, dissecting, reducing it to its components and negating its wholeness. This is the trend in testing children for learning deficits, and the focus is on the deficit, not the whole child. This process negates wholeness, and its effect, as Sacks perceived on Rebecca, is to 'decompose'. What use is a child broken into her functions or inadequacies? The theory behind this is to treat the specific problem with the specific treatment. This is the whole approach of pathological medicine today, that we must isolate the disease, then isolate the drug which treats it,

Specialisation makes everything complicated

otherwise it is seen as unscientific. Any therapy, which is claimed to treat a wide range of conditions, is seen as suspect and at risk of being dubbed 'snake oil'. Yet wholistic therapies always treat a multitude of conditions because they are treating not the disease, not the deficit, but the person as a whole, vibrant, living, connected being.

Wholism is simpler Therapies which support greater internal connectedness fall under the umbrella of sensory integration therapies. These include movement, Sound Therapy, vision therapy and nutritional support. Used in conjunction with learner-centred education, these methods give the best possible support for any child to become an avid, successful learner.

Nature is wholistic It is often difficult to predict what benefit sensory integration therapies will have for an individual, because an individual is far too complex for us to chart and predict which learning, which integration will occur next. But, somehow, nature knows; nature can apply the miracle of healing if given the right tools: love, nurturance, poetry, narrative and music, to name a few.

☺ PRACTICAL ACTION TIPS

Activities to make learning fun

✪ Sing together as you do your daily activities.

✪ Teach your child the songs you loved when you were young.

✪ Let your child make music on the pentatonic scale. Get special instruments which use this scale so the child's music will be pleasant to the ears.

✪ Read to your children at bed time, at nap time or any time you want them to settle.

✪ Read the books you loved as a child.

✪ Develop a good relationship with your child's teacher, be on the same side.

✪ Practice active listening. Listen to your child talk on a set topic for two minutes or so. Then let your child listen to you talk on the same topic for two minutes. Then each take one minute to tell the other person what you heard them say.

✪ Discuss why listening is important. What are three good things that can happen when people listen. What are three bad things that can happen when people don't listen.

✪ Include your child when you are working out to music.

✪ Listen to a piece of classical music which tells a story, such as The Sorcerer's Apprentice. Tell the story while the music is playing.

✪ Play a piece of music and help your child make up a story to go along with it.

✪ To help with study, have your child highlight important points in her study materials. Then have her summarise the important points and read them onto a tape recorder. When preparing for a test she can play back the tapes and listen to them. This will trigger her memory of the material as she understood it.

✪ Put on some music and suggest your children dance around, mimicking their favourite animals.

✪ Sing songs which have good 'acting out' words such as the Hokey Pokey, Swing Low, Sweet Chariot or Row, Row, Row Your Boat. Have fun acting out to them together.

Continued overleaf

✪ With older children, play 'In the manner of the adverb'. A person chosen to be 'it', goes out of the room, while the group chooses an adverb such as, for example, 'happily', 'slowly' or 'excitedly.' Then 'it' returns and asks different people to act out a task like 'go and put on David's hat' or 'do a gymnastic routine.' The person must perform the act 'in the manner of the adverb'. 'It' can keep asking people to do things until 'it' guesses the adverb. Then the person who did the best act, that enabled 'it' to guess, becomes the new 'it.'

References

[1] Sacks, Oliver. *The Man Who Mistook His Wife For A Hat*. London: Picador, 1985.

[2] Fox, Mem. *Reading Magic*. Sydney: Pan, 2001.

[3] Ostrander, S. Schroeder, L. *Superlearning* 2000. New York: Delacorte Press, 1994.

[4] Sheil, M. L. and Dyson, M. *SAMONAS Sound Therapy: Rationale and Results,* Private publication, 1996. 34.

[5] Sidlauskas A. E. 'Language: the Ideas of Dr Alfred Tomatis,' *Revue Internationale D'audio-psycho-phonologie.* No 5 Special–April-May (1974). 36.

[6] Sacks, Oliver. *Ibid.* 172.

[7] *Ibid.* 176.

[8] *Ibid.* 175.

[9] *Ibid.*

[10] *Ibid.* 176.

[11] Freire, P. *Pedagogy of the Opressed,* Harmondsworth: Penguin, 1972.

[12] Clark, Michael. Interview conducted for video: *Sound Therapy: Creating Enhanced Listening Around the World,* Sound Therapy International, 2003

Chapter 6

WE MOVE WITH OUR EARS

CONTROL YOURSELF, AUNTY — I'M A HYPERSENSITIVE CHILD!

– Sensory integration

Tracy had problems mixing with other children. She never had friends over and when she got invited to parties she wasn't too keen to go. All she really liked doing was playing with her Barbie dolls. She hated getting her hands dirty and she didn't like rough and tumble play or moving around much at all. She reacted very badly to anyone trying to brush her hair, touch her head or fix up her clothing. She was also not doing too well in school, but her mum didn't know why because she loved to read, though the books she chose were a couple of years below her age level. She said it was because she was reading them to Barbie, and she would sit and mutter away for hours. She could only read if she followed along with her finger. She had been tested for hearing problems, eyesight, ADD and dyslexia but nothing showed up. Her mother didn't know what to do.

Finally she heard of a kinesiologist and learning difficulties specialist who did movement programs for children. She thought that might help because Tracy certainly didn't like to move. In fact she sulked all the way to the appointment and wouldn't even look at the kinesiologist. Tracy started going for sessions where the kinesiologist did gentle exercises and guided movement to stimulate the vestibular and tactile senses. Tracy enjoyed the sessions and so it was easy to get her to go. The kinesiologist also recommended Sound Therapy and behavioural optometry. After three months on this combined program Tracy was like a different child. She started hanging out with friends, going to the swimming pool, and gave all her Barbie dolls to her cousin. Tracy had been suffering from Sensory Integration Dysfunction, and the multiple therapies had helped her to overcome the problem.

Balance is important for learning

This chapter examines the connection between learning, and the senses which tell us about touch, movement and balance. When children with learning difficulties are examined for sensory integration, problems will often be picked up in vestibular and proprioceptive areas. This means the brain is not properly processing information about position and movement.

The ear is for balance as well as hearing

The ear is two organs in one: the hearing organ (the cochlea) and the balance organ (the vestibular system). Both are housed in the same bony labyrinth, both are filled with fluid, and each has its own set of hair-like cells which pass electrochemical signals on to the nerves. The vestibular and auditory nerves are two branches of the same nerve — the eighth cranial nerve. Our balance organ, then, is part of our ear.

The pioneers

We speak with the whole body

Some pioneering educational specialists have discovered the vital role that the ear plays in our co-ordination, and how that affects learning as a whole. Dr Tomatis says: 'We transmit language through our whole body. What we intend to communicate is neither sounds, words, phrases, nor acoustic phenomena; they are instead profoundly felt sensations experienced within our sensory neurons...'[1]

90% of learning problems originate in the ear

Dr Levinson, a world renowned psychiatrist and neurologist, also did ground-breaking work in the 1970s and 1980s on the role of the vestibular system and the cerebellum in learning difficulties. Though made on different continents and different decades, these discoveries corroborate Dr Tomatis' findings. Levinson concluded that 90% of learning problems originate in the ear. After examining over 35,000 subjects, Dr Levinson states: 'Over 90% of patients referred with a primary diagnosis of dyslexia, LD (Learning Disability) or Anxiety Disorder, manifest significant degrees of overlapping or associated symptoms of ADD/ADHD and balance/co-ordination/rhythmic disturbances. Only inner ear/cerebellar vestibular mechanisms can explain all the signs and symptoms characterizing ADD/ADHD, dyslexia/LD mood/anxiety, psychosomatic and balance/co-ordination/rhythmic disorders.'[2]

Much earlier, the celebrated anthropologist, Dr Raymond Dart, pioneered our understanding of developmental reflexes and postural integration. Dart was aware that the vestibular organs of balance, situated in the ear, play a key role in controlling all muscular movement. In 1947, Dart wrote: 'The striated musculature, which was elaborated for movement of the body as a whole, can only work in a balanced way when it is responding without impediment to the vestibular organs of balance through the mechanisms elaborated for that purpose by the central nervous system.'[3]

The vestibular system helps us control our muscles

Development of the central nervous system

It is not surprising that children with ADHD, dyslexia or other specific learning difficulties often have co-ordination or movement problems, once we understand the role of the ear in both. This connection takes us into the realm of sensory integration, meaning the ability of the brain to receive and interpret the relationship between all of the different sensory information it receives.

Sensory integration is essential for learning

The development of the central nervous system in the early months of life sets the child up for later performance. A baby comes into the world with several primitive reflexes for the purpose of basic survival. They enable him to perform movements such as sucking, grasping and turning the head when touched near the mouth. Each of these reflexes must be either inhibited or transformed at the appropriate stages of development. Sensory integration is affected if the primitive reflexes are not adequately suppressed. Over the first two to four months they are gradually replaced with postural reflexes (such as the head righting reflex) which allow the baby

Primitive reflexes must give way to conscious movement

to develop control of its sensory body and his ability to manipulate his environment. As this happens, the cortex, the thinking brain, takes over from the more primitive brain systems.

Low muscle tone in a baby may indicate a future learning difficulty. If a baby sleeps with her hands open, this is an indication of a lack of muscle tone. This may also be an early clue to food intolerance, or to sensory integration problems.[4]

Motor sensory development

Movement programs can help children catch up Many motor sensory programs exist that can be helpful in improving co-ordination and working with primitive reflexes. These programs teach the children to engage in simple movement patterns that may have been missed in their development, leaving gaps in their neurological development, which impair movement. For example, it is essential for a pre-toddler to crawl in order to develop the brain's left-right awareness and integration, as a foundation for more complex movements.

Children with sensory integration difficulties may be helped by learning to cross crawl, like marching lying down, in order to enhance this ability. In the past school children would march around the playground to music. Perhaps this helped learning-disabled children to improve co-ordination and therefore learning.

The senses

The external senses

Five senses we know well: sight, hearing, smell, taste and touch. These are called external senses, as they inform us about the world outside us. These respond to external stimuli. In addition there are some little known senses, which respond to internal stimuli. [5]

The internal senses

1. Interoception is the sense of the internal organs, muscles and blood vessels. It lets us feel internal stimuli such as pain, nausea or butterflies in the tummy.[6]
2. The vestibular sense is the sense of movement, gravity and balance, informed by the semi-circular (vestibular) canals.

3. Proprioception is the sense of muscles, ligaments and joints, which informs us of the angle of our joints and the position of our limbs.[7]

These internal senses should operate automatically, so that the child can turn her attention to the outside world. If they do not, it is very difficult to direct the attention outwards.

What is sensory integration?

Our senses allow us to make 'sense' of the world, but only if they communicate smoothly with each other. Our senses must work together to do an effective job. Together, they provide the brain with a menu of balanced stimuli. The brain that is nourished with a well balanced menu of many varied senses, operates well.

Over 80% of the nervous system is involved in the reception, integration and processing of sensory information. The primary role of the brain is to be a sensory-processing machine. Inefficient sensory integration is like a traffic jam in the brain. There are three requirements for smooth traffic flow in, for example, the process of speech:

The brain is a sensory processing machine

- Sensory intake must be efficient
- Neurological organisation is essential
- There must be efficient motor language output

Otherwise, it's like a short in the circuitry, causing inefficient brain processing. Responses to stimuli may be too extreme, or, there may not be enough response. Sensory integration is the whole integrative process needed for our brain to tell our body what to do.

Facts about Sensory Integration Dysfunction

Sensory Integration Dysfunction is the inability to process information received through the senses. Some key facets of this disorder are:

- The inefficient processing of information from the senses (including tactile, vestibular, proprioceptive, auditory and visual).
- Occurs in the central nervous system. The flow between sensory reception and motor output is disrupted.
- Neuronal connections in the central nervous system are inefficient.

- Occurs before, during, or shortly after birth.

Sensory integration therapy

Several professions and independent thinkers in the field of learning difficulties are now identifying more specifically the problem of Sensory Integration Dysfunction. This is an inadequacy of the neuronal wiring. What is required is an intervention which increases what is called neuronal plasticity. Essentially this is the ability of the brain to become more flexible and develop new pathways for learning.

Dr Tomatis was way ahead of his time when he realised the role of auditory therapy in assisting the sensory integration required for learning. Dr Levinson narrowed down which part of the brain is central to sensory integration: the cerebellum. (See Chapter 10 for more detail on the role of the cerebellum.)

Physiotherapists worked out sensory integration therapy

Sensory integration therapy is an offshoot of the physiotherapy profession. However, few people recognise the condition, which was identified by the occupational therapist, A. Jean Ayres Ph D, who first described it. She formed her theory about forty years ago, and developed integration strategies. Her book: *Sensory Integration and the Child*, presents a thorough explanation of this much misunderstood problem.

Dr Jean Ayres led her profession in developing intervention strategies through physical therapy programs. Her work is outlined in the fascinating and highly accessible book *The Out of Synch Child*, by Carol Stock Kranowitz, MA. Parents who find this chapter particularly relevant would certainly benefit from her book. Sensory Integration Dysfunction plays a significant part in ADHD, autism and learning difficulties.

Does my child have Sensory Integration Dysfunction?

SID makes it hard to participate

Children with Sensory Integration Dysfunction (SID) look normal, yet subtle areas of their nervous systems are not functioning correctly. These children will lack self-help skills, will become aggressive or withdrawn in a group and may refuse to participate in physical activities or sports.

These children may have problems processing information received through their senses. They will have trouble interpreting sights and sounds, and sensations of touch and movement. They are likely to become abnormally upset by loud sounds or bright lights, or by being touched or moved unexpectedly.

Co-ordination problems may mean, at a gross motor level, that they have trouble mastering running, jumping, hopping or climbing. Small motor difficulties will affect their abilities at buttoning, zipping or tying, colouring, cutting or writing. Essentially, it is a difficulty in getting their body to do what their head is thinking. It will create problems, too, with catching and throwing balls, and managing forks, pencils and combs — and so many other essential life skills.

Poor co-ordination causes clumsiness

Most parents and professionals have difficulty recognising this problem. Hence, the child's behaviour, and low self-esteem issues, etcetera, are often mistaken for emotional problems, hyperactivity or learning difficulties. In fact, the strange behaviours stem from a poorly functioning nervous system. Unfortunately, many paediatricians who are not yet familiar with the syndrome may mistakenly dismiss it as a problem which the child will outgrow. Sensory Integration Dysfunction does not mean that the child is mentally deficient nor that the parenting is inadequate.

It is important to identify the problem when the child is young. This, of course, is because the brain is most receptive to change while it is still developing. If you wait until the child reaches school age and has already run into trouble with reading and writing, there is more damage to be undone, including confusion, humiliation and low self-esteem.

Points for Diagnosis

- It is easy to miss a Sensory Integration Dysfunction.
- These disorders are often mistaken for ADHD, which has become the most popular label in the last decade and is a condition familiar to most family doctors.
- Professionals who have not heard of, or been trained in, Sensory Integration Dysfunction may unfortunately dismiss it, thinking that if they are not aware of it, it cannot be very important.

- There is a tendency for parents to go into denial, hoping their child's problem will go away.

- Accepting the child as he or she is can be used as a reason not to seek treatment. Acceptance is great in that the child needs to feel unconditionally loved. However, no child is truly happy when he senses that he doesn't have the abilities others have and cannot participate, as he longs to, in many group activities. It is the parents' responsibility to seek help, to do it early and not be put off by whitewashing from uninformed professionals.

- Special needs children often excel in a particular area because they compensate for certain lacks by developing other skills. To a degree, this is a good thing; but it should not be used to justify dismissing, or not addressing, the area of special need.

- A child will perform differently on different days. This should not be used to dismiss the problem. There will be 'on' days and 'off' days. The 'on' days may be enough to reassure the parents that nothing is wrong, but in fact this inconsistency is itself one of the hallmarks of neurological dysfunction.

Hyper or hypo

*Too much
or too little
sensation*

Sensory integration disorders generally reflect either over or under-sensitivity to certain stimuli. A child may also have a combination of hyper and hyposensitivity in different areas.

Hyper-sensitive or over-sensitive child seeks to avoid stimulation

General responses

- Brain registers sensations too intensely
- Reacts with irritation and annoyance
- Cannot screen what is relevant from what is irrelevant
- Reacts as if minor inputs were annoying or threatening
- Highly distractible because cannot screen out what is not useful
- May misinterpret a casual touch as a life threatening blow
- Will often withdraw from situations and cut himself off from people
- May misinterpret gestures
- May go out of his way to avoid touch or movement activities

Situations

- Child may avoid touching and being touched
- Child may overreact to light stimulation, being accidentally brushed against or contact of clothing
- Child may avoid moving and overreact to being moved unexpectedly
- Extreme sensitivity to losing balance or becoming dizzy
- May avoid running, climbing, swinging
- Likely to get travelsick in cars or lifts
- May be rigid and seem unco-ordinated
- May avoid challenging playground equipment that requires good body awareness

Specific dislikes

- May become overexcited by too much sensory stimulation, light, visual variety
- May be hyper-vigilant, always on the alert
- May cover over ears to avoid sounds or voices which are too loud
- May overreact to certain appliances such as vacuum cleaners, juicers, power tools
- May have a strong dislike and intolerance of certain food textures such as lumpy foods or slimy foods
- May have a stronger than usual reaction to certain odours

Hyposensitive or under-sensitive child craves and seeks more stimulation

- Brain does not register sensations very strongly
- Not getting enough sensory information
- This child needs lots of stimulation just to achieve a normal state of alertness
- This child may constantly touch and feel things or crash and bump into things due to lack of motor control, or to get more stimulation
- He has the impulse to act but cannot co-ordinate those actions
- May be easily tired, and withdrawn
- May lack initiative and seem 'spaced-out' a lot
- May be unaware of pain, of different temperatures, or the feel of objects
- May seek out physical contact, constantly touching things, chewing clothing or rubbing up against walls and furniture
- May obsessively repeat movements such as spinning or rocking. May fidget constantly or love being upside down

- May slump a lot and have very poor posture
- May need to touch everything to learn about it, because visual sensory input is not being efficiently processed
- May miss important visual cues such as facial expressions or landmarks and directions
- May have difficulty following verbal instructions, and speak too loudly or softly, not being aware of own voice
- May be oblivious to unpleasant odours, may constantly sniff people, food and other objects

Behaviour problems resulting from Sensory Integration Dysfunction

- Poor muscle tone: very loose and floppy or tense and rigid
- Poor motor planning or 'praxis'. This refers to the ability to conceive of, plan and carry out a sequence of movements. May have difficulty learning ordinary tasks like climbing stairs, using playground equipment, bicycle riding, getting dressed and using eating utensils
- Lack of clear laterality (hand preference) by the age of four or five
- Poor eye-hand co-ordination, trouble using building blocks and art materials, tying shoes, handwriting
- Resistance to change. Child may react badly to leaving the house, meeting new people, learning new games or tasting new foods
- Refusal to move from one activity to another, objecting to minor changes in routine
- High level of frustration and anger over minor obstacles. Need to always win, perfectionism
- Difficulty changing state of excitement, unable to 'rev up' activity level or calm down easily
- Academic and social problems
- Emotional problems, overreaction to hurt feelings, disorganised, inflexible, irrational and needy
- Low self-esteem – this is one of the most telling signals of poor sensory integration

Distinguishing Sensory Integration Dysfunction from other conditions

The most prevalent indicators of poor sensory integration are unusual reactions to touch and movement. Clearly the vestibular system is a fundamental key to the whole sensory integration question.

Trouble with touch and movement

Carol Stock Kranowitz suggests that children are commonly affected by three separate, but potentially overlapping conditions:

- Learning difficulties
- ADHD
- Sensory Integration Dysfunction

Any of these can exist separately, or in any combination.

Medicine may control the symptoms of ADHD but it does not fix sensory integration problems. Therapeutic inputs which work through the senses are able to treat the nervous system at a causal level and deal with the fundamental problem. Physical therapy aimed at sensory integration is crucial in resolving conditions where the vestibular and tactile senses are involved.

Auditory language integration problems

A child with auditory dysfunction will have trouble processing what he hears. It is common for auditory processing and vestibular dysfunction to occur together. The child will likely show language difficulties and may seem disobedient as he has difficulty understanding and following instructions.

Hearing and balance problems often go together

Speech and articulation difficulties may cause problems pronouncing difficult words. This may be linked to proprioceptive or kinaesthetic problems; the child may lack awareness of how his mouth, lips and tongue work together. These children have difficulty positioning the muscles correctly for articulation, and will often come out with the wrong word — such as saying 'tool' instead of 'school', or 'dese' instead of 'these'.

Vestibular dysfunction influences eye movements.

Poor binocular vision can make it hard to accurately perceive what is seen. Even with good eyesight, the brain may have difficulty linking the visual information with incoming input from auditory, tactile and movement

Seeing and hearing are interlinked

senses. Messages get scrambled. The child doesn't know where a sound is coming from, cannot judge the weight or texture of an object by its appearance, cannot avoid objects in his path. Eye-hand co-ordination is poor. It is very difficult for him to piece together all the sensory inputs and make sense of the world.

Identifying particular sensory disorders

There are eight senses Any sense may be poorly developed. There may be a problem with any of the basic five, including auditory or visual. On the other hand, there may be difficulties with one of the lesser known, internal senses, which include: interoception, vestibular or proprioceptive.

These symptoms are very subtle and hard for the parent to recognise. When these functions are impaired, the child relies more heavily on visual clues. When she closes her eyes, or when it's dark, she is deprived of essential information to help her orient herself in space. This may explain why many learning-disabled children are afraid of the dark.

The central issue is the integration of all the senses. Stimulation to improve this integration can be given through any one of the senses. Visual exercises, auditory training, and physical movement programs can all be helpful. Some children will respond more to one form of input than another.

Examples of how the internal senses affect everyday skills

I will now examine in more detail how a child may be affected by a disorder of the tactile, proprioceptive or vestibular sense.

The effect of a disorder of the tactile sense

Tactile perception allows us to feel and gauge texture, temperature and pressure. If these inputs are amplified or dulled, the child feels out of touch with the world and may have trouble learning new skills and using his hands.

Body awareness is greatly informed by the sense of touch. It is difficult for a child whose tactile sense is distorted to form a clear self-image.

Motor planning. A lack of motor planning—also called dyspraxia—hampers the ability to undertake complex motor activities, including speech.

Visual perception is affected by tactile deficiencies because so much of learning comes from relating the appearance of an object to its feel.

Academic learning is hampered when a child is reluctant, or unable, to get physically involved with touching and manipulating objects, due to a tactile deficiency.

Emotional security is affected by tactile dysfunction, beginning with the primary bond with the parents which begins through touch.

Social skills depend on a child's ability to handle the rough and tumble of daily contact, and to be at ease in groups or brushing up against other children in play. Someone with a tactile disorder often makes others uneasy, or gives the impression of being aloof and unfriendly.

The effect of a disorder of the proprioceptive sense

The proprioceptive sense is the sense that tells us about ourself (proprio means self) and the position of our joints and limbs. It tells us whether our muscles are stretching or contracting, and how our joints are bending or straightening.

Motor Planning is affected, because co-ordination is difficult without adequate information from the joint receptors.

Grading of movement means being able to judge how much pressure and muscular effort is required for a particular task. A lack of proprioceptive information makes this difficult, so a child may use too much or too little force for an activity.

Postural stability is compromised by a weak sense of proprioception. New movements and positions can easily throw the child off-centre, making him feel insecure and vulnerable.

Body awareness is lacking when there is inadequate proprioceptive information in the nervous system.

The vestibular sense

The sense of orientation in space More time will be given here to the vestibular sense, due to its fascinating interlocking role with ear function. The vestibular system detects two basic types of movement: spinning, and swinging. It communicates about the relationship of our head to the force of gravity. It is the sense of balance and movement, and tells us where our body is in space. It tells us whether we are moving or standing still, and whether other objects are moving or motionless in relation to our body. Sensory messages are taken in by the neck, eyes and body; and, after processing in the brain, the nervous system generates muscle tone which allows for smooth and efficient movement.

The receptors in the vestibular system are stimulated by movement and gravity. However, the visual system plays a key role in co-ordinating with the vestibular sense. The two work together, hand in glove.

You have probably experienced vestibular disturbance when you were on a train stopped in a station, and the train beside you began to pull out of the station. You were watching it, and did not know if it was moving or your train was moving. The momentary sense of disorientation and confusion throw the nervous system into a slight state of shock. When you figure out which train is moving, you quickly reorient to knowing where you are in space. Imagine being in a constant state of disorientation of your vestibular sense. How hard would life be? Our need to know where we are in relation to the earth and to gravity is one of our most compelling needs, stronger even than the need for tactile comfort.

Can you balance with your eyes closed? One easy way of testing your vestibular and proprioceptive acuity, is to stand on one foot and have someone observe how much you wobble. Then stand on one foot with your eyes closed. Do you wobble more? Can your vestibular system work well without visual assistance?

The vestibular system is fundamental to sensory integration. The vestibular system plays a unifying role as it reports on the relationship of the person to the outside world and to the force of gravity. All our other sensations are processed in relation to this basic vestibular information. The vestibular input primes the nervous system to be receptive, and able to integrate other sensory information. If we do not have efficient vestibular function, other sensory inputs will become distorted and inaccurate.

Development of the vestibular system

As the child grows, he develops reflexes gradually as the brain matures. The brain learns to distinguish vestibular sensations, so that the baby can feel himself move, he becomes self-aware, he understands and learns to manipulate his position in space. He is able to manipulate his motor responses.

Babies love movement

He learns to enjoy all kinds of movement. There is linear movement: up and down, or side to side, or back and forth. This is soothing and has been used since time immemorial to rock the baby to sleep. Another kind of movement is rotation, spinning on the spot as on a twisted swing, or moving in a circle like on a merry-go-round. Children normally enjoy this twirling motion too, unless they have a problem with their vestibular sense.

The effect of a disorder of the vestibular sense

Muscle tone depends on information from the vestibular centre. The vestibular system informs the brain to send messages about muscle tone to all parts of the body. This is why, when standing on one foot, if we wobble we are able to auto-correct so efficiently. The vestibular system says, 'quick, the head is tilting, the body must be falling to the left.' A message is then sent to contract the muscles on the right side of the body to correct the tilt, and the body stays upright. A child with severe vestibular disorder lacks these signals, sometimes even to the extent of falling off her chair.

The vestibular sense tells you the angle of your head

Emotional security may be profoundly affected by vestibular disturbance. A child with vestibular problems feels disoriented in the world, will have difficulty undertaking many tasks that others can do, and will lack confidence and self-esteem.

Being disoriented is upsetting

Auditory language processing involves the vestibular system. Both functions are housed in the same labyrinth of bony chambers. They are fed by different branches of the same nerve, the auditory/vestibular nerve. The vestibular system influences motor control and motor planning, which are essential for the co-ordination of all the fine muscles which are used to produce speech. Therefore, a poorly functioning vestibular system is often involved in poor language development. Movement can encourage the speech functions to work. Stimulation of the vestibular system benefits language as well as movement dysfunction. Putting a child in a swing during speech therapy can produce amazing results. Movement encourages verbal thinking and voicing. Swinging while listening to Sound Therapy may enhance its effects.[8]

Movement may improve speech

Intolerance to movement is a sign of a vestibular disorder. A child with an intolerance to movement will experience travel-sickness, and will tire or get sick or dizzy on playground equipment. Movement needs to be introduced more gradually in a safe and supervised environment so that the nervous system can develop tolerance.

You may have to introduce movement gradually

Gravitational insecurity is identified as abnormal distress and fear of falling. The fear of falling is a primal fear which occurs as the brain overreacts to a change in gravity — even from such a simple action as standing up or being picked up by a parent.

Vestibular problems increase the fear of falling

Poor bilateral co-ordination. Both sides need to be co-ordinated in an efficient way. This indicates good interconnections across the corpus callosum, the big chasm which connects the right and left hemispheres of the brain. By the age of three or four, a child should have mastered the art of crossing the midline — so that, when painting or making models the right hand can cross into the left visual field and still work in a co-ordinated way. If she passes the paint brush from hand to hand when working on either side of the easel, this may indicate a failure of bilateral co-ordination. She may also have difficulty visually tracking an object which passes from the left to the right visual field. She may have trouble jumping with both feet together or doing a complex, two-handed task like holding and cutting paper.

Vestibular function affects right and left integration

Visual spatial processing. Eyesight only plays a small part in our visual perception. When surgery gives sight to a congenitally blind person, the process of learning to see

Spatial awareness involves more than the eyes

then begins. Eye movement — ocular-motor skills — is a big part of seeing, and is highly integrated with the vestibular system.

Other essential visual skills include:

- Fixing — holding our eyes on a fixed object or moving it from one fixed position to another, as in reading print.
- Tracking — following a moving object as it traverses space, as in watching a ball or a moving car.
- Focussing — the ability to change the gaze from a near to a distant object and back. This skill is essential for copying from a blackboard.
- Binocular vision — the ability to form the picture seen with each eye into a single mental image.

The development of spatial awareness, which is essential for moving around, avoiding objects and participating in most activities, is a skill which is highly influenced by the vestibular sense in tandem with the visual sense.

Motor Planning, called praxis, is the ability to plan and carry out a series of movements in order to accomplish a particular task. It requires motor planning to scratch your nose, put on your shoes or catch a ball. This skill requires a good integration between the vestibular, proprioceptive and tactile senses.

Planning of movements involves the vestibular sense

Possible causes of Sensory Integration Dysfunction

A condition such as this usually has a combination of several causes.

Causes may include:

- Genetic disposition
- Prenatal chemical exposure, hormone imbalances, viruses, illnesses or extreme stress
- Premature birth
- Birth trauma
- Lack of usual sensory experiences to support normal development

How common is Sensory Integration Dysfunction?

Dr Ayres estimated in 1979 that 5% to 10% of children had sufficient Sensory Integration Dysfunction to require intervention. Today, estimates vary between 12% to 30%.[9] The mildest and most common example is repeated ear infections due to poor immunity and diet.

As with many learning difficulties, a higher percentage of boys is affected — 80% of cases being boys. More girls may go unnoticed, however, as they are likely to be less aggressive and troublesome.

Of course, everyone has these problems to some extent. The difficulties are classed as Sensory Integration Dysfunction only when the brain is sufficiently disorganised that the individual has difficulty functioning in daily life.

The building blocks of sensory integration

Here is a brief outline of the normal sequence by which a child develops sensory awareness and movement:

First two months
- Sense of touch – tactile sense
- Balance and movement – vestibular sense
- Awareness of body position – proprioceptive sense
- Sight - developing visual sense
- Hearing – developing auditory sense

First year
- Awareness of body parts – body map
- Use of both sides of body – bilateral co-ordination
- Hand preference, eye and ear preference – lateralisation
- Organised for mobility - motor planning - praxis

First three years
- Auditory language perception
- Visual interpretation and perception
- Pencil skills – eye-hand co-ordination
- Purposeful activity – visual motor integration

First six years
- Academic abilities
- Complex motor skills
- Regulation of attention
- Organized behaviour and self-control

- Separate awareness of body and brain
- Self-esteem.

Unless the first level of essential skills is in place, the additional levels are built on shaky foundations. In any remedial program, lacks in the basic sensory systems must be addressed first if other interventions are to be fruitful.

First things first

A preschooler needs the following abilities:

Tactile discrimination
Discriminate and interpret varied types of tactile stimuli, heavy/light, and sense and interpret the weight and texture of external objects.

Vestibular awareness
Be able to adjust and judge the use of one's body in relation to gravity and be comfortable moving through space.

Proprioception
Awareness of limb positions and ability of co-ordinated movement.

Bilateral co-ordination
Ability to use both sides of the body in tandem, in a co-ordinated and integrated way.

Praxis, motor planning
Ability to organise and implement a series of movements to achieve a particular task.[10]

Treatment for Sensory Integration Dysfunction

As children acquire more efficient motor sensory skills they become more relaxed and focussed and are able to enjoy school and learning.

Early intervention

Early intervention is very important because the still developing nervous system is rapidly changing and highly susceptible to influence. It is easier to change the shape of a plant which is very young, pliable and growing rapidly. The future shape of the tree trunk is set forever after a few years. However, even older children, teenagers and adults can show remarkable change when given the opportunity.

Early treatment is much more effective

But help is possible at any age

Sometimes, rapid and unexpected changes are seen in people at a variety of ages with the introduction of sensory integration exercises. For example, a girl who had balance problems was sent to gymnastics for therapeutic reasons. She loved gym so much that she ended up becoming an Olympic athlete.

Even simply using Sound Therapy can produce changes in sensory integration.

Here are a few examples:

- A Masters student who used Sound Therapy found her grades went up by 20%.

- A woman who had always suffered from an unidentified condition described her first experience of Sound Therapy like this: 'the minute I put the music on, I felt as though someone had placed a warm hand between two wet blankets in my brain.'

- A woman in her forties had a stroke, which affected her speech and language ability. She was faced with having to give up the degree course she was enrolled in. After a few weeks of Sound Therapy she made a recovery which left the doctors astounded, and went on to finish her degree.

Integrated treatment programs

Integration may be enhanced by any sensory treatment

Many individual therapists and centres are beginning to offer programs which address Sensory Integration Dysfunctions. It is, of course, important to treat a condition which involves several senses with several forms of sensory treatment, and these therapists will be helpful in cross-referring to help you find all the support you need. Of course, if you are already doing Sound Therapy at home, you do not need to spend extra money also attending a specialist Sound Therapy treatment clinic or practitioner. Each centre will have their own preferences, but ultimately it is your choice.

Sound Therapy International's portable program allows physical therapists and other remedial practitioners to easily add Sound Therapy to their program as an integrated part of their work. This is of particular advantage in country and isolated areas.

Helen Milbourne is a trained sensory integration therapist working with the program 'N.O.D. to Learn'.

Helen explains: 'The key to learning difficulties is in the relationship between normal brain function and the Central Nervous System. For many people this relationship doesn't work very well. This reveals itself in many developmental ways — physical, social and emotional. 'N.O.D. to Learn' provides Neuro/Sensory/Motor Programs which stimulate early childhood patterns which are crucial for learning.'

There are also organised networks of centres which address different aspects of learning and sensory integration support.

There is a network of Dore Achievement Centres in the UK, the US and Australia, where a specially tailored program is designed for children to practice at home. The organisation was established by Mr Wynford Dore, who drew together many experts on the vestibular aspect of learning difficulties in order to help his own daughter. Neurologists and neuro-psychologists working in the US and the UK, combined efforts to develop a program bringing together the latest neurological knowledge with advances in remedial education.[11]

'Toddler Kindy GymbaROO' has centres around Australia. GymbaROO is a structured program of movement activities which parents and children do together to stimulate learning abilities from infancy to early school years. Activities are aimed at assisting normal development and co-ordination. By encouraging correct neurological integration, children are given a strong foundation for later cognitive learning. GymbaROO is a 'watch dog' program to make sure that children are going through all their developmental stages. The instructors observe them and work with them and if there are any little 'hiccups' (just noticeable differences) in the child's development, they point this out to parents and provide extra stimulation during the program. GymbaROO was begun twenty years ago by Margaret Sasse, who has a nursing and teaching background. Her excellent book *Tomorrows Children* [12] gives many suggestions of exercises and structured programs which can be done at home.

Find a specialised exercise centre for toddlers

Helen Milbourne has many years experience running a GymbarOO centre in Albury Wodonga. Helen has incorporated Sound Therapy into her program and finds it assists children with many conditions, including poor sleep, emotional problems, speech problems and many sensory / motor skill challenges.

Helen believes that in listening to Sound Therapy the brain is being stimulated and getting just as much of a workout as she is giving the children at GymbaROO. By offering Sound Therapy as well, she says, the children get a sort of 'double whammy'.

Helen explains, 'It's ideal for a child who might be a little bit upset, just at that moment. After a few minutes, the child will be able to take the headphones off and go onto a slide or a trampoline, perhaps without having the tantrum they were having a moment before.'

Three year olds may need help with sleep In particular, Helen has noticed in dealing with young children that there are major issues with sleeping problems. This occurs with little babies, and especially children around the age of three. Helen says, 'I will often have parents of three-year-olds come to me and say "My child has been sleeping beautifully until now".' An explanation for this, she believes is, 'We know that the creative side of the brain becomes very strong around the age of three. Dreaming — especially nightmares, are consciously occurring. It is very stressful, so Sound Therapy is something I would recommend for that age group in particular.'

Julia Dive is another learning difficulties tutor who has developed her own program, drawing largely on the work of Barbara Pheloung and others. Barbara Pheloung's books: *Help your child to Learn, Overcoming Learning Difficulties* and *Help your Class to Learn* [13] are another excellent tool for parents and educational specialists. Julia lives near Bega in NSW, and has a passion for making educational resources available in isolated country areas.

Make sure your child has a strong foundation to build on Julia has fitted out a shed on her rural property, where she offers a remedial movement program after school hours. Julia explains that the brain can actually be restructured through sequenced movements. If the early reflexes are not properly inhibited, it leaves the child being unable to adequately absorb sensory input. Julia describes it as being like a tower of blocks with the bottom blocks made of sponge. Wobbly to say the least!

She explains, 'Before you can read and write there are certain movements you have to be able to perform, and if you can't do those properly then reading and writing will be a challenge.' Julia has had excellent results in helping children through her combined program of movement activities and portable Sound Therapy. She explains how general schooling, movement programs and Sound Therapy relate to remedial education.

'If you think of what schools offer as a basic criss-cross infrastructure, for most kids, that's all they need. The movement program gives a finer net to catch the kids who are falling through. The Sound Therapy is a finer net again, and it just catches more of those children who will fall through, even from the basic movement program.

A finer net to catch the problems

'I had a little girl who was doing trampoline exercises with the movement program and she was very stiff on the trampoline, she wasn't fluid, she didn't feel good, she didn't have good spatial awareness. And then one day I laid her down flat on the floor and asked her to do some eye exercises and she got dizzy! Well if you can't even do eye exercises lying down, how on earth can you jump up in three dimensions? And that's what made me realize there was an inner ear issue and that Sound Therapy maybe was going to help with that.

'I think generally there's not a big enough appreciation of how important the hearing is, to the actual act of learning. I think that's been overlooked in the general desire to effect mass education. Because if children can't hear the sounds, if they can't relate a sound to the symbol, then they have trouble having it register in their head and understanding it and then relating that sound again to that symbol next time they see it. They need to able to see the letter, hear the letter and reproduce the sound of that letter next time they see it. And then they need to be able to blend that letter in with all the other letters that form a word, and be able to reproduce that sound again. On top of that, besides just being able to voice the letter, they have to have an understanding inside their head of what that letter means. And Sound Therapy, I think actually helps that process of what happens after the sound goes into the head, and then where it goes inside your brain and what your brain does with it, and how it spits it back out again on the other side.

Most educators don't appreciate how important hearing is for learning

'Sound Therapy isn't the only tool you use to help a child with learning problems. But I think it's a tool that would make all the other things that you do, work that much better. I'm thinking of a child who has used a lot of reading programs and writing programs to help with her learning problems, and I think Sound Therapy has helped her to get the best out of those programs that she can get.'

Inhibition and facilitation – the Alexander Technique

Inhibition allows the brain to control random activity

Inhibition is the neurological process which reduces connections between sensory intake and behavioural output. It enables us to have control, instead of constantly twitching and waving our limbs about. Without adequate inhibition, our nervous system would be overloaded by sensory excitation. The Australian actor, F.M. Alexander, developed a technique for increasing sensory awareness. In applying the technique, the student learns to make inhibition conscious. This means that intention is brought to every muscular contraction and to each split second of response to an external stimulus. This gives the person a superior level of control and awareness of movement.

Facilitation lets the brain direct our actions

Check the web

Facilitation is the opposite of inhibition. It describes the neurological process which promotes connections between sensory intake and behavioural output. Alexander used the term 'direction' to describe intentional, conscious volition of muscular action. The brain makes a conscious decision to engage in an action which is meaningful and beneficial. A correct balance between inhibition and direction leads to smooth transitions, and moderate, useful neuromuscular activity.

The Alexander Technique is taught worldwide by several thousand practitioners. The conscious development of inhibition and direction takes the student in the opposite direction to the ADHD sufferer who has very little inhibitory control. Willing teenagers, or children with ADHD or sensory integration difficulties, could benefit from the Alexander Technique. The technique has been found valuable for a range of people with conditions varying from poor posture and co-ordination, twitching or clumsiness, to severe disabilities of the nervous system. It is also used to improve performance for musicians and sports people, or others wanting to have more awareness of, and be more comfortable in, their bodies.[14]

How to find a sensory integration therapist

Therapists who specialise in assisting children with sensory integration may be called physical therapists, occupational therapists, learning difficulties centres, sensory integrative therapists or brain gym practitioners.

Try the phone book

Ask for referrals at your school or ask other local practitioners and educators who have assisted you.

Ask at the school

Check our website www.soundtherapyinternational.com for Sound Therapy outlets near you. Your local Sound Therapy distributor may be able to help with local referrals. Also see the Resources section at the end of this book for other contacts.

Check the web

At the end of this chapter there are some suggestions you can try at home.

The role of vision in learning

Sue Larter is a Specialist Behavioural Optometrist practicing in Pennant Hills in Sydney. I visited Sue at her office, and she generously shared her wealth of knowledge from her twenty or so years of clinical experience.

Behavioural Optometry has a different philosophy for looking at the vision system. Normal eyecare professionals look to make sure you can see clearly and your eyes are healthy, and if that's okay, they assume that all is fine. A behavioural optometrist goes further, looking at not just 'can you see', but 'can you keep it clear over time, keep it single, maintain your place on the page, and while you're doing all that, understand what you're looking at?' The focus is not on vision, as such, but on neuro-developmental dysfunctions. It addresses developmental issues concerning integration with motor function, vision and auditory perception. Behavioural optometrists do retraining, as well as corrective lenses.

How do you interpret what you see?

Sue Larter explains that there is a huge overlap between neuro-developmental dysfunction and learning difficulties. In the vision system, mechanical issues are just one component. However, and this can be a huge issue, 'If every time you try and read everything's gone blurry, gone double, you get sore eyes or headaches, your inclination to

Blurry vision, double vision, sore eyes, and headaches make reading hard

read is generally a bit lowered. Some kids will just read on regardless, but they don't have a learning problem.'

These mechanical vision problems may be solvable with lenses, or prisms, or vision therapy, and this will enable the child to read more easily. However, Sue recognises that just getting the vision system together is not going to solve most true learning disabilities, because there are often other aspects to the problem, such as motor or auditory components or metabolic issues concerning diet.

Special lenses help eye mechanics

There are two strands to behavioural optometry. Part A addresses the mechanical visual issues. Typically, the children who are provided with support lenses to address these issues have been told by a number of eye care practitioners that they don't have a problem. Behavioural optometry can stabilise the mechanics of vision through lenses and prisms. This does not necessarily mean long-term use of these tools. They may be needed for 18 months or so. Lenses and prisms are one of the main tools used for stabilising the mechanics of the system. This can have a flow-on effect into the more perceptual areas because a support lens really works on reducing visual stress. Stress reduction has many spin-offs, as Sue explains, because focus is driven by adrenalin, which is your stress hormone. When you have a vision system which is stressed, if you can reduce that stress it helps to widen out your visual field. If you have a wider visual field you can take in more information more efficiently, so maintaining your place on the page will be easier.

Behavioural optometrists prescribe differently

The lens used by a behavioural optometrist is very similar to a normal lens someone would get from an optometrist. The difference is the way it's used and how it's prescribed. They are not normally very weak lenses. The main difference is that they use what is called a yoked prism. Because prisms are normally used if you see double, you can push the eyes to see single or you can make the system go double by using prisms — by just changing the direction the light enters the eyes. A yoked prism has no optical effect, but it has a really big spatial effect. Spatial interpretation is a really huge issue in the area of sensory integration. In research which Sue did for her Masters Degree, she found that the speed of spatial judgement, tied in with eye-movement skills, is one of the best predictors of reading age.

Sue explained, 'Spatial judgement has to do both with depth and with movement between letters. In the act of reading what is important is knowing where you are on the page and being able to maintain that, but in order to do that you need awareness of space around you. If you're only looking at a single letter or two, it is very hard to apply any sort of comprehension to what you are doing. You need to be able to take in the whole page and quickly switch between central and peripheral focussing, and that sort of thing.'

Spatial judgement is an important part of reading

Spatially, a lens will either magnify or shrink an object something. The impression it makes is not to just make it bigger or smaller; it literally does make the object appear to subtly shift in space. If something looks smaller, you perceive that it's further away. If it looks larger, you tend to perceive it as closer. So this brings us into the perceptual component of vision. This process occurs in the brain, but the lens can help. You put the lens on and the brain makes that perceptual shift. This is one of the applications for the yoked prism, which is a very powerful way of making shifts through the whole body in the way the person relates to space. Sue explained that you can put a yoked prism on and really feel the shift. For example, if you're just standing in a balanced position and you put on a yoked prism, you can feel the weight shift either to the heels or the toes, depending which way you put the prism, up or down. This means you can make quite big shifts in perception of space by changing input into the eyes.

This can change a child's orientation to the world in a way which affects behaviour. How a yoked prism works is this: imagine you have a horizon that you can see. It's a reasonable assumption that anything above the horizon is going to be further away, and anything below the horizon is going to be closer. What a yoked prism can do is to seem to shift the horizon. This would be done only minutely, but enough for the brain to think, 'Oh, that's closer, I can converge more easily.' Or 'That's further away, I can relax out and take in more information'. This can help the kids who are highly distractible, and very peripherally aware — which is a really useful thing to do in some instances, but not, unfortunately, in the classroom. If you want them to centre their attention more, you can a use a yoked prism

With the right lens, the horizon may shift

which effectively lowers the horizon a little bit, so they just get that feel that it's okay to be centred more here, close in.

Optimal seeing improves performance

Besides the mechanics of vision, the other strand of behavioural optometry is the visual/perceptual components, which is referred to as 'visual information processing skills'. A practitioner will do a lot of developmental, visual processing training. In addition to working a lot with children who have learning problems, behavioural optometrists may also work with sports vision. In this case they are taking an already efficient system and making it even better. They are able to train speed, depth, judgement, eye-hand co-ordination, and central and peripheral awareness.

The eyes can be trained to work better

The retraining exercises include a lot of processes which superficially may look like occupational therapy, for example, lots of cross-pattern movement activities. However, this progresses to doing visually-led movement activities and visual coding, which involve a lot of body movement as well. Sue explains some of these:

'We have a computer program which has a little stick man on it and you either have both legs and arms out and one arm up, or whatever it may be. But the picture on the screen is only 3cm tall and if you're intensely watching what the arms are doing you sometimes forget to watch what the legs have done. So you're not being as aware as if you're taking in the whole picture even though it is a small picture. This is training visual attention to detail. In the auditory system you have to have the attention to detail to really get the whole story. We do a lot of therapy where you're using the vision system to drive the motor system, because you'll learn most effectively if you do it multi-sensorily. We use metronomes a lot as well, because once you've learned to do a particular visual motor task, for example, you can then put a metronome on and see if you can maintain that level of function with an auditory load. Of course, a lot of kids will fall apart at that point, so you slowly have to build that in again. So we really try and work as multi-sensorily as possible.'

The length of the basic program is at least three blocks of eight weeks. The therapist will work with the children for three quarters of an hour, one-on-one, and then give them homework which needs to be done at least five times a week for about fifteen to twenty minutes. Most of the exercises do not involve computer programs and can easily be done at home.

Sue has a very positive, welcoming manner which no doubt sets her clients at ease. She says 'Success breeds success, because you can start building on skills and keep on building.' Like other sensory integration therapists, Sue recognises that learning difficulties are rarely purely visual or purely auditory. There is also usually some motor component.

Learning difficulties are never just in one area

Sue explains that there is definitely an interplay between the auditory and visual systems and helping one will often help the other, because auditory and visual information are both received by different layers of the Lateral Geniculate Nucleus — the part of the brain which is the primary processor of visual information. 'Due to these interconnections' she says, 'we do know that auditory processing speed will improve if we get the right support lens.'

There is also an interesting relationship with laterality. Some of the information received from each eye, crosses to the opposite side of the brain. This apparently complicated arrangement is engineered so that the right brain receives information about the left visual field, and the left brain receives information about the right visual field.

Some of what we see on the right and left, crosses over in the brain

On the subject of what causes visual integration problems Sue says:

'Some of it is trauma and that sort of stuff. But I think the dreaded TV is a component here. The lack of movement and learning through movement, because you sat like a blob and you've had all the pictures fed to you, you haven't had to develop your own pictures. You've had your attention span trained to be short. I think there's all those sorts of factors. Then you have the chemical toxins and that doesn't help.'

To find a behavioural optometrist go to www.acbo.org.au/

Chiropractic

The following is an excerpt from an interview with chiropractor, Daniel Danuser from Newcastle, who recommends Sound Therapy to his clients. We asked him about the importance of chiropractic treatment for children.

The spine affects our whole neurology

'It's my belief that normal spinal biomechanics are essential for normal neurological integration of the neck and the spine — but also for the brain. In a child, the brain is still developing, its still growing, so that to me seems a very important time when the neurology has to be maximised, and really I do think that's what chiropractic adjustment and manipulation does. It mechanically restores something in the spine, but more importantly it changes the program. It renews the programming at the level of the spine in the brain stem and in the higher centres of the brain; and that's where its most powerful effects are, and that's where Sound Therapy works, and incidentally, I believe where aromatherapy would work too.

After an accident a child should have a spinal check up

'I believe that children should be looked at if they have had a fall or an injury out of the ordinary and if their behaviour is different to normal — if there is an alteration in the way they act, the way they recover from tiredness, or the way they respond to normal interaction. If that is different over a few days in a row, I would think that is telling us that somehow the nervous system is not integrating and that's why the child is not behaving as normal, so that is the point in time where, especially if there has been any sort of fall or injury, I would recommend a chiropractic check-up.

'I think the chiropractor then should have the clinical skills to say "yes, we do need to do an adjustment", or "no, this child is great and we don't need to do an adjustment or a manipulation." I check children here when they come in with their parents and often there is nothing to adjust, nothing to change and that's how it should be.

Birth trauma may cause spinal misalignment

'If there is a normal birth and normal pregnancy, there really should not be any need to take the child to a chiropractor until he starts to be weight-bearing — so, sitting, about six months; walking, at twelve months. However, if there has been a difficult birth, a difficult position in the womb or a difficult delivery, it may be prudent to check the child earlier; especially if the child has difficulty gaining strength or thriving, is restless a lot, is colicky, seems upset — not because of some organic pathology but because something is obviously disturbing him — without him actually being ill. At that point in time, I think a chiropractic assessment is very worthwhile.

'Lastly, I believe that the brain governs the way we live, the brain makes it possible to interact with our environment and express and do and make things happen as a person. It is my view that the brain controls the nervous system, it controls the immune system and it controls the hormonal system — and if all of those three work well and the brain is working well, we are in a state of maximum health and we can cope with whatever is thrown at us and expected of us. If our level of health is diminished it would then make sense that we look at our primary senses to gain access to the brain to help it. So sound — hearing — is one of those primary senses; as is tactile input, and that's why I think people like massages and also why chiropractic is a good therapy. I also think that aromatherapy works through the senses of the nose, and we know that light therapy works through the senses of the eyes, and that good healthy unadulterated food is also playing an important part. Any therapy which treats us directly through our senses is a natural and safe way to heal the nervous system.'

The immune system is affected by the nervous system

Finally, to close with some words form Carol Stock Kranowitz:

'It is critical to understand that no matter how much advanced brain power a child has, intelligence alone is not sufficient for organised, daily functioning if the underlying senses are not integrated. Sensory integration depends on a sensory processing machine that is in good working order.'[15]

PRACTICAL ACTION TIPS

What you can do at home

If you do not have access to a trained therapist and you have the skills yourself to begin working with your child, here are some activities you might try. Children will love doing these things with you anyway, as this type of physical activity is a part of fun, normal, healthy play.[16]

Do a few of these each day. Do not overdo them, as the child's nervous system must adjust to each new stimulus.

Cross crawling Laterality activities

Squirming

Get baby or child to squirm along the floor on its belly

One-sided crawling

Let baby or toddler lie face down. Take hold of the right leg and arm, and move them forward as if to wriggle along the floor, bending the elbow and knee. Have another person sit on the other side, and then move the left leg and arm forward. At the same time, move the right arm and leg back down. Keep alternating sides. This helps to develop laterality and reflex integration.

Next step. Get child to push right hand and knee into the floor, straightening the arm and pushing up on the knee. Then do left side, and turn head from side to side with each movement.

Cross crawling

The same as above, but move the opposite arm and leg together, i.e., the right arm goes forward with the left leg.

Vestibular stimulation activities

Spinning in an office chair or a tyre swing. Spinning is very important for developing eye-movement control and balance. If you are spinning a young child, do it slowly at about two revolutions per minute. Older children can spin themselves at the speed they like. Do not spin a child against her wishes, as over stimulation of the vestibular system can be distressing and counterproductive.

Rocking from side to side. Child can lie on parent's body and rock with parent; or she can be in a cradle, across a big beach ball, or in a hammock or blanket. Bounce her on your knee.

Rolling along the floor or down a hill is fun, either with hands by the sides or above the head. Rolling can also be done wrapped in a blanket.

Somersaults

Frog jumps

Hanging upside down over the bed or on a swing.

Wheelbarrow. Pick up your child's legs and let the child walk along on her hands.

Playing with boxes. Let the child play with different sized boxes, building towers, playing cubby house or making obstacle courses.

Walking on unstable surfaces, like sand, long grass or a water-bed.

Tightrope walking balancing on a low wall or furniture.

Lateral movements, like making angels in the snow or the sand. Child lies on his back and moves arms and legs out and up in a big arc along the floor.

Bouncing in time to music, or on a mattress, rebounder or trampoline.

✪ Bounce with legs apart, then legs together.

✪ Bounce putting one arm and leg out to the same side, or both to the front or both to the back. This challenges the vestibular and proprioceptive responses to compensate for the changed conditions of balance.

Marching to music. Practice marching lying on your back. Then get up and march around the room.

Tactile stimulation activities

Water play. Provide a series of containers and flexible length of plastic hose in a big tub of water. This assists child to learn about gravity, pressure and co-ordination.

Finger painting. Encourage children who enjoy it to do as much as they like. Encourage the hesitant ones to have a go. Try adding other textures to paint, like sand, shaving cream, pudding.

Hand in the bag. Put a few objects with different textures in a cloth bag or pillowcase. Let the child reach in and guess what the objects are.

Trust walk. Blindfold the child, then lead him around the house letting him feel things and guess what they are.

Contnued overleaf

Quick tips to help a tactile learner

There are children who may have trouble learning through their auditory or visual senses. They may need tactile stimulation to help them learn.[17]

✪ Let them hold a soft squeezable ball and squeeze it while learning.

✪ Touch them when you talk to them.

✪ To help learn left and right play Simon says. Simon says 'hop on your left foot'. Simon says 'touch your right ear'. Touch your toes. Whoops! Simon didn't say so!

✪ Teach your child to skip as this helps to co-ordinate both sides of the brain.

✪ Let your child spin, or swing him around. This is good for the ear and children love it. They need to rock, swing and spin to develop the ear's motion sense.

✪ When you are driving ask your child to direct you. 'Which way do I turn here?'

✪ Sort items around the house by different types of categories, colour, shape, size etc.

✪ Sleeping in a hammock has been known to help some children as it increases vestibular stimulation.

✪ Martial arts training is good, because they have to think about their actions quite consciously. It is structured, can provide good mentoring and may be an alternative to team sports for a child with poorer co-ordination. It will help to develop self-esteem and self-confidence. It is best to have three sessions a week to make a significant difference.

✪ Dancing lessons can have similar effects.

✪ Do not use walkers, play pens or other devices which encourage a child to artificially stand before he can balance. This will take away from his crawling time and interfere with his normal development.

References

1   Tomatis, A. A. *The Ear and Language*. Phoenix: Moulin, 1996. 161.

2   Levinson, Harold. 'Thirty Five Years and 35,000 Patients Later,' in the *All in One guide to ADD and Hyperactivity*, eds Ali, Elvis et al. New York: Ages Publications, 2001.26.

3   Dart, R. 'The attainment of poise' S. Afr. Med. J., pp. 74-91, cited in, Fjordbo, G. D., *On the Development of Habit - from the viewpoint of the Alexander Technique and early neuromotor patterns of development*. Private Publication. Thesis submitted to the study-council for the Audiologopedic Studies at the University of Copenhagen, 1993.

4   Dengate, Sue. *Different Kids: Growing up with Attention Deficit Disorder*. Sydney: Random House, 1994.

5   Kranowitz, Carol Stock. '*The Out of Synch Child*.' New York: Penguin, 1998.

6   Cameron, Oliver G. 'Interoception: The Inside Story — A Model for Psychosomatic Processes.' *Psychosomatic Medicine* 63: 697-710 (2001).

7   Garlick, D. *The Lost Sixth Sense*. Sydney: The University of New South Wales, 1993.

8   Kranowitz, *Ibid*. 114.

9   Kranowitz, *Ibid*.

10 *Ibid*. 50 -54.

11 http://www.ddat.co.uk

    http://www.ddat.com.au
    http://www.dorecenters.com

12 Sasse, Margaret. *Tomorrow's Children*. Australia: GymbaROO, 2002.

13 Pheloung, Barbara. *Help your child to Learn*. Move to Learn, 2003, *Overcoming Learning Difficulties,* Move to Learn, 1992 and *Help your Class to Learn,* Move to Learn, 1997.

14 Alexander, F.M. *The Use of the Self*. London: Victor Gollancz,1985.

    Society of Teachers of the Alexander Technique. http://www.stat.org.uk

    An Introduction to the Alexander Technique: *The Head Leads and the Body Follows*. DVD, produced by In Such a Way, 1997. http://www.alexandertrust.org.uk/#projects

15 Kranowitz, *Ibid*. 277.

16 Sasse, Margaret. *Tomorrow's Children*. Australia: GymbaROO, 2002.

17 Block, Mary Ann. *No More Ritalin*. New York: Kensington, 1996.106.

Chapter 7

NOT ANOTHER LABEL !

Dyslexia, ADHD, ADD, autism, Asperger's, Down syndrome, fragile X syndrome, dyspraxia, learning difficulties, epilepsy, sensory integration dysfunction….what next?

Helga had multiple problems. She had first been diagnosed with dyslexia when she was in grade two. She was way behind in reading and didn't pay attention to the teacher. She used to look out of the window and daydream. In grade four, her mother took her to a new family doctor who diagnosed her with ADD. He did not recommend Ritalin though, because her behaviour was not a problem and there was a history of tics (muscle twitches) in the family. In grade six, she was still struggling and on the teacher's suggestion her mother took her for a series of specialist learning evaluations. This time, Helga was diagnosed with Asperger's syndrome, which is higher-functioning autism. This explained why she was hypersensitive to sound, why she was so methodical and got very upset if her routine was broken, and why she got so obsessively interested in certain subjects and would stay up all night studying them for months at a time. It also explained her slightly odd social mannerisms and why she had trouble making friends. She was enrolled in a remedial tutoring program and one of the special education teachers suggested to Helga's mum that she also try Sound Therapy. Helga loved the music and listened to it more than the recommended three hours a day. In fact, she used it for about eight hours a day—she slept with it, ate with it, studied, travelled to school, and watched TV with it on. She told her mother that it made her feel more connected to the world, she could express herself better and was now able to make sense of what the teacher was talking about. She overcame her sound sensitivity and started a jazz ballet class where she made some friends.

Labels have their uses Parents may wish to avoid having labels put on their children in case it causes stigma, teasing and affects the child's self-image. On the other hand, it is sometimes a relief to have a label to identify the problems your child is struggling with. The identification of a difficulty opens the way to seek remedial treatment which is essential for your child's development.

Don't delay

Don't use not labelling as an excuse not to get treatment If you suspect your child may have learning difficulties or special needs, take every action you can to get all the treatment you can as soon as possible. Every year, every month and every week that your child struggles on without help, he is getting further behind and missing out on crucial developmental stages of learning, brain mapping and social development. You will also save a great deal of money by seeking out solutions as early as possible, because you won't need as many therapeutic interventions later on.

If you think there is something wrong, get help Don't wait and see what the doctors say, do all you can to help him, now, because you care about him more than anyone else ever will. Unfortunately many doctors, not being expert on early identification of learning disorders, and wishing to reassure the parents, will proclaim the child 'fine' or take a 'wait and see' approach. This is valid in the case of drug treatment or surgery, since these interventions, if misplaced, could be harmful. However, non-invasive programs will have only beneficial effects and the leverage of early intervention will be compounded many times. These programs may include Sound Therapy, movement programs, fitting of assistive devices such as eye glasses or hearing aids, and removing toxins from the diet or environment. Even if your child does not have a problem, these interventions will help him or her to develop maximum potential and lead as fulfilling a life as possible. Often the parent is the first to notice a difference, but may be lulled into passivity by well-meaning doctors or teachers. Don't let that happen! Keep seeking, and get your children the help they need.

Adults with learning and developmental difficulties

While the focus of this book is on children, adults with any of the problems discussed here can also benefit significantly from sensory integration therapy. There are many cases where an adult has lived all their life with vestibular problems, auditory processing problems and other disorders which were never properly identified or treated. Sensory integration therapies have only recently become prevalent, so were not available when today's adults were in school. There are a few adult's stories included in Chapter 8, Listeners' experiences with Sound Therapy. Also see the book: *Sound Therapy: Music to Recharge Your Brain*, by Patricia Joudry and Rafaele Joudry

Finally, an explanation of what is wrong!

The history of labels

From the 1950s through into the 1970s, the most common learning disorder to be identified was dyslexia. It was a popular label and any child displaying a certain list of symptoms was given this diagnosis. A host of specialists then came up with treatments they believed would help the sufferer.

We used to call it dyslexia

In the early 1980s, the new term ADD (Attention Deficit Disorder) was coined to cover both symptoms of inattention and hyperactivity. Subsequently, two different types of ADD were isolated, ADD and ADHD. The H stood for hyperactivity and meant that as well as the concentration problem of ADD the child was also hyperactive. Many theses were written on the exact difference between these two brain disorders. It was generally accepted that the hyperactive component existed more frequently in boys.

There are several types of ADD

Definitions

There is considerable overlap between the symptoms of dyslexia and ADHD, as there is a tendency for the preferred label and its proponents to take more and more symptoms

The labels overlap

under its umbrella. Sensory Integration Disorder is a new term which now lists many of the symptoms previously attributed to dyslexia or ADHD (See Chapter 6). Sensory Integration Disorder is probably the most accurate label yet as it is closer to the fundamental cause of the disorders, which involve the inner ear/vestibular system and cerebellar function.

Most common uses   For simplicity's sake, and to attempt to achieve the clearest possible distinction between the most frequently used labels for learning and sensory disorders, I give below a brief list of those behaviours or deficits most commonly associated with each label. Many symptoms overlap. Practitioners or professions tend to have a favoured label under which they build the others as sub-categories. Thus, if you take your child to enough professionals, she could end up with several labels. These disorders are not like infectious diseases that can be clearly identified and segmented; rather, they are a result of some error in brain wiring in the developing child.

Primary and secondary dysfunction

Let's get to the cause   To achieve effective diagnosis and treatment, it is essential that efforts be directed to the root cause of the problem. We must address the primary, not the secondary, dysfunction. To understand the distinction between primary and secondary dysfunction, imagine a plant with a primary problem within its root system. The effect of this illness would be seen in the leaves and upper part of the plant. But would we be right if, in examining the leaves, we determined that the source of the problem was in the leaves? Sensory Integration Dysfunction is probably the best way of describing the primary dysfunction causing most learning difficulties.

Sensory Integration Dysfunction

- Poor performance of some sensory systems
- Poor communication or integration between the sensory systems
- Over- or under-sensitivity to certain senses
- Hyper or hypo-sensitive to proprioceptive or vestibular input (senses of position and movement)
- Poor functioning of the cerebellum (a part of the brain which controls basic co-ordination)

Dyslexia

- Lateral confusion (not clear which side is leading)
- Poor co-ordination
- Poor visual/auditory integration
- Distorted sensory perception
- Poor memory
- Poor linguistic ability

ADHD/ADD

- Inability to focus and maintain attention
- Hyperactivity and impulsiveness
- Dreamy inattention
- Emotional reactivity
- Inability to project awareness to others' needs

Autism

- Social isolation
- Sensory reception—hyper or hypo
- Limited literal interpretation of interaction and meaning
- Inability to perceive emotion and meaning
- Emotional overreactivity
- Self-absorbed, inability to identify with others.

Spectrums

Then, each major label has sub-categories which make up a spectrum of associated conditions. Here are some of the common sub-categories.

Sensory Integration Dysfunction

- CAPD — Central Auditory Processing Disorder
- Tactile dysfunction
- Vestibular dysfunction
- Proprioceptive dysfunction
- Hypersensitivity
- Hyposensitivity

ADHD

- ADHD predominantly inattentive—or ADD
- ADHD predominantly hyperactive/impulsive
- ODD Oppositional Defiance Disorder
- CD Conduct Disorder
- OCD Obsessive Compulsive Disorder

Autism or Pervasive Developmental Disorder

- Autistic disorder
- Asperger's syndrome sometimes called higher-functioning autism
- Childhood Disintegrative Disorder (CDD)
- Retts disorder
- Pervasive Developmental Disorder — Not Otherwise Specified (PDD-NOS).

Learning Difficulties

- Dyslexia
- Visual learning difficulty
- Auditory learning difficulty

Central Auditory Processing disorder CAPD

CAPD is a complex group of symptoms describing a difficulty with integrating auditory information. To assist understanding and treatment, speech pathologists have broken this disorder down into sub-categories. The following table is based on the work of Dr. Teri James Bellis' Subprofiles of CAPD [1]. To this excellent outline, I have added the relevance and benefits of Sound Therapy for the different types of CAPD.

Sub categories of CAPD

Profile	Description	Region of Dysfunction	Associated Problems	Educational Intervention	Benefits of Sound Therapy
Auditory decoding deficit	The classic type of CAPD. Children may appear to have hearing problems even when their hearing tests as normal. Information processing is slow and inaccurate. This means they have to work much harder to interpret what they hear.	Primary (left) Auditory Cortex	Difficulties with spelling (word attack), hearing amid noise, sound blending; poor analytic skills; mimics hearing loss	Improve acoustic clarity; speech- sound training; auditory closure activities; speech-to-print skills training	Stimulates connections in auditory cortex. Improves clarity of hearing. Increases information- processing speed.
Auditory Associative Deficit	These children have difficulty applying the rules of language to sounds they hear. Background noise often reduces their ability to understand speech. They tend to perform less well with language demands in the classroom.	Left (associative) Cortex	Receptive language deficits, including semantics and syntax; difficulty comprehending information of increasing linguistic complexity; poor reading comprehension; poor maths application	Rephrase using smaller linguistic units; systematic learning approach; multi-sensory augmentation; speech-language therapy focusing on receptive language	Stimulates connections in auditory cortex. Improves processing speed. Improves linguistic comprehension and spontaneous use of greater vocabulary.
Integration deficit	These children demonstrate difficulty across modalities with any task which requires efficient hemispheric communication. They have trouble tying together auditory and visual information. They frequently exhibit long delays in responding.	Corpus Callosum Cerebellum	Difficulty linking prosody and linguistic content; poor speech-in-noise skills; phonological deficits; auditory language and memory deficits; poor bimanual co-ordination; difficulty with any task requiring interhemispheric integration	Limit or discontinue use of multimodality cues; provision of note-taker; sensory integration therapy; interhemispheric exercises; specific academic intervention	Stimulates sensory integration via the cerebellum. Improves auditory visual linkages. Stimulation of right-ear/left-brain improves efficiency of corpus callosum and auditory processing.

Table continued overleaf

Sub categories of CAPD part 2

Profile	Description	Region of Dysfunction	Associated Problems	Educational Intervention	Benefits of Sound Therapy
Prosadic deficit	These children talk or read without intonation, stress or rhythm. They often have difficulty with pragmatic communication skills, sequencing, social judgement, gestalt patterning and spatial abilities. They have difficulty perceiving the prosadic cues which underlie humour, sarcasm, question forms — which rely heavily on intonational cues to gauge intent.	Nonprimary (right) Auditory Cortex and associated areas Cerebellum	Difficulties with spelling (sight word), judging communicative intent, perception and use of prosody; monotonic speech; visuospatial and mathematics calculation difficulties; socio-emotional concerns	Placement with animated teacher; prosody training; keyword extraction; psychological intervention	Increases high frequency sensitivity and therefore emotional appreciation of meaning in sound. Whole brain stimulation and integration through use of complex melody, rhythm and harmony. Integration of right hemisphere with multi-sensory inputs via cerebellum.
Output organisational deficit	These children have trouble organising, sequencing, recalling and/or expressing an answer. They have listened to, analysed, correctly connected and pulled together the information, but still have difficulty responding correctly. In general, these children have difficulty with tasks where success is dependent on motor and or planning skills.	Temporal-to-frontal and/or efferent system Cerebellum	Poor hearing amid noise; poor organisational skills; motor planning difficulties; difficulties with expressive language and word retrieval; poor sequencing and follow-through	Highly structured environment; training in use of organization aids; speech-language therapy focussing on expressive language; may benefit from assistive listening technology	Improves motor praxis through stimulation of the cerebellum. Activates efferent auditory pathways. Improves whole brain connections and auditory memory.

Speech problems

Speech develops at different speeds and there is a range which is considered normal development. The following is a rough guide of what to look for in the early years.

The first three years By 12 months or so, most children have one or two words which they say with meaning, and can comply with simple requests (e.g., 'Can I have your cup?') or commands (e.g., 'Don't touch!') and understand little questions (e.g., 'Where's your tummy?').

By 2 to 3 years of age, your child should be able to follow two-part instructions ('Get your teddy and put it on the chair') and string two or three words together to talk about and ask for things.

Two part instructions

If a child is not reaching these levels and you have concerns that her language may be delayed, introduce Sound Therapy right away. The stimulation it provides will help to develop brain pathways, establish clear laterality, and ensure that the child does not miss out on crucial developmental time.

Use Sound Therapy if there is language delay

Language and laterality

Language problems, according to Tomatis, are frequently associated with left-ear dominance which causes auditory confusion. In poor lateralisation there is an extra step in the auditory feedback process.[2] The two ears communicate with opposite hemispheres of the brain. Therefore, if a child is using the left ear, the message is sent to the right hemisphere of the brain. The message must then be sent on to the left hemisphere, thus incurring loss of time and causing slowness and fatigue.[3] In contrast, lateralisation to the right has the effect of facilitating and accelerating the patient's processing of sensory and cognitive information.[4] Sound Therapy consistently produces right laterality. It not only provides the right ear with a higher volume of sound, but also trains the right ear in its intended role of being the main receiver and decipherer of high frequency tones.

Sound Therapy trains the right ear to take the dominant role

Left-handedness

Children who are left-eared are sometimes also left-handed. These children may take longer to adjust to Sound Therapy and may resist using it at first. However, they are the ones who stand to benefit most, and it is most important that

Left-handed children may need it more

167

they are encouraged to push through their resistance and persist with the program. Once children achieve their breakthrough with Sound Therapy, if they are still quite young, they may spontaneously switch to be right-handed. This is not intended as a bias against left-handed people, who are often multi-talented and creative in unusual ways. However, the process of establishing laterality may be streamlined by the use of Sound Therapy.

Trauma or injury may cause an apparent reversal Some practitioners may advise that a child has reversed brain hemi-spheres and that the child should therefore reverse the headphones. In the vast majority of cases, this is not correct. Those fully versed in neurological development confirm that it is extremely rare for the hemispheres to be naturally reversed. (This would occur in the case of mirror-image twins.) Most often an apparent reversal will have been caused by trauma or injury and the child will be better if it she corrected to adapt to right ear lateralisation.

Stuttering

Dr Tomatis says that two conditions are always present in a stutterer:

1. Incompatibility between the directing ear and the general lateralisation of the individual, or the absence of a 'directing' ear, owing to the absence or inadequacy of general lateralisation.

2. A trans-cerebral delay time in the order of 0.15 seconds, or 0.2 seconds for English language. This delay is different in each language! 0.2 seconds is the average length of a syllable in English.[5]

Stuttering is an easy condition to measure and some good research has been done on treating this condition.

82% of stutterers got relief Jaarsveld and du Plessis at the University of Potchefstroom studied forty-three stutterers. 82.55% experienced significant relief. However only 54% maintained their results for 1 year indicating perhaps that long term Sound Therapy treatment is necessary for this condition to fully resolve. It is not always possible to change a lifetime of habit in a few weeks of treatment.[6]

Many other studies on learning and language difficulties have supported the efficacy of Sound Therapy for language development. See Chapter 10, *Research,* for more detail on these studies.

For examples of children who have been helped in their speech function by Sound Therapy see Chapter 8, *Listeners' experiences.*

Dyslexia

'There are devastating effects on personal development for the person who has failed to listen effectively and cannot read.' [7]

What is dyslexia?

Dyslexia is a language-based learning disability which is neurological in origin. Dyslexia refers to a cluster of symptoms, which result in people having difficulties with specific language skills, particularly reading, accurate and/ or fluent word recognition and poor spelling and decoding abilities. It is referred to as a learning disability because dyslexia can make it very difficult for a student to succeed academically in the typical instructional environment. These difficulties typically result from a deficit in the phonological component of language, which is often unexpected in relation to other cognitive abilities and the provision of effective classroom instruction. Studies show that individuals with dyslexia process information in a different area of the brain than do non-dyslexics. Many people who are dyslexic are of average, to above average intelligence.

Dyslexia is a problem with analysing sounds

New terminology

Dyslexia technically means 'reading difficulty'. Many educational specialists now break this condition down more specifically. The new term used is 'Specific Learning Difficulty' and this is broken into sub-categories of 'Visual learning difficulty' or 'Auditory learning difficulty'. In fact, because the visual and auditory pathways are so closely linked, most people with dyslexia are bound to have difficulties in both areas. Many also experience co-ordination problems and balance or movement disorders, because of problems in the vestibular system and poor integration of all sensory inputs to the brain.

Dyslexia includes visual and auditory problems

How common are language-based learning disabilities?

- 15-20% of the population have a language-based learning disability.

- Of the students with specific learning disabilities receiving special education services, 70-80% have deficits in reading.
- Dyslexia is the most common cause of reading, writing and spelling difficulties.
- Dyslexia affects males and females nearly equally, and people from different ethnic and socio-economic backgrounds as well.

Can individuals who are dyslexic learn to read?

- Yes, if children who are dyslexic get effective phonological training in Kindergarten and 1st grade, they will have significantly fewer problems in learning to read at grade level than do children who are not identified or helped until 3rd grade.
- Early introduction of Sound Therapy will support and enhance other interventions and make learning much easier.
- It is never too late for individuals with dyslexia to learn to read, process and express information more efficiently. Research shows that programs utilising multi-sensory structured language techniques can help children and adults learn to read. See Chapter 6, *We move with our ears.*

What causes dyslexia?

Dyslexia is a problem in the connections between ear and brain

The causes for dyslexia are neurobiological and may be partly genetic. It is often the case that one of the child's parents, grandparents, aunts, or uncles is dyslexic. However dyslexic-like traits may also develop, in childhood or later in life, as a result of stress and toxic exposures. Anatomical and brain imagery studies show differences in the way the brain of a dyslexic person develops and functions. People with dyslexia have been found to have problems with discriminating sounds within a word, a key factor in their reading difficulties. For this reason, certain researchers, including Dr Tomatis, have identified dyslexia as primarily a problem in the functioning of the ear and auditory neurological system. See Chapter 10, *Research, the brain and Sound Therapy* for more details on the link between dyslexia and ear function. Dyslexia is not due to either lack of intelligence or lack of desire to learn; with appropriate teaching methods dyslexics can learn successfully. They are often gifted in areas which do not require strong language skills, such as art, computer science, design, drama, electronics, maths, mechanics, music, physics, sales and sports.

Is there a cure for dyslexia?

There is no cure as such for dyslexia, as it is not a disease. However the right sensory integration treatment, in particular Sound Therapy and behavioural optometry, may remove and repair many of the neurological processing problems.

Common signs of dyslexia

- May talk later than most children.
- May have difficulty pronouncing words, i.e., 'busgetti' for 'spaghetti', 'mawn lower' for 'lawn mower'.
- May be slow to add new vocabulary words.
- May have difficulty with rhyming.
- May have trouble learning the alphabet, numbers, days of the week, colours, shapes, how to spell and write his or her name.
- May be unable to follow multi-step directions or routines.
- Fine motor skills may develop more slowly than in other children.
- May have difficulty telling and/or retelling a story in the correct sequence.
- Often has difficulty separating sounds in words and blending sounds to make words.
- May be slow to learn the connection between letters and sounds.
- Has difficulty spelling phonetically.
- Makes consistent reading and spelling errors such as:
  - Letter reversals - 'd' for 'b' as in: 'dog' for 'bog'
  - Word reversals - 'tip' for 'pit'
  - Inversions - 'm' for 'w', 'u' for 'n'
  - Transpositions - 'felt' for 'left'
  - Substitutions - 'house' for 'home'
- May have difficulty learning new vocabulary.
- May have trouble remembering facts.
- May be slow to learn new skills; relies heavily on memorising without understanding.
- May have difficulty planning, organising and managing time, materials and tasks.

- May have poor 'fine motor' co-ordination, with illegible handwriting .Often uses an awkward pencil grip (fist, thumb hooked over fingers, etc.).
- May have difficulty spelling; spells same word differently on the same page.
- May avoid reading aloud.
- May have trouble with word problems in maths.
- May have difficulty with written composition.
- May have trouble with non-literal language (idioms, jokes, proverbs, slang).

How widespread is dyslexia?

Current studies suggest that 15-20% of the population hve a reading disability. Of those, 85% have dyslexia.

What are the effects of dyslexia?

Dyslexia causes literacy problems

The impact which dyslexia has is different for each person and depends on the severity of the condition and the approaches of the remediation. The most common effects are problems with reading, spelling, and writing. Some dyslexics do not have much difficulty with early reading and spelling tasks but do experience great problems when more complex language skills are required, such as grammar, understanding textbook material, and writing essays.

Speech can be affected too

People with dyslexia can also have problems with spoken language. They may find it difficult to express themselves clearly, or to fully comprehend what others mean when they speak. Such language problems are often difficult to recognise, but they can lead to major problems in school, in the workplace, and in relating to other people. The effects of dyslexia reach well beyond the classroom.

Dyslexia affects self-esteem

Dyslexia can also affect a person's self-image. Students with dyslexia often end up feeling 'dumb' and less capable than they actually are. After experiencing a great deal of stress due to academic problems, a student may become discouraged about continuing in school.

How is dyslexia diagnosed?

A formal evaluation is needed to discover if a person is dyslexic. The evaluation assesses intellectual ability, information processing, psycho-linguistic processing, and academic skills. It is used to determine whether or not a student is reading at the expected level, and takes into account the individual's family background and overall school performance. The testing can be conducted by trained school or outside specialists.

How is dyslexia treated?

Dyslexia is a life-long condition. With proper help, people with dyslexia can learn to read and/or write well. Early identification and treatment is the key to helping dyslexics achieve in school and in life. Most people with dyslexia need help from a teacher, tutor, or therapist specially trained in using a multi-sensory, structured language approach. It is important for these individuals to be taught by a method which involves several senses (hearing, seeing, touching) at the same time. Many individuals with dyslexia need one-on-one help so that they can move forward at their own pace. For students with dyslexia, it is helpful if their outside academic therapists work closely with classroom teachers. The inclusion of Sound Therapy in an integrated program will make the other interventions easier and more effective, because Sound Therapy addresses the fundamental processing problem in the inner-ear system at its most fundamental level. Students will often find that when they begin Sound Therapy their language comprehension and recall improves — along with spatial awareness, co-ordination, listening spelling and reading.

Multi-sensory treatment is important

Schools can implement academic modifications to help dyslexic students succeed. For example, a student with dyslexia can be given extra time to complete tasks, or help with taking notes, and/or appropriate work assignments. Teachers can give taped tests or allow dyslexic students to use alternative means of assessment. Students can benefit from listening to books-on-tape and from writing with computers.

Teachers can make it easier

Students may also need help with emotional issues which sometimes arise as a consequence of difficulties in school. Mental health specialists can help students cope with their struggles.

Dyslexia and the ear

> 'The foundation on which reading and writing are based, is spoken language. If the sounds which form the basis of language are not thoroughly analysed this can pose an obstacle to the development of written language skills.' [8]

Reading involves rapid analysis of letter forms, and their translation into sound. Decoding letters into sounds and recognising their meaning requires well-developed auditory processing skills.

Dyslexics process sound more slowly Analysis of auditory function often shows that dyslexics have difficulty detecting the relationship between high and low sounds. Their auditory processing speed is slow, making it hard for them to identify consonants, which are high frequency sounds and require rapid auditory processing.[9] Other symptoms of dysfunction of the auditory and vestibular system are:[10]

- dips in the perception of certain frequencies in one or both ears
- lack of proper awareness of their bodies
- poor concepts of time and space
- left ear dominance or no clear lateralisation

Laterality
The Right/Left argument

Left ear dominance causes learning difficulties A debate has raged for decades over whether lack of left brain dominance causes dyslexia. The mistake made by most of these theorists is that they used left-handedness as the measure of right-brain dominance. Tomatis, however, looked more deeply into the question, and learned that it is not the dominant hand which is at issue, but the dominant ear. Left-earedness is sometimes, but not always, reflected by left-handedness. In the words of one specialist educator from Los Angeles who has spent decades studying and treating dyslexics, 'it doesn't matter if the person is left-eyed, left-handed left-legged, or 'left' anything, it will not necessarily cause a problem. But if they are left-eared, they will have a learning difficulty.'

The right ear serves the virtuoso Tomatis believed that the right ear must be the leading ear and that this is the key to proper listening. Another way he expressed the roles of the two sides of the brain is that the right hemisphere is the instrument, and the left hemisphere is the virtuoso, or the one which executes. Right is passive, left is dynamic and active.[11] Tomatis' findings in this regard were experimentally reproduced. By having people monitor themselves with the left ear, they produced experimental dyslexics.[12]

ADHD – Attention Deficit and Hyperactivity Disorder

Terminology

ADD was first identified in 1917-1918 when an outbreak of encephalitis in the United states left children with ADD-like symptoms. This mislead doctors for many years to believe that ADD was due to brain damage. As a result, the condition was called Minimal Brain Damage (MBD) in the 1950s. This was changed in the 1960s to Minimal Brain Dysfunction, because by this time doctors had realised that there was often no history of brain damage. At the same time the terms 'hyperactivity' and 'hyperkinesis' were also being used to describe the same condition. The description was widened in the 1980s to include short attention span and impulsive behaviour. To distinguish between the two types, a definition was then created for ADD without hyperactivity and ADHD with hyperactivity. This was listed in the DSM III—the Diagnostic and Statistical Manual of Mental Disorders—which is used in the United states and Australia. In Europe they use the ICD - International Classification of Disease of the World Health Organization.

This was revised again in 1987 DSM III and changed to ADHD. By 1994, in DSM IV, it became ADHD divided into Predominantly Inattentive or Hyperactive/Impulsive. In some cases there could be a combination of the two.

Now Dr Russell Barkley, perhaps the most respected expert in the field and a member of the DSM committee which decides on the diagnostic criteria, is proposing that an 'inhibition disorder' is the main feature of ADHD.[13]

ADHD includes short attention span and hyperactivity

Recognising ADHD

Recognising ADHD is usually a gradual process for the parents. First the behaviour is put down to the 'terrible twos', but when they turn into the 'terrible threes' and 'terrible fours' and 'terrible fives', parents realise something is definitely amiss.

When the terrible twos don't end

Denial - Oh no, my child isn't hyperactive

On the other hand, sometimes parents of hyperactive children do not realise their child is hyperactive, yet it is patently obvious to outsiders who are not used to being exposed to such a whirlwind of activity. If several outsiders have commented, it may be wise to look into getting help for your child.

Girls and Boys

There are more girls with ADD that the diagnostic statistics usually show. Girls are more likely to have ADD without the H, so they are dreamy, low energy, poor learners, or disorganised chatterboxes, but are less likely to be hyperactive and therefore do not come to the attention of specialists. Many girls probably miss out on assistance because their problem remains unrecognised.

Varied symptoms

No two are the same. This makes ADHD hard to diagnose. Here are a few of the common but very varied symptoms parents may notice.

- Class clown
- Impulsiveness
- Dreamer who gets nothing done
- Learning-disabled in reading or maths or both
- Sugar cravings
- Sensitivity to food textures and lumpy food
- Hates chewing
- Can't sleep
- Can't stay asleep
- Sleeps long hours like a 'stunned mullet' and hard to wake
- Fails to finish things
- 'But he can't have ADHD, he can concentrate so well when he's interested.'
- Co-ordination problems
- Speech problems

ADHD diagnosis

ADHD is a point on a scale ADHD, which includes the former definition of ADD, is believed to be a disorder of the brain's neurotransmitter chemicals, noradrenaline and dopamine. However, the only way of diagnosing the condition is by assessing the child on a number of behavioural standards. These behaviours relate to the ability of the child to focus attention and to use judgement and inhibition. This assessment is done by a doctor or a psychiatrist. Since it is simply a matter of ticking off a number of criteria on a list, the diagnosis really marks an arbitrary point where the experts say, 'this child has enough problems that we will call it ADHD'. The child who doesn't quite make the score still may have the same problems, but to not quite as high an extent.

There are no laboratory tests to diagnose ADHD. *There is a* Some research has begun to identify possible areas of the *change in brain* brain which may be involved. Dr Alan Zametkin, et al, *metabolism* undertook positron emission tomography (PET) scans, which showed differences in the brain metabolism of adults with ADD compared to those without. The greatest reduction in brain metabolism was in areas believed to be important in the control of motor activity, attention, and the inhibition of inappropriate responses.[14]

ADHD is currently diagnosed by the child's score on a list of behaviours, according to the assessing doctor. The full DSM IV evaluation criteria is included in Appendix III. This is a brief summary of the two scales.

1. Inattention

- Makes careless mistakes or fails to pay close attention to detail
- Has difficulty paying attention
- Seems not to listen
- Fails to finish schoolwork or tasks
- Is disorganised
- Dislikes or avoids tasks which require attention such as schoolwork
- Loses necessary items
- Is easily distracted
- Is forgetful

2. Hyperactivity

- Fidgets with hands or feet or squirms in seat
- Leaves seat
- Runs about or climbs excessively (in adolescents or adults: feels restless)
- Has difficulty playing quietly or relaxing
- Is 'on the go' or acts as if 'driven by a motor'
- Talks excessively

3. Impulsivity

- Blurts out answers
- Has difficulty awaiting turn
- Interrupts others

Denial

Prior to your child receiving a diagnosis, you may find that many professionals will try to reassure you by dismissing the problem as part of normal development. They may say things like:

- 'Don't worry, he'll grow out of it.' Unfortunately, if untreated the child may well grow out of this problem and into a worse one.
- 'There's nothing wrong with your child.'
- 'Would you like a prescription for some tranquillisers?'
- 'Could do better if he tried', on the school report card.
- 'He just needs some proper boundaries.'

The child cannot control her behaviour However, you will find that behaviour modification is not helpful when a child is reacting to a health problem. A child cannot be expected to control her behaviour if she is going through chemical upsets like low blood sugar or a toxicity reaction. See Chapter 9 *What's this on my plate?* to address these areas.

The cause

Environmental causes may be being blamed on genetics The cause of ADHD today is largely attributed to genetics, but this may be a function of the fact that genetics is the latest new area of research and is therefore receiving credit for almost everything that ails us. More and more evidence is now pointing to the fact that ADHD is an environmental disease, meaning that it is caused by our increasingly toxic environment. Some cases of ADHD have responded well to dietary change, allergy treatment and supplementation. Some respond well to Sound Therapy. Some are controlled by prescription drugs. Some doctors trace the cause to the inner ear system and its corresponding brain pathways. In Chapter 9, *What's this on my plate?*, I go into some depth as to the possible environmental causes of ADHD and the evidence to support this. Also see the section below on the causes of autism.

Gifted Children

Bright children and children with ADHD can have some of the same symptoms, such as high activity level, being easily bored and underachieving in school.

Being gifted is like the flipside of ADHD. Perhaps which

way the child goes, depends entirely on his environment — by which I mean parenting, family, food, education and opportunities available to the child.

High achievers

Famous people believed to have had ADHD include Beethoven, Einstein, Leonardo da Vinci, Winston Churchill and Thomas Edison. ADHD children who are able to draw on their inner potential and turn their lives around can become incredibly productive and successful adults. They often have a superabundance of energy, and need little sleep. They may be workaholics, and are often non-conformists who think outside the square and are highly intuitive and creative.

People with ADHD may be very talented

Do kids grow out of ADHD?

The symptoms of ADHD change and evolve through life. Where it used to be thought that children grew out of ADHD, it is now recognised that the symptoms are different and not as noticeable in adults. A reduction in activity level at about age seven may appear to be an improvement; but at the same time it is likely the child will be showing co-ordination problems which show up in sport, and social problems with peers may become difficult. If there are reading difficulties these will also show up at the beginning of school. Now secondary behaviour problems, resulting from the child's awareness of his own difficulties, will start to arise.

The symptoms change but don't go away

ADHD is sometimes described as 'limbic immaturity', meaning the ability to control and have judgement over one's emotions is underdeveloped. This means there may be a big improvement in mid- to late adolescence. The limbic system does not fully mature until the early twenties and some males show significant behaviour change at that time.

Adults with ADHD

Adults may feel as though they are ten years behind everyone else in the stages of developing maturity. Adolescence seems to happen in the twenties, instead of the teens. Frequent change — changing jobs, changing addresses — is typical of ADHD adults. The condition can continue right through life, threatening careers and causing marriage problems.[15]

Adults tend to have lots of changes

Adults symptoms include
- Restlessness
- Mood swings
- Irritability
- Disorganisation and distractibility

These symptoms can be a problem in relationships and may make work life difficult. What these adults need is plenty of leeway, and to be encouraged to follow their ideas. Most important of all, ADHD adults report, is someone to believe in them.

Defiance ODD and CD

Two new categories are now coming into common usage. These are Oppositional Defiance Disorder and Conduct Disorder.

Oppositional Defiance Disorder is a behaviour pattern where the child constantly says 'no', stubbornly refuses to co-operate with requests and intentionally breaks rules. You would have to meet and spend time with one of these children to understand that this is more than the 'terrible twos', and is not due to poor parenting.

Their common behaviours include:

- Losing temper
- Arguing with adults
- Refusing adult requests or defying rules
- Deliberately annoying other people
- Blaming others for his or her own mistakes
- Touchy or easily annoyed
- Angry and resentful
- Spiteful or vindictive

This syndrome puts excessive strain on families, even beyond that normally experienced with ADHD children. There is a greater likelihood that these families will experience marital problems and other emotional problems.

Conduct Disorder (CD) is a pattern of constantly violating the rights of others. Children with Oppositional Defiance Disorder often go on to develop Conduct Disorder.

The behaviours associated with CD are:

- Stealing
- Running away
- Lying
- Fire-lighting
- Breaking and entering
- Truancy
- Vandalism
- Cruelty to animals
- Rape
- Use of a weapon
- Physical aggression
- Mugging, armed robbery or extortion
- Physical cruelty to people

This condition is also associated with poor school performance, drug use, teenage pregnancy, sexually transmitted diseases and increased risk of suicide attempts.

Solutions for ADHD

Tutoring

If a child is behind and struggling in school, tutoring may be an important part of the remedial program. ADHD children respond much better in a one-on-one situation, so tutoring is sometimes necessary to help them catch up and improve their academic achievement. This would have to be done by a skilled tutor who is able to build rapport with the child and gain the child's interest and trust. Tutoring will be much more successful if sensory integration therapies and nutritional issues are addressed at the same time.

One on one attention is very helpful

Treatment

Medication and diet. There is a place for both medication and diet in the treatment of ADHD. Often proponents of one or the other will present it as the only way. Some parents may need to use medication for a certain period simply to cope and get the situation under control. This does not mean that other methods which address the more fundamental issues should be abandoned. For more detail on the issues surrounding medication and dietary support,

181

please see Chapter 9, *What's this on my plate?*

Sound Therapy is highly recommended for children with ADHD. It is easy to apply and may be very effective in improving brain integration and, therefore, inhibition, behaviour and learning ability.

Sensory integration therapy, including movement activities and possibly visual exercises, may be an important part of recovery for some ADHD children.

Discipline and behaviour control

Specific rewards work best

The methods used to teach responsible behaviour to most children may not work with an ADHD child. In order for a child to learn better behaviour, she needs to be able to listen, plan ahead, remember, consider before acting and be motivated by rewards. These are all the things which ADHD children often cannot do. They lack judgement and impulse control. An American psychologist, Dr Russell Barkley, author of the book *Attention Deficit and Hyperactivity Disorder: A Handbook of Diagnosis and Treatment,* suggests that ADHD is more of a motivation deficit than an attention deficit. The implication of this theory is that ADHD children need a different type of motivation from others. They tend not to be motivated by praise and appreciation, but more by rewards. This is the basis of the behaviour management program now recommended for defiant children.[16]

Be wary of punishment

Punishment, with the intention of forcing the child to regret his behaviour, is usually counter-productive and only serves to gradually build defensiveness and resentment. Punishing an ADHD child will have even worse repercussions than with other children. This is particularly true for any form of physical punishment. Never use punishment as a way for you to deal with your anger. The furthest one should go in applying discipline, is to use 'time out' or withdrawal of privileges. Any punishment which is given should be used sparingly. If you have to use some form of punishment, use the following safeguards:

Safety tips for punishment[17]

- Give clear warnings first, so the child has a choice
- Think before you act

- Communicate calmly
- Have a clear beginning and end to the punishment
- Let the matter drop once it's over

For tried and true techniques that work for children with ADHD, see the section on Practical Tips at the end of this chapter.

Autism

Autism is a complex developmental disability which typically appears during the first three years of life. The result of a neurological disorder which affects the functioning of the brain, autism impacts the normal development of the brain in the areas of social interaction and communication skills. Children and adults with autism typically have difficulties in verbal and non-verbal communication, social interactions, and leisure or play activities.

A brain state that causes isolation

Prevalence

Autism and its associated behaviours have been estimated to occur in 2 to 6 per 1,000 births.[18] Autism is four times more prevalent in boys than girls, and knows no racial, ethnic, or social boundaries. Family income, lifestyle, and educational levels do not affect the chance of autism's occurrence.

People with autism process and respond to information in unique ways. In some cases, aggressive and/or self-injurious behaviour may be present.

Persons with autism may also exhibit some of the following traits:

- Insistence on sameness; resistance to change
- Difficulty in expressing needs; using gestures or pointing, instead of words
- Repeating words or phrases in place of normal, responsive language
- Laughing, crying, showing distress for reasons not apparent to others
- Preferring to be alone; aloof manner
- Tantrums
- Difficulty in mixing with others
- May not want to cuddle or be cuddled
- Little or no eye contact

- Unresponsive to normal teaching methods
- Sustained, odd play
- Spinning objects
- Inappropriate attachments to objects
- Apparent over-sensitivity or under-sensitivity to pain
- No real fears of danger
- Noticeable physical over-activity or extreme under-activity
- Uneven gross/fine motor skills
- Not responsive to verbal cues; acting as if deaf, although hearing tests in normal range

Different categories on the spectrum

Autism can be mild, severe, or anywhere on the spectrum

Autism is one of five disorders coming under the umbrella of Pervasive Developmental Disorders (PDD), a category of neurological disorders characterised by 'severe and pervasive impairment in several areas of development', including social interaction and communications skills (DSM-IV-TR). The five disorders under PDD are: Autistic disorder, Asperger's disorder, Childhood Disintegrative Disorder (CDD), Retts disorder, and PDD-Not Otherwise Specified (PDD-NOS). Each of these disorders has specific diagnostic criteria as outlined by the American Psychiatric Association (APA) in its *Diagnostic & Statistical Manual of Mental Disorders* (DSM-IV-TR).[19]

Asperger's or higher-functioning autism

Asperger's children may be brilliant in some areas

The terms more advanced autism, high-functioning autism, Asperger's syndrome and Pervasive Developmental Disorder (PDD) refer to individuals within the autism spectrum who do not experience severe intellectual impairments. Although more advanced individuals with autism may score below average on standardized intelligence tests, they often learn at, or above, normal rates in certain areas. Areas of ability will differ across individuals. For example, an individual may learn academic content easily, but have difficulty performing activities of daily living. Or a student who is very good at memorising may not be able to answer essay-type questions.

They respond well to praise

Individuals are usually extremely good on rote memory skills such as facts, figures, dates, times. Many excel in maths and science. There is a range of severity of symptoms within the syndrome, the very mildly affected child often goes undiagnosed and may just appear odd or eccentric. They often use language in a slightly odd way and take literal meanings from what is read or heard. They are happiest with routines and a structured environment; finding it difficult to decide what to do they fall back on their preferred activities. They love praise, winning and being first — but find losing, imperfection and criticism very difficult to take. Bad behaviour often stems from an inability to communicate their frustrations and anxieties. Some children with Asperger's, boys in particular, may be prone to outbursts of anger. Children with Asperger's need love, tenderness, care, patience and understanding.

One of the hallmarks of Asperger's syndrome is the child's pre-occupation (or obsession) with certain topics, often on themes of transport — trains in particular — or computers, dinosaurs, maps etc. These preoccupations, usually in intellectual areas, change over time but not in intensity, and may be pursued to the exclusion of other activities. We now believe that my older sister suffered from Asperger's syndrome. She exhibited many of these symptoms, including spending her early childhood obsessed with trains and her adulthood fascinated by computers. See the special tips at the end of this chapter for handling autism or Asperger's.

They may be obsessive about hobbies

Retts disorder

This condition, (first described by Rett in 1966), is a pervasive developmental disorder which follows a very specific progression. Children with this disorder seem to develop normally for the first six to eight months of life. Parents may notice excessive levels of hand patting, waving, and involuntary movements of the fingers, wrists and arms. However, these signs are subtle and may go unnoticed. There is a slowing of normal development and a failure to reach developmental milestones on time. Particular problems occur with the acquisition of skills requiring balance, such as walking. Head deceleration occurs (the head fails to grow larger at the proper rate.) Children undergo a rapid deterioration in behaviour, including loss of acquired speech and purposeful use of hands. A lack of interest in social relationships occurs, and stereotyped

Hand washing is typical

behaviours may develop. The most prominent symptom in Retts syndrome may be 'hand washing' movements, which develops after the ability to move hands purposefully is lost. These children are generally mentally retarded. Episodes of screaming or tantrums may occur. Sleep abnormalities and seizure disorder are present in over half of the children with this disorder. The lack of interest in social relationships, loss of expressive language and the development of stereotypes can cause this disorder to be confused with autism. Retts disorder is much more prevalent in girls. Sound Therapy may be very helpful for children with this disorder. For information on the effect of Sound Therapy on a child who matches this description see Chapter 8, story by Pietro and Shaylene Garofalo.

Childhood Disintegrative Disorder

Autism can come later and cause deterioration

Childhood Disintegrative Disorder (CDD) is a term given when a child with a history of normal development, rapidly deteriorates into autistic-like symptoms between the ages of two and three. Previously developed skills are lost, such as bowel and bladder training, language skills and social skills. The child may become essentially mute, lose the ability to play purposefully and develop autistic-like stereotypes. Prior to this period of marked deterioration, the child may exhibit periods of agitation or dysphoria. From the perspective of environmental medicine, it seems likely that such a child has been affected by toxic poisoning at a later date; or perhaps a later vaccine, as Dr Scheibner says, 'was the straw that broke the camel's back.' As with Retts syndrome, Sound Therapy may still be helpful in these cases, and should be begun as soon as possible after symptoms appear.

Causes

Research is revealing neurological causes

While understanding of autism has grown tremendously since it was first described by Dr. Leo Kanner in 1943, the official medical line is that there is no known cause of autism. However, it is generally accepted that it is caused by abnormalities in brain structure or function. Brain scans show differences in the shape and structure of the brain in autistic versus non-autistic children. Researchers are investigating a number of theories, including the links between heredity and genetics, and environmental factors such as viral infections, metabolic imbalances, and exposure to environmental chemicals.

Genetics versus environment

With the preference today for finding genetic causes for so many diseases, medical and official channels tend to downplay the contribution of environmental factors. Looking at the contribution of artificial chemicals to health issues is quite confronting since so many chemicals have become an ingrained part of our lifestyle, from insect spray, to painkillers to talcum powder. Many large chemical companies also have a financial interest in downplaying the possible dangers of their products. Research scientist, Dr Viera Scheibner is a recognised authority on the subject of autism and its probable link to damage caused by vaccination. Although controversial, her views are backed up by years of painstaking personal research on the subject. Her work was done from the passion of her own conviction to uncover the truth, and was not funded by any outside body. Dr Scheibner explains the weakness in attributing autism to genetic causes:

> '*I also view with caution statements of Bax (1994) that it is a well-established fact that "there are certainly genetic factors in the origins of autism". This adage is no more valid than when we say that everything has a genetic component, but this does not prove genetic factors as a causal link. A trigger is necessary to activate the genetic predispositions to action. We are all allergic (sensitive) to, and affected by, toxic substances; that does not justify continued exposure and then blaming the bad recipient's genes for the observed reactions.*'[20]

Thus she explains the inherent weakness in the tendency today to attribute most diseases to genetic causes. Finding a link does not prove causality, and the preoccupation with this search is dangerous in that it can divert us from putting resources into searching for environmental causes, over which we could have more control.

The genetic argument has weaknesses

Purkinje neurons and vaccination

The loss of Purkinje neurons has been linked to autism

Dr Scheibner has noted that one of the most prominent changes in the brains of autistic children is a loss of Purkinje neurons. Purkinje cells are a particular type of neuron which exist in large quantities in the cerebellum, where crucial aspects of sensory integration take place. This abnormality was first discovered by Williams et al. (1980), and has since been substantiated by 16 more studies from nine laboratories involving 240 autistic patients, using quantitative magnetic resonance imaging (MRI) and autopsy.[21]

Dr Scheibner explains how she was able to link this evidence to the administration of vaccines:

> *'Purkinje neurons are vulnerable to the destructive force of viruses only during a relatively brief period of development. It is a well documented fact that the vast majority of autism occurs after a brief period of normal development, usually after the first year of life. This is usually after a number of vaccine rounds have been administered. The last round, which seems to break the camel's back, is usually the MMR vaccine, and/or the boosters of other vaccines (such as DPT (diptheria), HiB and polio), administered around 18 months of age.*

> *Loss of Purkinje neurons triggers loss of other neurons. Loss of neurons causes misconstructions of cerebellar circuits. Purkinje neurons normally provide the only cortical inhibitory control over output of neural activity from deep cerebellar neurons.'*[22]

> *'This misconstruction of intrinsic cerebellar circuit structure and function begins with the loss of Purkinje neurons early in brain development, and ends with the loss of ability of the cerebellum to transform input signal into precise spatiotemporal patterns of output. Output activity will be abnormally reduced. It will be either excessive or poorly modulated bursts of excitation, or abnormal spatiotemporal patterns of excitation and inhibition.'*[23]

Toxins may have intergenerational effects

Some harmful substances ingested during pregnancy have been associated with an increased risk of autism. Environmental researchers also observe that, where there is intergenerational autism there is usually evidence of toxic exposure in previous generations. It appears that chemical toxins can cause genetic or prenatal damage which is passed on from parent to child.

Autism tends to occur more frequently than expected among individuals who have certain medical conditions, including Fragile X syndrome, tuberous sclerosis, congenital rubella syndrome, and untreated phenylketonuria (PKU).

Whatever the cause, it is clear that autism and pervasive developmental disorder (PDD) are caused by inputs which cause damage to the functioning of the brain and the nervous system. Autism is not a mental illness. Children with autism are not unruly kids who choose not to behave. It is not caused by poor parenting. Furthermore, no known psychological factors in the development of the child have been shown to cause autism.

Autism is no longer considered a psychological problem

Why haven't we heard?

Many concerned experts and parents around the world are acting to educate the public on this issue, but it is not being covered in the mainstream media. Fortunately, today, if you wish to educate yourself on other points of view, much information from reputable sources can be found on the internet. Many concerned experts are gathering at small professional conferences to address the issue. One such three-day event was held at Loyola University, where researchers shared growing evidence which indicates that vaccines are linked to increasing rates of brain problems and that government health agencies have done little to recognise this. Here are some excerpts from their press release:

The internet covers issues that are not on the media

> 'Autism One, a non-profit group dedicated to learning more about autism, sponsored the meeting. Parents of children with autism at the Chicago conference said the disease has a way of isolating parents because of the time-consuming task of raising a child with autism.
>
> "I did not leave my son's side for four years," said Edmund Arranga, with Autism International Association. "It keeps people from connecting." Arranga said he estimates that 40 percent of parents of children with autism believe vaccines cause the disease.
>
> 'Many parents described previously normal children who appear to regress suddenly

with signs of autism within days of receiving vaccinations. Those vaccinations often include measles, mumps and rubella vaccines and large doses of thimerosal.' [24]

Similar conclusions were reached at the Mind of A Child conference in Sydney convened by Dr Robyn Cosford. In the conference conclusions she writes:

'It is apparent that ADHD/ADD/Autism represents a spectrum of disease, in which the clinical picture is determined by a combination of genetic predisposition, the severity of the insults to the system, and the age at which these occurred. Autism, in particular, is associated with metabolic and immune abnormalities, and in some cases has been linked clearly— temporally, biochemically (Paul Shattock) and immunologically (Dr Andrew Wakefield) with MMR vaccination, and is not simply a psychiatric disease.' [25]

Diagnosis and treatment

Autism often appears from 18 months to 2 years

The characteristic behaviours of autism spectrum disorders may or may not be apparent in infancy (18 to 24 months), possibly because the causal damage has not yet occurred, but usually become obvious during early childhood (24 months to 6 years).

As part of a well-baby/well-child visit, your child's doctor should do a 'developmental screening', asking specific questions about your baby's progress.

These five behaviours signal that further evaluation is warranted:

- Does not babble or coo by 12 months
- Does not gesture (point, wave, grasp) by 12 months
- Does not say single words by 16 months
- Does not say two-word phrases on his or her own by 24 months
- Has any loss of any language or social skill at any age.

If you are concerned, find out more

If your child does exhibit any of these 'red flags', it warrants having further evaluations by a multidisciplinary team which may include an environmental doctor, neurologist, psychologist, developmental paediatrician, speech/language therapist, learning consultant, or other professionals knowledgeable about autism.

It is important that parents and professionals work together for the child's benefit. While professionals will use their experience and training to make recommendations about your child's treatment options, you have unique knowledge about his/her needs and abilities.

The impact of Sound Therapy on Autism

It is advisable to start Sound Therapy at home as soon as you suspect a difficulty or difference in your child. This therapy requires no supervision and will enhance the child's development whether or not there is a problem. It will also assist in making any other interventions more effective.

Research scientist, Dr Viera Scheibner explains that Sound Therapy creates new brain connections, repairing damage that has been caused by vaccination or other toxins. She says: 'Now you know that the brain has to be educated, so to speak. And the brain is re-educated by stimulus. So you stimulate it in a certain way and you create new connections.' Dr Scheibner has also observed that repair can be effected by homoeopathic treatment. However she cautions against relying on being able to repair such damage.

Sound Therapy may help to restore brain connections

> 'To repair brain damage requires a really effective and intense intervention. And as you know, it's easy to damage a child and hard to fix it. This is what some parents don't realise. Before it happens, they are quite flippant about the whole thing. They think that, "oh well, let's just do it, (vaccination) let's not rock the boat." They think if it causes damage then we do something about it, right? It's not that simple.' [26]

Much publicity was created about the exceptional healing potential of Sound Therapy for autism in the 1980s, when Annabel Stehli's best selling book: 'The Sound of a Miracle: A child's triumph over autism,' [27] was published. The book detailed how her daughter, Georgie, underwent treatment with the Berard method of Sound Therapy. Dr Berard developed an adaptation of the Tomatis Sound Therapy using a different filtering device and different music. He disagreed with Tomatis' psychological theories and did not want to be associated with Tomatis, thought it is clear that Tomatis was the originator for his whole concept

Sound Therapy has been found highly effective for autism

and technology. Both methods are equally effective in the treatment of autism, as is the portable, Joudry method.

Georgie's recovery was so complete that her family claimed she had no remaining traces of autism. Some practitioners disagreed, but there is no question that the treatment gave her back enormous areas of her functioning, enabling her to marry and carry on a normal life. The story makes very interesting reading for any family living with autism.

Down syndrome

Down syndrome is a chromosomal disorder

Down syndrome is a developmental disorder caused by a chromosomal abnormality. There is an extra, critical portion of the number 21 chromosome present in all, or some, of the cells of people with Down syndrome. This additional genetic material alters the course of development and causes the characteristics associated with the syndrome.

Typical physical characteristics include

- Muscle hypotonia, low muscle tone
- Flat facial profile, and a small nose
- An upward slant to the eyes
- An abnormal shape of the ear
- A single deep crease across the centre of the palm
- Hyper flexibility, an excessive ability to extend the joints
- Dysplastic middle phalanx of the fifth finger, fifth finger has one flexion furrow instead of two
- Excessive space between large and second toe
- Enlargement of tongue in relationship to size of mouth

Potential

Down syndrome children have great potential

Children raised at home and included in all aspects of community life can best reach their potential, and function in society with a greater degree of independence. Parental love, nurturing and support, as well as early intervention programs, educational opportunities and community involvement, have a direct relationship to the degree to which a person with Down syndrome is able to achieve his/her potential. Today, people with Down syndrome live at home with their families and are active participants in the educational, vocational, social and recreational activities of the community. They are integrated into the regular education system, and take part in sports, camping, music, art programs, and all the other activities of their communities. In addition, they are socializing with people with, and without, disabilities, and as adults are obtaining employment and living in group homes and other independent housing arrangements.

Medical issues

Individuals with Down syndrome have a higher incidence of certain medical problems and need special medical and educational intervention.

Heart disease: Up to fifty percent of individuals with Down syndrome are born with congenital heart defects. The majority of heart defects in children with Down syndrome can now be surgically corrected with resulting long-term health improvements.

Alzheimer's disease: Estimates vary, but it is reasonable to conclude that twenty five percent, or more, of individuals with Down syndrome over the age of thirty-five will develop the clinical signs and symptoms of Alzheimer's-type dementia.

Mental retardation: Most people with Down syndrome have IQs which fall in the mild to moderate range of retardation. Children with Down syndrome are definitely educable, and educators and researchers are still discovering the full educational potential of people with Down syndrome.

Ear infections: Children with Down syndrome are highly prone to ear infections and upper respiratory tract infections. This is due both to a depressed immune system and certain structural considerations:

- Small Eustachian tube
- Contracted nasopharynx
- Narrow external ear canal

It is extremely important to address these problems from the beginning to avoid increased loss of hearing in the developmental stages. Regular use of Sound Therapy from an early age, is a safe, non-invasive way to stimulate the middle ear apparatus and reduce infections and blockages.

Overcome early hearing loss to accelerate your child's potential

In addition, the diet must be kept healthy to support the immune system and avoid food intolerances. The addition of nutritional supplements is of benefit in supporting dietary balance. See Chapter 9 *What's this on my plate?* for more detail on diet.

Hearing

The incidence of hearing loss among individuals with Downs Syndrome is 60-75%.

Sound Therapy supports ear mechanics **Conductive hearing loss** is due to poor functioning of the middle ear apparatus, which consists of bones, muscles and the eardrum. The micro-massage provided by Sound Therapy can help significantly to keep these mechanisms in top form, and improve conductive hearing. It also helps to keep the Eustachian tube open, reducing blockages and infections of the middle ear. The importance of this intervention for a child with Down syndrome cannot be overemphasised. Many children with Down syndrome have more difficulty with expressive language than they do with receptive language; that is, understanding is usually more advanced than speech. The home based Sound Therapy program, offering a range of stories and music, is very beneficial as it helps to develop language and listening skills at the same time as exercising the ear.

It is vitally important with Down syndrome children to avoid middle ear infections so that the child is not disadvantaged in hearing during crucial developmental phases. Even mild hearing loss is important as it will affect the learning and communication ability of a child struggling to catch up with the rest of the world.

Otitis media, middle ear infection, produces a temporary hearing loss which can go unnoticed but has measurable detrimental effects on educational development. When having your child checked for suspected otitis media, if the eardrums cannot be seen by the paediatrician, due to the size and curvature of the outer ear canal, request referral to an ENT doctor. They have smaller instruments and microscopes available for better diagnosis.

Antibiotics will normally be recommended as a treatment for middle ear infections. Use these with discretion as too many antibiotics will affect your child's immune system.

Grommets. Another treatment offered to overcome recurrent ear infections is the insertion of grommets—little plastic tubes which puncture the ear drum, allowing fluid to drain out. These have mixed results, for while they may reduce the impact of otitis media, they do cause trauma to the ear and may interfere with the natural ability of the middle ear to release pressure through the Eustachian tube. The regular use of Sound Therapy, and correct diet, may remove the need for grommets or antibiotics, leaving you with a much healthier, happier child. Chronic inflammation of the sinus cavities has also been found to respond very favourably to Sound Therapy in both children and adults.

Sensorineural (nerve loss) is another type of hearing loss where there is damage to the actual hearing organ inside the cochlea. It is believed that Sound Therapy can also help this type of loss, to some extent, by stimulating the cilia (the hair like cells in the inner ear) to function more actively. Again, for a child with Down syndrome this is one of the most important interventions you could provide.

Sound Therapy provides stimulation for the nerves

It is very important to have your child's hearing assessed at an audiology clinic, as the fitting of a hearing aid at an early age will greatly assist development. Sound Therapy can still be used in conjunction with a hearing aid.

The importance of early intervention for Down syndrome children

Early intervention can help in many ways. During the first three to four months of life, for example, an infant is expected to gain head control; and the ability, with help, to pull to a sitting position with no head lags, and enough strength in the upper torso to maintain an erect posture. Appropriate physical therapy may assist a baby with Down syndrome, who may have low muscle tone, in achieving this milestone.

Physiotherapy helps develop upper torso strength

One of the fine motor skills which an infant is expected to achieve is the ability to hold and reach for objects. Here again, the baby with Down syndrome may need help before mastering these tasks. Physical therapy, and practice in achieving these and subsequent milestones, can assist a baby with Down syndrome in the four areas of development.

Keep moving beyond the plateau

Early intervention can also prevent a child with Down syndrome from reaching a plateau at some point in development. Thus, the goal of early intervention programs is to enhance and accelerate development by building on a child's strengths, and by strengthening those areas that are weaker, in all areas of development.

The importance of gross motor development

Physical exploration helps mental development

All areas of development are equally important, although the emphasis changes as the child grows. Nevertheless, before birth and in the first months of life, physical development remains the underlying foundation for all future progress. Babies learn through interaction with their environment. To do this, an infant must have the ability to move freely and purposefully. The ability to explore one's surroundings, the ability to reach and grasp toys, to turn one's head in order to follow a moving object with one's eyes, the ability to roll over, and to crawl in pursuit of a desired objective — all of these behaviours are dependent upon gross, as well as fine, motor development. These physical, interactive activities foster understanding and mastery of the environment, stimulating cognitive, language and social development. See Chapter 6, *We move with our ears,* for more detail on motor development programs. Movement activities from an early age will enhance the development of the motor areas of the brain, and assist greatly in the areas of muscular development, co-ordination and motor planning.

Communication

Help them participate

People with Down syndrome may have many barriers to effective communication. The receptive language skills of children with Down syndrome — how well they understand what is being said — are often much stronger than their expressive language skills, i.e. how well they can say it. Parents often comment, 'He knows what he wants to tells us, he just can't seem to put the words together, or we can't make out what he is saying.' Classroom participation is therefore more difficult as well. The child may express his frustration by acting out or by inattention.

Because of the communication problems discussed above, people with Down syndrome may have difficulty taking about things which make them sad or angry. Major life changes, such as loss or separation, may prompt decreases in appropriate behaviour at school or work.

Although there are common speech and language problems, there is no single pattern of speech and language common to all children with Down syndrome. Certain linguistic areas, such as vocabulary, are usually easier for children with Down syndrome than other areas, such as grammar. Sequencing of sounds and of words may be difficult for many children. Many children have difficulties with intelligibility of speech and articulation. Some children have fluency problems. Some children use short phrases, while others have long conversations. All of the speech and language problems that children with Down syndrome demonstrate are faced by other children as well. This means that there is a great deal of knowledge and experience that can be applied to helping a child with Down syndrome with his/her specific areas of challenge. It is vital to provide support in the form of speech therapy for children with Down syndrome.

Speech therapy and Sound Therapy go so well together

Tactile sensitivity and articulation

Many infants and toddlers with Down syndrome are very sensitive to touch. They do not want to be touched, don't want their teeth brushed, or do not like certain textures of foods or perhaps mixed food textures. The term 'tactilely defensive' is sometimes used. It can be helpful to use oral massage and direct muscle stimulation, which often results in infants and toddlers being increasingly able to tolerate touch in the lip and tongue area. The massage program begins with the arms and legs and gradually moves toward the face and oral area. Babbling and sound-making generally increase as a result of these activities. Once the child can tolerate touch, and can freely move the articulators, an oral motor skills program can be introduced. The parents can begin this with activities such as blowing whistles, blowing bubbles, making funny faces, and sound imitation activities. Generally, it works better if you imitate the child rather than providing a model to imitate.

Touching and massage help develop oral skills

During this stage, speech therapy is important so that sounds and specific sound production can be targeted; articulation therapy could begin. But the therapy would also include oral motor exercises and activities, on an ongoing basis, to strengthen the muscles and improve the co-ordination of muscles. Intelligibility is the goal of the speech component of therapy.

Sound Therapy is the essential 'mirror program' for speech therapy, for, as Dr Tomatis discovered, a child can only produce sounds that he can hear. Sound Therapy increases the frequency range, and clarity of hearing. In addition, it supports motor development and planning, which are needed for correct articulation.

Fragile X syndrome

Fragile X is a problem with the X chromosome

Fragile X syndrome, also called Martin-Bell syndrome, is an inherited condition and is linked to a problem with the X chromosome. It is the most common inherited mental handicap and can cause significant learning difficulties. The full mutation appears in approximately 1 in 3600 males, and 1 in 4000 to 6000 females.

Boys are more affected as girls have two X chromosomes

Boys are generally more severely affected than girls increasingly probably because girls carry two X chromosomes, one of which is presumed to be normal. Most boys will need extra help at school and may never be able to live on their own. Most boys will show some level of mental retardation, with an IQ of 60 or 70 (normal or 'average' IQ is 100). An estimated eighty percent of affected boys, and thirty-five percent of girls with the syndrome will have some degree of intellectual handicap. Girls may have milder learning problems and many grow up to live independently.

It can skip generations

Unaffected family members can pass the genetic mutation onto their own children or grandchildren, and in some cases the disorder has been passed on in families for many generations. In other circumstances, the syndrome can skip several generations before it shows up again. An estimated one in 250 women carry the fragile X permutation.

Physical and behavioural problems result

Fragile X syndrome also has some physical characteristics which affect some individuals. Adult males may have a long face, large ears and large testicles. Affected girls may have a thin face, and prominent ears. The physical features seen in males appear in a smaller percentage of females, and often to a lesser degree. Sufferers of both sexes may have double-jointed fingers, flat feet and a heart murmur. Learning difficulties include slow learning, delayed speech, attention deficit disorder, and hyperactivity. Affected individuals may also show some form of autism and/or aggression. The syndrome may not be recognised until mid-childhood. Behavioural characteristics in some males include attention deficit disorders, speech disturbances, hand biting, hand flapping, autistic behaviours, poor eye contact, and aversion to touch and noise.

Treatment and remedial therapy

There is no cure for fragile X syndrome, but special education is available to help affected children.

Get help from Sound Therapy, speech therapy and occupational therapy

Various forms of therapy can help including Sound Therapy, speech therapy and occupational therapy. Educational programs should be developed to meet the individual's strengths and weaknesses. The child's behavioural problems and physical needs must also be addressed. Medication can also be used in some cases to control hyperactivity, aggression, and/or depression. Children with fragile X syndrome may also be diagnosed with ADHD. See section on ADHD for more detail.

Other Sources of Information www.fragilex.org

Speech and language

Intervention by a speech pathologist is essential for boys with fragile X syndrome. Often, delayed speech is the first sign that something is wrong with a young child, and the speech pathologist is the first person to evaluate the child. Speech pathologists are integral people on the multidisciplinary team which sees a child, whether in early intervention, early childhood, or school-age programs.

Children with fragile X syndrome have unique speech and language disorders. Boys with fragile X often have particular problems with conversational skills. Their speech and language are affected by physical, oral-motor, attention, and behavioural characteristics, meaning that an integrated approach to treatment is necessary. Sound Therapy will assist greatly in strengthening brain pathways to enable language skills to be improved.

Strengthening brain pathways improves language skills

Girls with fragile X often have many good verbal skills, but have difficulty in pragmatic speech, with anxiety and shyness affecting their social interactions. They, too, may benefit from the services of a speech pathologist.

Uncontrolled squalling and flapping are seen in the more severe cases. Here the effect of Sound Therapy can be seen quite dramatically as it starts to reduce these

Involuntary movement may be reduced

199

behaviours and restore voluntary control to the nervous system.

Medical intervention

Several therapies together works best Several areas need to be observed medically in order to best foster speech and language development. As ear infections are common to boys, and as such infections may cause intermittent hearing loss, it is important to be vigilant in treating them. Try preventative treatment, such as Sound Therapy and dietary changes, before resorting to antibiotics. Grommets may be recommended, but may be deemed unnecessary if Sound Therapy and correct diet are used regularly. Hearing should be tested by an audiologist regularly, to be sure there is not a mild hearing loss.

Low muscle tone and oral-motor problems

Most boys with fragile X syndrome require oral-motor assessment and goals. This assessment, and the writing of goals, might be carried out jointly by a speech-language pathologist and an occupational therapist.

Speech pathologists can work with occupational and physical therapists to intervene in the area of low muscle tone and oral-motor weakness. Trunk support, sometimes in the form of specially constructed chairs, may be an issue — to help with breath support and vocalisation for some children. Posture sometimes spontaneously improves with Sound Therapy.

Touching the face is helpful There are many activities which speech pathologists can use to help increase tolerance-to-touch around the face, neck, and mouth, and thus improve chewing, swallowing, and speaking. Speech pathologists may work jointly with occupational therapists to design oral motor activities appropriate for a child. These may include physical activities which begin away from the mouth, but which gradually allow the child to build up tolerance around the face and mouth.

Using the mouth prepares the child for speech Both foods and toys can be used in oral-motor activities in order to provide incentives. Blow toys, whistles, and straws can be used to help build up oral-motor strength and functioning. Speech pathologists may recommend a variety of foods to help with chewing and oral-motor strength. These might include crunchy and chewy foods, such as fruit snacks, celery, bagels, and gum. In addition to helping with speech and language, such oral stimulation may help prevent the child's chewing on clothing, straps, or skin.

Cerebral Palsy

Cerebral palsy is a term that describes a group of disorders which affect movement control. These are chronic disorders which appear in the first few years of life and generally do not worsen over time. Cerebral palsy is caused by faulty development of, or damage to, motor areas in the brain, which disrupts the brain's ability to control movement and posture. Symptoms of cerebral palsy include difficulty with fine motor tasks (such as writing or using scissors), difficulty maintaining balance or walking, and involuntary movements. The symptoms differ from person to person and may change over time. Some people with cerebral palsy are also affected by other medical disorders, including seizures or mental impairment, but cerebral palsy does not always cause a profound handicap. Early signs of cerebral palsy usually appear before three years of age. Infants with cerebral palsy are frequently slow to reach developmental milestones such as learning to roll over, sit, crawl, smile, or walk. Doctors diagnose cerebral palsy by testing motor skills and reflexes, looking into medical history, and employing a variety of specialised tests. Although its symptoms may change over time, cerebral palsy, by definition, is not progressive, so, if a patient shows increased impairment the problem may be something other than cerebral palsy.

Motor areas in the brain are affected

What is the prognosis?

At this time, cerebral palsy cannot be cured; but, due to medical research, many patients can enjoy near-normal lives if their neurological problems are properly managed.

Treatment

There is no standard therapy that works for all patients. Drugs can be used to control seizures and muscle spasms, and special braces can compensate for muscle imbalance. Surgery, mechanical aids to help overcome impairments, counselling for emotional and psychological needs, and physical, occupational, speech, and behavioural therapy may be employed. Sound Therapy has been found helpful for many similar conditions, including brain damage due to injury or stroke, seizures and delayed development,

Sound and physical therapy will help posture and movement control

201

and sensory integration and co-ordination problems in conditions such as autism, Retts syndrome and fragile X syndrome. Sound Therapy is part of the solution for all of these conditions which affect motor control. It is, therefore, possible that Sound Therapy may help to reduce involuntary movement and restore a certain amount of motor control to those with cerebral palsy by building new brain pathways and stimulating the cerebellum, (the part of the brain fundamental to sensory integration). Sound Therapy has also been found to improve the posture of people with cerebral palsy, when used in conjunction with psychomotor exercises and physiotherapy.[28]

Causes and prevention

Brain injury and lack of oxygen are the cause

There is not one specific cause of cerebral palsy. However, it can be caused by injury to the brain before, during, or after birth. Lack of oxygen to the brain, or trauma to the head, during labour and delivery can cause cerebral palsy. If the infant does not get enough oxygen the brain can be injured. Cerebral palsy may also be acquired from damage to the brain in the first months, or years, of life. The injury may be a brain infection (bacterial meningitis, viral encephalitis), or head injury following an accident.

Cell development in pregnancy may be involved

Research also suggests that cerebral palsy results from incorrect cell development early in pregnancy. For example, a group of researchers has recently observed that more than one-third of children with cerebral palsy also have missing enamel on certain teeth. Scientists are also examining other events — such as bleeding in the brain, seizures, and breathing and circulation problems — which threaten the brain of a newborn baby. Some investigators are conducting studies to learn whether certain drugs can help prevent neonatal stroke, and other investigators are examining the causes of low birth-weight. Other scientists are exploring how brain insults (like brain damage from a shortage of oxygen or blood flow, bleeding in the brain, and seizures) can cause the abnormal release of brain chemicals and trigger brain disease. Good diet and health management of the mother during pregnancy could therefore assist in prevention. Using Sound Therapy during pregnancy is an excellent way to assist with the mother's health.

Epilepsy

Epilepsy is a neurological condition which makes people susceptible to seizures. A seizure is a change in sensation, awareness or behaviour, brought about by random electrical activity in the brain.

Seizures vary from a momentary disruption of the senses, to short periods of unconsciousness or staring spells, to convulsions. Some people have just one type of seizure. Others have more than one type. The type of seizure a child has depends on which area of the brain is affected. Some seizures involve convulsions, or strange and confused behaviour, but others, such as absences, may be harder to recognise. Some may be unnoticeable to everyone except the child experiencing the seizure. Despite the appearance of some seizures, the child is not in pain.

Some seizures are hardly noticeable

Although they look different, all seizures are caused by the same thing: a sudden change in how the cells of the brain send electrical signals to each other.

Many people have a **single seizure** at some point in their lives, but this does not mean that they have epilepsy. If a person has a tendency to experience repeated seizures which originate in the brain, then that person may be diagnosed as having epilepsy.

One seizure alone does not mean you have epilpesy

The brain is a highly complex structure composed of millions of neurons, which are a particular type of nerve cell. Neurons in the brain are responsible for a wide range of functions including:

- consciousness
- awareness
- movement
- body posture

Nerve cell activity is usually well organised. A sudden, temporary interruption in some or all of the functions of the nerve cells may be called a 'seizure' or 'fit'.

What causes epilepsy?

Any person's brain has the capacity to produce a seizure under certain conditions, but most are not likely to do this spontaneously. There are several possible reasons why some people develop epilepsy.

Each individual has a 'seizure threshold', or level of resistance to seizures. This threshold varies from person to

Many factors can cause seizures

203

person, depending on factors including genetic propensity, stress, brain injury and other forms of interference with brain function — such as a tumour, stroke, **an infection which affects the brain**, or birth trauma. Some people develop epilepsy following infections such as meningitis or encephalitis.

Many people believe that the onset of their seizures was due to stress or periods of emotional upset, or to a relatively minor blow to the head. Although this type of factor may trigger individual seizures, it is not the underlying cause of the epilepsy. In these cases, it is likely that a family tendency to have seizures plays an important role.

How common is epilepsy?

I in 100 children has epilepsy Epilepsy is the most common serious neurological condition. A neurological condition is one which involves the nervous system. Around 1 in every 200 adults, and 1 in every 100 children, has the condition.

Anyone can develop epilepsy; it occurs in all ages, races and social classes. Seizures often start in infancy or by late adolescence, but the likelihood of developing epilepsy rises again after the age of sixty-five.

How is epilepsy diagnosed?

Observing a seizure is part of the diagnosis Seizures can occur for many reasons, not just epilepsy. Other types of seizures include febrile convulsions, breath-holding attacks, and fainting.

If your child has more than one seizure, your GP will usually refer them to a specialist for diagnosis. Often the doctor makes the diagnosis using an eyewitness description of the seizure and other information about the child's medical history. However, to help with diagnosis, a number of investigations may be used. For example:

- a physical examination and, in some cases, a blood test.
- a CAT (computerised tomography) or MRI (magnetic resonance imaging) scan
- an EEG (electroencephalogram)

Certain brain scans help with diagnosis These tests will not diagnose epilepsy, but they may help provide additional information to help establish the cause of the seizures. Normal results from these tests do not rule out a diagnosis of epilepsy.

The tests are painless, but younger children or children

with learning disabilities may be given a mild anaesthetic to help them relax and stay still.

Who is responsible for my child's treatment?

Professionals who may be involved in a child's medical care include:

- a paediatrician - children's doctor
- a paediatric neurologist - who specialises in the brain and nervous system
- an epilepsy specialist nurse.

When a young person reaches the age of sixteen to eighteen, they may start seeing a specialist who treats adults. The GP is responsible for a child's care between appointments with the specialist.

How is epilepsy treated?

Most children with epilepsy are treated with anti-epileptic medication. This cannot cure epilepsy but aims to prevent seizures from occurring. Once the right drug or combination of drugs is found, many people on medication become seizure-free.

Medication may control seizures

Like all drugs, those for epilepsy may cause side effects in some people. These often wear off after a time, or may be minimised by adjusting the dosage. If you or your child are concerned about any aspect of the medication, you may want to talk to your pharmacist or doctor. Medication should not be changed or stopped without first consulting the doctor.

Other treatments which may help to reduce seizures are a low carbohydrate diet, such as the Zone diet, and mineral supplementation, and Sound Therapy.

A treatment option sometimes recommended for children whose seizures are not controlled by medication is the high fat, low carbohydrate ketogenic diet, which has been used to control epilepsy since the 1920s. However, recent studies from Boston University School of Medicine indicate that a low calorie diet, not a ketogenic diet, may be a superior way to treat epilepsy. The most important element in diet, for epilepsy, is keeping the blood sugar balanced. Dr Barry Sears' Zone diet offers a simple, easy way to achieve balanced blood sugar. It is a much more balanced form of reduced carbohydrate diet which can be followed without negative side effects. It is rich in the fruits

A low starch diet may be helpful

205

and vegetables that would supply enough bioflavonoids and Vitamin C to prevent the bruising which comes from a weakened collagen structure in the vascular bed. The Zone Diet coupled with high-dose fish oil was developed to treat neurological disorders. It is a lot safer and cheaper than any type of drug intervention. See Chapter 9, *What's this on my plate?* for more details on diet and supplementation.

How will epilepsy affect my child's life?

Leisure activities

Most children with epilepsy can participate in the same activities as other children. Simple precautions can help make activities such as swimming and bike riding safer for people with epilepsy.

People with epilepsy can do most things   The vast majority of people with epilepsy are able to go to discos, use computers and watch television, with no increased risk of having a seizure. Photosensitive epilepsy is when seizures are triggered by certain frequencies of flashing lights. It is usually detected during an EEG test and is often treatable with medication. If your child has photosensitive epilepsy you may need to take extra precautions.

Learning

Epilepsy does not necessarily affect learning ability   Most children with epilepsy have the same intelligence and learning potential as other children, and attend mainstream schools and colleges. However, having frequent seizures may interrupt your child's everyday learning.

Management of a seizure varies, depending on the type of seizure that occurs. It can be useful to talk to the school about your child's epilepsy, so that people can recognise and help to manage their seizures. Some seizure types may be very subtle and difficult to detect, and can go unnoticed.

Some children with epilepsy also have learning disabilities which may originate from the same cause as the epilepsy. These children may need extra help at school or may go to a school which provides specialist teaching and support.

Will my child's epilepsy change with age?

Seizures may be affected by hormonal changes   As a child gets older, their seizures may change in type and frequency. Some girls find that their seizures change when their periods start, becoming more frequent around the time of their period. The doctor may discuss making changes to their medication to help at this time.

Some children outgrow their epilepsy by their mid to late teens. This is known as spontaneous remission. If a child has not had a seizure for a number of years, the doctor may discuss the possibility of gradually reducing the level of medication, and eventually withdrawing the drugs altogether.

Sound Therapy for epilepsy

Several reports have been received of Sound Therapy helping to alleviate the symptoms of epilepsy. It has been used with some success both by adults and children, at home and in a classroom situation. Tomatis also observed these effects in his clinics, saying, 'Certain young clients showing symptoms of epilepsy have been found to improve considerably in the sphere of behaviour and socialisation after being educated under the Electronic Ear.' [29]

Sound Therapy may create dramatic improvements

A remarkable and profound case was the recovery of Hilary Peart who had experienced epilepsy all her life, suffering severely with the condition, and who achieved an almost total recovery through Sound Therapy. See Chapter 8, *Listeners' experiences,* where her story is included in her own words.

Some research has been done to explore stimulating the vagus nerve in order to stop seizures. This effort to apply frequency to a particular part of the brain is rather hit and miss. A much more direct and compatible way for the body to have the vagus nerve stimulated is via the ear; for, a branch of the nerve is lying across the ear drum, as one of our listeners pointed out, as if saying 'here I am!' The ear is where frequency is received by the body, so why not work through the body's own system?

The vagus nerve is easily stimulated via the ear

What else can be done to prevent seizures?

Some children's seizures occur in response to certain triggers such as stress and nervousness, over-excitement, certain smells, lack of nutrients, boredom or lack of sleep. It may be helpful to keep a diary of seizures to see if a pattern emerges. If this is the case, avoiding these situations as far as possible may help to make seizures less frequent. Gentle exercise is very helpful— such as swimming, stretching, and dancing, or anything else the child finds relaxing. Strenuous exercising which requires a lot of muscular tension, such as weightlifting, should be avoided.

Learn to observe what triggers seizures

Hearing Loss

While Sound Therapy is not a cure for hearing loss, it is helpful in most cases and can improve hearing to some extent. Many adults have reported that they hear better after using Sound Therapy, and since children heal faster than adults, and their cells and neuronal pathways are still developing, their potential to heal is even greater. The sooner hearing loss is addressed the more its impact on education and development can be reduced. The early fitting of hearing aids is important in affecting educational outcomes. Likewise, the earlier Sound Therapy is introduced, the greater its leverage for language development. Sound Therapy has a very different impact to a hearing aid since its aim is to treat the cause of hearing loss by stimulating and enhancing the function of the natural ear.

Sound Therapy is believed to improve the ability of the ear to receive sound accurately by exercising and strengthening the ear muscles. The ear's ability to convey sound to the brain may also be enhanced by stimulation of the cilia in the inner ear and of the auditory-neural pathways.

Children who use hearing aids can use Sound Therapy as well, and this may enhance the benefits they get from their hearing aids. Listening can either be done by placing the earphones on the outside of the hearing aids, or by having the child listen at a time when the hearing aids are not being worn.

PRACTICAL ACTION TIPS

I have included specific ideas for handling children with ADHD and autism, because these two conditions may require quite different approaches. For other children you may find that a mix of these techniques is effective.

Tried and true techniques which work for children with ADHD or other behaviour problems

✪ Provide regular routine, structure and consistency.

✪ Get the child's attention first, before giving instructions.

✪ Do not make a big issue of small matters or transgressions.

✪ Be gentle, firm and consistent.

✪ Avoid arguments. If the child keeps challenging and whining, simply keep answering with 'you know the rule'.

✪ Give fair warning – after making a request, count to three, slowly, (five seconds between each number). This avoids the likelihood of the child refusing point blank, and gives him time to think over the situation and decide to comply.

✪ Use 'time out', after counting to three. The aim is not to punish, but to allow the child and everyone else to calm down. 'Time out' lasts for 1 minute per year of the child's age. Remove the child from the situation into a quiet chair or room. Do not react if the child protests or calls out during this time. When time out is over, the child starts with a clean slate and the matter is forgotten.

✪ Reward good behaviour, it is much more effective than punishing bad behaviour. Reward even the smallest gains. Use little trinkets, stickers, etc., not junk food.

✪ Novelty is important for rewards. It doesn't have to be new and expensive, just different.

✪ With young children use immediate rewards or withdrawal of privilege. Delaying does not work.

✪ For older children use tokens. Depending on age, children can be rewarded with stars or tokens which can later be redeemed for cherished rewards or privileges.

✪ Develop consistent rules.

✪ Have a pre-arranged discipline plan which both parents follow.

Continued overleaf

✪ Use all the tools at your disposal, sensory training programs, teacher liaison, nutritional support as well as consistent parenting.

✪ Make sure the child gets one-on-one attention. ADHD kids play well 1 on 1 but not in a group.

✪ Suggest alternatives rather than confronting a disagreement head on.

✪ Allow the child time to have his or her view heard, but remove yourself from the situation if the child becomes loud or aggressive.

✪ Always use distraction rather than confrontation.

✪ Think of yourself as being on the same team as your child and solving problems together.

✪ Regularly give your child quality, one on one time, love and encouragement and opportunities for leadership.

✪ Prepare for going into public places, which are highly stimulating. Tell him beforehand exactly what is going to happen so he is prepared: 'we're going to go to Target and get that blanket, then we are going to the baker to get some bread and some rolls, then we are going to pick up the dry cleaning and then we will go to the park before we come home.'

✪ Explain again before each segment. 'Now we are going into Target to get the blanket. If you behave well in there you will get a reward such as a new book or a ride on the rocking horse in the mall.' Rewards must be short-term and immediate.

✪ If he gets ratty, stop in the shop and talk. 'Look at me.' Get eye contact, 'If you keep doing what you're doing you won't get your new book. If you come calmly with Mummy, I will get you the book.'

✪ These must be short-term rewards, one for each shop. The child cannot contain his behaviour for two hours and get a reward for the whole trip.

✪ Exercise is really important, go for a walk, a bike ride, to the playground to let their energy out.

✪ Get a swimming pool. This is one of the very best ways for overactive children to work off their excess energy. It takes up a relatively small amount of space and can occupy them for hours at a time. Kids don't have to be well co-ordinated to enjoy splashing around in the pool for hours. Being in water also provides relief form the overload normally experienced by those with poor cerebellar function. When their system gets a break from having to cope with gravity, they have more attention available for other brain functions and feel greatly relieved by this.

Tried and true techniques for handling children with autism or Asperger's

✪ Begin early to teach the difference between private and public places and actions, so that they can develop ways of coping with more complex social rules later in life.

✪ Children may categorically object to going into new situations because of fear of the unknown, social awkwardness, or not knowing how to handle new situations.

✪ Give the child clear advance instructions on what will happen and how she/he should respond.

✪ Anger- when anger is coming up try directing it appropriately, i.e., into recycling, by providing cans to crush, boxes to break down, telephone directories to tear up.

✪ A child with higher functioning autism may be highly intelligent and advanced in some academic areas. If the child is frustrated by being in a class below his/her age capability, try to arrange for him/her to be in a more advanced class.

✪ Keep all your speech simple—at a level the child can understand.

✪ Keep instructions simple; for complicated jobs use lists or pictures.

✪ Try to get confirmation that they understand what you are talking about - don't rely on a stock 'yes' or 'no', which they like to answer with.

✪ Explain why they should look at you when you speak to them; encourage them, give lots of praise for any achievement - especially when they use a social skill without prompting.

✪ With some young children who appear not to listen, the act of 'singing' your words can have a beneficial effect.

✪ Limit any choices to two or three items.

✪ Limit their 'special interest' time (on favourite hobbies) to set amounts of time each day, if you can.

✪ Use turn-taking activities as much as possible, not only in games but at home too.

✪ Pre-warn them of any changes, and give warning prompts if you want them to finish a task: 'when you have coloured that in we are going shopping'.

✪ Try to build some flexibility into their routine; if they learn early that things do change and often without warning - it can help.

Continued overleaf

⭐ Don't always expect them to 'act their age'; they are usually immature and you should make some allowances for this.

⭐ Try to identify stress triggers and avoid them if possible; be ready to distract with some alternative 'come and see this...', etc.

⭐ Find a way of coping with behaviour problems — perhaps trying to ignore it if it's not too bad, or hugging can sometimes help.

⭐ Promises and threats you make will have to be kept — so try not to make them too lightly.

⭐ Teach them some strategies for coping — telling people who are teasing perhaps to 'go away', or to breathe deeply and count to 20 if they feel the urge to cry in public.

⭐ Let them know that you love them, 'wart's an' all' — and that you are proud of them. It can be very easy with a child who rarely speaks not to tell them all the things you feel inside.

⭐ Remember, they are children just like the others, they have their own personalities, abilities, likes and dislikes — they just need extra support, patience and understanding from everyone around them

References

1 Bellis J. Subprofiles of CAPD. www.angelfire.com/bc/capd/.

2 Tomatis, A. A. *The Conscious Ear,* New York: Station Hill Press, 1977. 104.

3 Spirig, E. 'Dyslexia, Mental Deficiency and the Electronic Ear', IVth International Congress of Audio-Psycho-Phonology, Madrid, May 1974, translated by Jacques J Waters, Child Study Centre, University of Ottawa.36.

4 Weeks, B. S. 'The Therapeutic Effect of High Frequency Auditon and its Role in Sacred Music,' in *About the Tomatis Method,* edited by Gilmour, T. M., Madaule, P. and Thompson, B. Toronto: The Listening Centre Press, 1989.

5 Tomatis, A. A. *The Conscious Ear,* New York: Station Hill Press, 1977.104.

6 Jaarsveld, P. E. and du Plessis, W. F. *Audio-psycho-phonology at Potchefstroom: A review.* Potchefstroom University of Higher Education, 1988.

7 Morgan, A.V.M. 'Listening and Learning Disability.' in *About the Tomatis Method,* edited by Gilmour, T. M., Madaule, P. and Thompson, B. Toronto: The Listening Centre Press, 1989.195.

8 Gilmour, Timothy M. 'School Listening Training Programs.' in *About the Tomatis Method,* ed. Gilmour, et al.106.

9 Spirig, E. 'Dyslexia, Mental Deficiency and the Electronic Ear', IVth International Congress of Audio-Psycho-Phonology, Madrid, May 1974, translated by Jacques J. Waters, Child Study Centre, University of Ottawa.18.

10 *Ibid.* 22.

11 Sidlauskas A E. 'Language: the Ideas of Dr Alfred Tomatis,' *Revue Internationale D'audio-psycho-phonologie.* No 5 Special–April-May (1974).22.

12 Spirig, *Ibid.* 10-11.

13 Dengate, Sue. *Different Kids: growing up with Attention Deficit Disorder.* Sydney: Random House. 1994.

14 Zametkin, A. J. et al. National Institute of Mental Health. 1990, cited in Dengate, *Ibid.* 155.

15 Dengate, Sue. *Different Kids: Growing up with Attention Deficit Disorder.* Sydney: Random House. 1994.

16 Dr Russell Barkley, *Attention Deficit and Hyperactivity Disorder: A Handbook of Diagnosis and Treatment,* New York : Guilford Press, 1998. (cited in Dengate, ibid.)

17 Green, C. and Chee, K. *Understanding ADHD.* Sydney: Doubleday, 2001.

18 Centres for Disease Control and Prevention, 2003.

19 American Psychiatric Association: *Diagnostic and Statistical Manual of Mental Disorders,* Fourth Edition, Text Revision. Washington, DC, American Psychiatric Association, 2000.

213

[20] Scheibner, V., *Behavioural Problems in Childhood.* Blackheath, NSW: Scheibner, 2000.10.

[21] Williams, R.S., Hauser, S.L., Purpura, D.P., DeLong, R., and Swischer, C.N., 1980. 'Autism and mental retardation: Neuropathologic studies performed in four retarded persons with autistic behaviour.' *Arch Neurol*; 37: 749-753, cited in Scheibner, *Ibid.* 7.

[22] Scheibner, *Ibid.* 8.

[23] *Ibid.*

[24] Benjamin, M. 'Autism, vaccine link considered', United Press International, 5/6/2003 2:59 PM www.upi.com/view.cfm?StoryID=20030505-123913-6672r

[25] Cosford, R. 'The Mind of a Child' - conference summary, www.acnem.org/journal/19-1 april 2000/mind of a child conference.htm

[26] Scheibner, V. Interview at Blackheath, transcribed by Rafaele Joudry. 2002.

[27] Stehli, Annabel. *The Sound of a Miracle: A child's triumph over autism.* New York: Doubleday, 1991.

[28] Spirig, *Ibid.* 30.

[29] Tomatis, *Ibid.* 189.

Chapter 8

LISTENERS' EXPERIENCES
WITH SOUND THERAPY

The following accounts from families who have used Sound Therapy, are included to give the reader a sense of the spectrum of difficulties and the range of results which may be possible with this therapy. Hearing people's varied journeys, how and when they introduced Sound Therapy and how it interacted with other approaches, I hope will be of benefit to other families on this journey. These stories include accounts from adults who themselves had learning difficulties as children, and as adults were helped by using Sound Therapy. They also include accounts of parents who, while using Sound Therapy to help their children, also listened and obtained other benefits for themselves — such as reduced stress, more energy, better communication, patience, understanding, and joy that they could share with their children.

Sound Therapy can help in so many ways

Help for Primary children

Some brief comments from students and parents at Quaama Public School after using Sound Therapy.

9-year-old girl: 'I can play handball better now. I can read properly. It helps me think properly. I feel free inside. My

Time and co-ordination

stomach's not tied up in knots any more. Julia, Julia, I can tell the time now!'

Under water **9-year-old girl:** 'It doesn't sound like I'm under water all the time anymore'

Anxiety **10-year-old girl:** 'It reduces anxiety and stress before swimming carnivals and overnight excursions.'

Confidence **10-year-old girl:** 'Feels much more confident. Participated in talent quest for the first time.'

Grief **12-year-old boy:** 'Settled him down. He had had some nightmares since his grandmother passed away a few months earlier. After a few weeks was able to talk about his grandmother. It was a great relief.'

Help for disadvantaged teenagers
Some brief comments from students at St. Peter's College Vocational School, Muenster, Canada

After a few months of listening to the cassettes on portable cassette players issued by the school:

Susan Stroeder:

Attention 'I enjoyed this therapy and learned to pay more attention in school. I wake up easier in the morning — my Mom doesn't have to call me anymore. I don't have to ask questions twice, but hear things the first time.'

Kyle Bauer

Headaches 'I don't get headaches now and am much more active.'

Marian Niekamp

Energy 'Don't need as much sleep and am not tired in the mornings. My speaking is much clearer.'

Keith Carroll

Calm 'It made me much more calm and relaxed.'

Lyle Witt

Rock music 'My right ear seems to bug me when I listen to hard rock now.'

Debbie Nagy

Study 'I've been listening to the Walkman™ for over 600 hours. I find it very relaxing. I can sleep a lot better at nights. I wake up more easily in the mornings and find myself in better moods. I don't mind listening to it at school, and on weekends I try to get as many hours as I can. I find I can study a lot better and I'm more prepared for tests. I'm really enjoying the classical music.'

Carla Gaunt
'a brain-damaged, mentally handicapped teenager in Saskatoon, has been doing Sound Therapy for the past three months and loves listening to the tapes. Her parents report that there has been a great improvement in her ability to handle stress; her speech has developed and also her recall of past events.'

Brain damage

Posture pick up
Maureen Boyko – Watson, Sask. Canada:
'Our son, Mitch, is going to St. Peter's Pre Vocational Centre in Muenster. He has been listening to Sound Therapy tapes on an Auto-Reverse Walkman™ in school since he started there, and we've had them at home since our purchase two months ago.

'Sister Miriam, one of Mitch's teachers and also principal of the school, said she has noticed a real change in Mitch in the final two months of the school year. My husband and I have noticed a real difference as well. His posture has improved. He used to walk really slouched. We're not reminding him to stand straight nearly as often. He is more relaxed; he speaks out more clearly and more often. He used to speak so softly and did not articulate his words clearly. He feels that he has much better sleep, listening to the tapes. And last but not least he has developed a real appreciation of classical music.'

Posture

Let's Recite
Donalda Alder, Teacher of the Hearing Impaired – Long Beach, CA, U.S.A.
'The children's poetry tape has been a Godsend for my hearing impaired students. They love it! Their attention spans have increased dramatically since they have been listening regularly to the tape. My one very hyperactive youngster has settled down to her schoolwork because she knows she can listen to the tape as soon as she's finished. The tape has become a reward!

Hearing impaired children

'It's amazing to me that for the thirty-five years I have been teaching hearing impaired children, this is the first auditory training tape that uses only speech to which the children can listen comfortably. Patricia's speech is articulate and soothing. You have chosen the poems carefully so that they are amusing and hold the children's interest as well.'

Drug free and smarter
Judy and Gerrit Westerhof – Winnipeg

Not dyslexic any more 'Our son John is in Grade 6 and showing terrific improvement in reading since beginning on the Sound Therapy tapes two months ago. He says a lot of people don't even know he is dyslexic anymore. His teachers are amazed and thrilled, and even his friends have noticed the change in him. John came home last week and reported that two boys said, "Boy, John, you're a lot smarter this year. Last year you were so dumb, but this year you're not." We are so excited, because last year John was in a special program and this year he is in the regular program. He was on medication for his learning disability, but is now off the Ritalin. It makes him especially happy that he doesn't have to take the pills anymore, as they made him sick to his stomach. He loves the baroque music, listening with his Auto-Reverse Walkman™ all night until the batteries run out. He hated to read before, and now when we have our evening devotions he asks to read and does it very well. It is like a miracle and he improves daily. His grandfather says it's like an alarm went off in his head and he woke up.'

Longer sentences
Mrs. Marjorie Karpan – Keneston, Saskatchewan, Canada

Longer sentences 'I have noticed a remarkable change in my child's speech. The results were tremendous. The child is speaking in longer sentences, with more detail in speech. I am convinced that Sound Therapy really WORKS!'

Accident recovery
Mrs Joe Bentley

'Our daughter had a bicycle accident last spring, smashed her head on the pavement, and had two fractures to the head as well as brain concussion. The diagnosis was that she would never speak, walk, or have a memory. A friend sent her the first four Sound Therapy tapes, and she gradually learned to listen to them. She enjoys the music, as she is a pianist, and at the end of five weeks she could play the piano and read music again, though she couldn't yet read a book. I read the Sound Therapy book to her. Now six months later, she can read slowly, and can do everything except communicate fully. I am sending for another tape, as they have done so much for her. We thank you for all the help you have given our daughter.'

Brain damage

Calm at last!
Mary Ann Scherr – Yorkton, Saskatchewan, Canada

'My son Aaron, aged 10, was diagnosed as Attention Deficit Disorder, formally Hyperkinetic Syndrome. In December I read about Sound Therapy and the possibilities of this helping hyperactive children. We purchased the tapes at Easter, and Aaron started therapy. A week and a half later, at a teacher interview, his teacher remarked that he was so much more calm and pleasant. She said "I had my first decent religion class because Aaron didn't butt in and interrupt. Is he on medication or what?" I confessed that Aaron had started Sound Therapy but I didn't think it necessary to tell the teachers. "Whatever it is," she said, "keep it up, because whatever it's doing is helping him." Two weeks later I asked the teacher if Aaron could listen to the tapes during school. Now he takes his Walkman™ to school and does his three hours in the a.m. All around, Aaron is much more relaxed with himself and with others. Because of his attitude I have been able to introduce new foods into his diet to determine which food groups he is really sensitive to. With Aaron's new positive approach, his life can only get better.'

ADHD – hyperactivity

Interrupting in class

Mellow and happy
Brandy Graham – Saskatoon, Saskatchewan, Canada

'My five year old son, Quannah, has always been very hyperactive with an energy that just bounces off the walls. He also showed a lot of anger. I obtained the Sound Therapy story tapes, and let him listen to these for an hour or so each day – letting him feel it was a privilege, and in

Hyperactive, to mellow and calm

219

no way forcing the therapy on him. In about two weeks there was a noticeable change in his behaviour. He became very quiet and calm, and somehow mellow – and he also seemed much happier. When he contracted the measles, I let him have the Walkman™ and the stories to listen to in bed, and there was great improvement in his sleep *Ear infection* pattern. Some time later, when he caught an ear infection at a public swimming pool, and was in a lot of pain and distress, I again played the story tapes for him, and the pain went out of his ears. I'm sure the Sound Therapy was responsible for his rapid healing.'

Those tapes are making me smarter!

Pat Engbers, RN – Victoria, British Columbia, Canada

Dyslexia 'My son, Marty, was diagnosed as dyslexic and has had special education since Grade 1. He started using the Sound Therapy tapes during Grade 8. School authorities, counsellors and special education teachers, on evaluating Marty after the first Grade 8 term, were all of the opinion that he would be unable to complete the grade because of his problems (lack of reading comprehension, inattention, short-term memory difficulties). However, we were able to persuade them to keep him in his present school and to give the tapes a chance to work.

'Marty used the tapes overnight, every night for nine months, and he himself reported improved hearing and concentration after about three weeks. The best news of all came after six weeks when he came home from school *It's making me* very excitedly and said, "you know, those tapes are making *smarter!* me smarter! I was half way through an essay this morning and realised that I had actually heard and understood the teacher. I knew the answers and it was easy to write them down!"

'From then on, even though Marty never became a scholar, his previously strained expression grew happy and relaxed. His ability to deal with Math and English improved greatly. He left school after Grade 10, and is now working at a full-time job and has no trouble at all with the math and language skills he needs.

Posture 'I should add that our other son, David, also used the tapes, for improved concentration and memory. After a few weeks we noticed that his very bent back had straightened right up – and has stayed that way.'

Schizophrenia is not for life

Reba F. Adams, RN – Dallas, Texas, USA

'The psychiatrist told me, "Your daughter is a schizophrenic and always will be." At the age of sixteen she underwent a complete personality change as a result of a severe hypoglycaemic attack, and a fall in which she struck her forehead on a file cabinet. From being active and popular, with a wonderful sense of humour, she became irritable and suspicious, dropped her friends and became a regular recluse. She would not talk on the phone nor eat at the table, but took her meals to her room to eat behind closed doors. Her co-ordination was poor, very mechanical, like a doll. She became unable to sleep and would go days without even an hour's sleep. That was ten years ago. She has been doing Sound Therapy for six months and is better in so many ways I hardly know where to begin. She will initiate conversations again, and occasionally I hear her deep joyous laughter that I have missed so much these past years. She is calmer, and has obtained her driver's licence, she has started work on her education, with the assistance of a tutor provided through a special program, and she wears a Walkman™ to class. The Walkman™ is worn from the time she gets up until bedtime every day. She has come so far that I really cannot say enough about this wonderful therapy. *(Schizophrenia)*

'As for myself, I have recently been working a twelve hour shift, doing private duty on a stressful case. Before Sound Therapy, I did well to get out of bed and work just eight hours, and never kept a clean house. During this case, I am able to do chores at home too. I listen a short time and get twice the amount of projects accomplished. *(Energy)*

'Then there is my mother, who had a massive coronary and came to stay with me after ten days in hospital. I put her to listening to the Sound Therapy tapes as many hours a day as possible. After two months, the doctor said she was well enough to live alone again, so she is now back in her own apartment. Every morning she gets up at 7:30, puts her Walkman™ on and takes a walk around the apartment complex. Not bad for eighty-four years old! *(Eighty-four and doing well)*

221

Depression 'Now I have begun an experiment with a man who has been in and out of psychiatric wards for the past twenty-five years. He is presently home but goes to a day care centre. I loaned him my music tapes and my Gregorian Chant tape. He has been listening for two weeks now, and says his depression is lifting, and also says, 'I feel alive between my ears for the first time in twenty-five years.' He wears the Walkman™ to the day care centre, Veteran Administration Hospital, where one of the psychiatric nurses also is wearing a Walkman™ and Sound Therapy tape.'

Dental cold turkey
Kathleen Boyd Sharp – Camrose, Alberta

Epilepsy 'Because of epilepsy I have always had to take dental work cold turkey, no anaesthetic. If I take the anaesthetic it means an instant epileptic seizure. Even when I did not take it, a few hours later at home I would still have a seizure of six or eight hours duration. Well it was mid-September when I started using Sound therapy, very faithfully from four to ten hours a day. In February I had a cavity to be filled and wasn't even dreading it. I had the tapes running while I sat in the chair, with the dentist working on my tooth. I was as relaxed as if I was sitting in the recliner chair in my own living room. I was hardly aware of the drill (that had to be a first). This was something I had never experienced before in my entire life. There have been many times when I had to be carried — literally — out of the dentist's office, driven home and carried into the house, and it would be hours before I started functioning. This time, I felt so very good, and when I got home, no seizure, I didn't even have to lie down, but crocheted for a while and played the guitar for a few hours.

Spasticity I am deriving untold benefits. I was paralysed about thirty years ago with spinal meningitis, and have tended to have bad falls ever since. Sound Therapy has helped my spasticity and caused a noticeable improvement in my walking. My feet were quite toed-in, but now I actually walk with both feet pointing straight ahead. I sleep better, am calmer, and wake up ready to get up and start the day. The tapes are worth three times their weight in gold to me. I had a male relative visiting, and he helped himself to my Walkman™ batteries for his razor and ruined the charge. I declare if anyone touches those batteries again they will meet with instant death! Would I kill someone over a messed up charge on my batteries? You bet I would, and sit in jail and listen to Sound Therapy.'

Nightmares away
Helen Hill – Regina, Saskatchewan, Canada

'Our eleven year old son reports that he "never slept better in his whole life." He had been troubled with terrible nightmares. He now will not part with, nor go to bed without Tape # 1 in your program. Thank you so much.'

Nightmares

Computer fatigue
Mary Finnie – Medicine Hat, Alberta, Canada

'My daughter works with a computer and has been exhausted at the end of every day. She started listening to the tapes, and the very next day was amazed at how good she felt. She asked if she could listen at work and they agreed to it. She tells me they think she's crazy, but she feels so good that she doesn't care.'

Computer exhaustion

Grades climbing
Mrs Joyce Saben – Vancouver

'Our son has been on the Sound Therapy program for two years and it has helped him to overcome his learning disabilities. He started off listening all day and all night to complete his first 300 hours. He is allowed to listen to the tapes in his classes at school. His letter grade at school has increased from a C to where he is now on the B Plus Honour roll. It happened that he was asked to give a testimony in a court case about the experience of having dyslexia, and he ended up telling the Judge all about his experience with Sound Therapy - to the great interest of the Judge!'

Higher grades for dyslexia

In my own words
Larissa Amy, 13-year-old girl with ADD and Higher Functioning Autism – Sydney

'My pain is not as sharp and my sleep is less. The colours are beautiful. They stand out heaps and are richer and brighter. Reading — there are more gaps in between the letters. They stand out even more. This has helped a lot for me. Life is so much easier now. But of course I feel like a new person. The world has changed a lot.'

Higher functioning autism

Now he's speaking
Janice, mother of a child with Dyspraxia

Dyspraxia 'My son Jamie was diagnosed, at age three, as having "Severe Speech Dyspraxia." This disorder, I was told, would mean years of intensive speech therapy. I started Jamie on Sound Therapy and found after a short time his progress with his speech therapy increased. Jamie used Sound Therapy for three months and continued speech therapy for another year. I firmly believe that without the Sound Therapy his progress would have been much slower.'

Hey I can read!
Madonna Schoonder – Sydney

Dyslexic hearing 'I've always had bad concentration and memory. I also have what I call dyslexic hearing. People talk to me but I have no idea what they're saying most times. It makes no sense to me & I just shut off. I heard about Sound Therapy and wasn't sure if it would help, but wanted to give it a go. I listened for three hours the first night and slept the whole night through, and soundly — something that's never happened *Sound sleep* before. My whole life I've had trouble getting to sleep and staying asleep more than two or three hours, even when exhausted. So for me, that was great. Not only that, I've slept well every night since, even with my boyfriend there — who literally jumps all around all night and constantly bangs the bed with his legs.

Concentration 'I've also noticed my concentration has improved enormously. I can read a book now without my mind wandering, and I only need to read it once because it makes sense the first time. My conversations have improved also because people's words make sense now & don't seem all jumbled.

Calm 'The first time I listened to Sound Therapy was just a quick listen of a friend's. I didn't even really know what it was. I'd just had a huge fight with my boyfriend and was extremely upset. Within seconds of listening to the music, it calmed me down a lot.'

Goodbye epilepsy!
Hilary Peart – Perth

'When I first read of Sound Therapy in their newsletter, "Listeners' Voices" and read of the benefits others had received from listening to their tapes it sounded too good to be true. I thought if I could get a fraction of that help it would be worth trying, so I sent for the tapes, and both my husband and I started listening to them as soon as we received them.

'I have epilepsy and the medication I take was not completely controlling it. I had an almost constant "electric" feeling in my head, and looked out at the world through what seemed like a net curtain, or fog. I was constantly on edge, slept badly, felt exhausted, had difficulty reading and communicating. The simplest tasks had become complicated for me.

Epilepsy

'From the start, I listened to the Sound Therapy tapes ten to twelve hours a day and found it very soothing. Before I started listening to the tapes, my day consisted of about two hours of activity in the morning and the rest of the day mainly resting and unable to communicate. By the end of the first three months of listening, my day had improved to the extent that I could be active most of the time except for a couple of hours resting in the afternoon. The headaches, pressure in my head, and confusion gradually lessened.

'After about 6 weeks of listening, I visited my neurologist. He was pleased with my progress and said to carry on with what I was doing. At the next visit, six months later, he couldn't get over how my walking and posture had improved, and I later left the Sound Therapy book with him. On my next visit about eight months later, he again could see my improvement and was very pleased, and had enjoyed reading the book, as he had an interest in how music can help with restoring memory etc.

Posture

'Today, after about fifteen months of listening, what a change! I have my enjoyment and enthusiasm for life back. I have tried many alternative remedies over the years, as I have had a number of health issues. I have a heart problem which has culminated in me having a pace-maker fitted, chronic fatigue syndrome, fibromyalgia and of course, the epilepsy. I still carry on with acupuncture treatment, homeopathic drops, and magnetic therapy, plus nutritional supplements and a good diet, all of which have helped me and continue to do so. I was doing all this before I started on the Sound Therapy, but what I found with the Sound

It's given me back my life!

Therapy was it seemed to enhance all the other things I was doing.

'In conclusion Sound Therapy has improved my:

- Energy levels
- Co-ordination
- Memory
- Concentration
- Ability to do needlework (I had come to the stage that I was unable to do this any more)
- Communication – both written and oral
- Sleeping pattern
- General quality of life

In short, Sound Therapy has given me my quality of life back. Thank you Sound Therapy.'

A natural solution for ADHD

Liz Rayner – Sydney

'I thought I would take this opportunity to thank you both for your time and effort. It is rare these days to find a business that is so prompt, giving and kind.

'My son Jason has benefited greatly from the use of the Sound Therapy tapes, and the Natural Trio for his ADHD. Jason listens to the tapes mainly at night and has never complained or not wanted to listen to them. He settles a lot more easily and quickly — within ten minutes. Then there is the "miracle" of the Natural Trio combination. I say "miracle" because Jason's behavior was of great concern and stress for our family. If I had not seen the differences in my child, I would have though that this was a gimmick. However, it's not. My son is less aggressive, calmer, less fidgety, able to concentrate better and more centered.

Sound Therapy and supplements for ADHD

'His behavior in the school classroom has improved immensely and his schoolwork is steadily improving along with his self-esteem and confidence.

'It is evident through the positive changes my son has experienced, even after a short period of using the tapes and natural ADHD remedy (two months), that it is beneficial.

'My husband and I send you a heartfelt thankyou for all your help and time. Words cannot express the relief and gratitude we feel at finally finding a natural solution for our son.'

Interviews with families using Sound Therapy

Even after almost twenty years in this field, I am still warmed, awed and amazed when I talk to some of our listeners, and hear how Sound Therapy is changing their children's lives. Here are the transcripts of interviews done with some very dedicated parents, and others who care for children.

Leaps and bounds in language

Clara Rapp – Perth

'I have twin boys, Brendan and Jonathan, who were born very premature at twenty-eight weeks, and when they were born they were in the intensive care nursery. Because of the prematurity they couldn't swallow food, so they were being tube-fed. They were virtually on oxygen for three months. They couldn't breathe by themselves, their lungs were very weak. As a result they had developmental delay. Brendan, in particular, had all sorts of problems. He had a hole in the heart and lots of other problems, but the main problem was language delay. Brendan had auditory processing problems. Jonathan didn't have as many problems as Brendan, but he had seizures as well, and he had speech and language delay.

Premature birth

Developmental delay

'Over the years I tried many, many things to try and help them. I used speech therapy with them since they were two years old; I used to take them to the hospital for regular sessions once a week and I also took Brendan to many private speech therapists. I tried kinesiology. It did help to some extent, but I felt it was too time-consuming and expensive and I couldn't afford it, so I didn't keep at it for too long. It was a lot of work involved for me because I was working and it was very frustrating.

'When they were at school they used to get teased because they couldn't talk in full sentences, with the result that they wouldn't talk much to other kids. I was at the point where I just couldn't handle it any more.

Not talking in sentences

'When the boys were about six, I started Sound Therapy. That was when I first saw your mother's book in the bookshop. I read it and I got very, very keen and I then went and bought your tapes .

'I started Sound Therapy with both of them at the same

227

time. I noticed that their sentences started getting longer, they started talking to other kids. I felt very happy about it, and so I persisted with Sound Therapy by putting the music on their ears at night time when they went to sleep. I used it constantly for more than a year maybe, with the four basic tapes, putting them on at bedtime for one and a half hours every night. From there I found that their

Improved language ability

language ability just got higher and higher, that words were just coming through. It helped their studies as well; it helped them with their school work. Not a hundred percent, but it helped them to come to a standard, where they could perform, so at least they were not very below their age level, as they were before.

'I am convinced it was the Sound Therapy that helped them, because I had tried everything else. I tried so many therapies. Sound Therapy was what really made the difference, so I insisted that they keep using it. I bought your other four tapes, recently — Full Spectrum. I'm using that on them at the moment and I'm finding they're coping pretty well with their schoolwork.

'They stopped having speech pathology when we started Sound Therapy because it was just too hard to keep going to the appointments, but they continued to improve.

'My husband noticed the change in them, but sometimes he wouldn't admit it because he was thinking I was going crazy.

Family chaos

'Those years were like a nightmare, chaos, it was like a bomb that was dropped on us. We were in a lot of shock and denial and anger and all those states that we went through, because we expected normal happy kids. Of course, they were healthy — but just the speech and language and learning difficulties were enormous to deal with, so there was always a lot of pressure between me and my husband.

'My husband is a person who wants everything right and done correctly, and he was putting a lot of pressure on the boys with their education. With me being understanding about what their problems were — it was causing a lot of stress between me and my husband. That is why he was thinking I was going bonkers over the Sound Therapy!

'The boys are fourteen now, and all that has all changed. My husband is now convinced that it is the Sound Therapy that has changed their language. He is coming with me on that now.

'Brendan was left-handed before and we wanted him to be right-handed and we were trying to get him to do right-handed writing. He was totally confused as to which hand he was going to use. But then after doing Sound Therapy I found that his writing automatically changed to the right hand, and now he's a right-handed writer.

Left handed

'After they started speaking more clearly and at least being able to talk to a few kids at school, that made me feel so much better. I felt that they were being more normal now. I felt confident that at least they have some future. Because everything involves language. If you can't talk to people then you feel ostracised. So it made me feel very happy that now they can at least mix with other kids, and seem normal among other kids.

Mixing with other kids

'I would say, that if parents like me who have a child who is not fitting in and nothing works, then definitely give Sound Therapy a try.

'I'm so glad I came across the book in the book shop. If I hadn't seen it, maybe I would never have heard of Sound Therapy and maybe my children would still be struggling, and I would still be in the mess that I was so many years ago. I want to thank you for what Sound Therapy and your mother's book have done for my life.'

Healthier immunity - better focus
Daniel Danuser – Newcastle – 2004

'Talina is six. She is a very soft, sweet, energetic young girl. She is very kind and caring. She is very interactive and very cuddly.

'She has had an issue with recurrent earaches, and at various times we had thought that she wasn't hearing as well as she ought to, to the extent that we had taken her to a hearing centre to have her hearing analysed, to be told that "no, her hearing is fine." But we still thought that her perception was not as good as it might have been. It was affecting her school work because she can't concentrate on acoustic signals. If somebody talks to her it doesn't mean that it actually registers. It's what you would describe as daydreaming. You think, "oh dear, she is not listening." I think she is just inattentive and her hearing is somewhat

Recurrent earaches

diminished, but not within a measurable range. It looks as though she is daydreaming, though being in Year 1, it's not a big deal at this stage.

'Our concern was for her, because we see that she may be missing out at various times on being more interactive, she was missing opportunities because she wasn't paying any attention to her hearing.

'Sound Therapy, as you would know more than anyone, recharges the brain, and I have always thought that her *More attentive* hearing problem was more a tuner for the brain as opposed to a hearing issue. Even though it manifested as her not being attentive, I think it was the brain not being attentive, so with the Sound Therapy we tried to change that, and *Earaches* it worked. Now she is more attentive, she can hear more *decreased* easily and she hasn't had any recurrent ear infections for several months. Her reading has improved dramatically, and I think her phonetics has improved but she fluctuates a lot.

Less sleep 'Previously she had a great requirement for sleep, but if she uses the tapes to go to bed she is really bright and cheerful early in the morning. She definitely has less requirement for sleep than she would have normally; obviously suggesting that her brain is able to fully charge quicker, you don't need ten hours, you can do it in six or seven hours.

'So that reassured me that it's a great thing. It reassured me that, in my view, every household should have a set of tapes. I think at least every school should have a number of units that they can hand out to the children.

'For myself, similarly, I haven't had any middle ear *Phonetics* infections since I started using it. I also think my phonetics is better. But, more importantly, you have reconnected me with the past, it has made me aware of things gone by. That happened at what I, in hindsight, would recognise as the moment when the ear opened up, as you describe in the book.

Handwriting 'Like many others, at first I felt that I was calmer. I felt my handwriting was better. I felt I could concentrate better and stick to tasks better. I didn't want to drift away. That happened virtually as soon as I used the tapes. My sleep needs were less, I felt more refreshed, and I had more energy. All of that happened virtually immediately.

But within about two to three months, I had a profound period of tiredness, I thought that was the opening of the ears, but thinking back now, it wasn't. But subsequent to that, I had fond memories of my childhood that I could reconnect with, which I thought had been buried and lost forever. This was very special because they were important instances in my life; so to know that they are still there, and to know they still bear an influence in my life, was profound for me and very important.

Fond memories

'My youngest daughter has not used the tapes. She is not interested, she is very connected, she has unbelievable hearing and phonetic skills, and she is a very advanced child. Often the second child is more advanced, but she is quite exceptional. She has also not had any major illnesses, and that is perhaps the biggest difference. My first daughter, Talina when she was eighteen months old had a rota virus infection, a gastrointestinal infection that was quite severe. She was not well for two weeks, and ever since then we felt that her health had not been the same as prior to it. It hamstrung her immune system, and she then became prone to flus and ear infections. It left her vulnerable to get eczema or fungal spreads on the skin, and that to us means that she has a reduced level of wellness. So, as concerned parents, of course we try and do everything we can to make her stronger so she can overcome that early infection, and to succeed we have to be careful with the diet. But tiredness was still something that was common. It was still common that she couldn't get out of bed easily in the morning or she would be grumpy. Whereas, with the Sound Therapy, she comes running into the room and she is cheerful and happy and switched on right from the word "go". She has had enough sleep by six, instead of by eight o'clock.

Low immunity

'She loves lying in bed listening to the children's stories and she loves drawing and painting. That photo that I sent you of her, where she has propped up a unicorn next to herself and is drawing a unicorn and painting and colouring it in—that's what she loves to do. If you let her, she would do that, twenty-four hours a day. She never has any objections to putting on the headphones for that.

'We have several of the children's stories tapes that she listens to. She loves the ones about elves, fairies and unicorns.

231

'I would say to other parents that it is money well spent, and they should not to be too hesitant and too closed-minded. It seems a lot to spend $500 or $600, but I really think it's a very good investment because there are multiple members of the family who can benefit from it.'

Wrestling with hearing loss
Ian Patterson – Melbourne – 2001

Ian is a qualified electrician and also a massage therapist. He began his career in his teens as an amateur wrestler. Having his injuries treated with massage lead him into that line of work, starting at the age of eighteen. He later learned Reiki, and when he came across Sound Therapy he decided to try it to help his hearing problems. Ian shares his story:

Ear abscesses 'My own experience of hearing as a child was disastrous! I was late starting school because of continuing hearing problems, multiple abscesses in the ear, sometimes both ears at once. Then when I started school I was called a problem child, because I couldn't hear so I kept asking questions.
Back of the From an early age I was often sent to the back of the room
class to read a book, but fortunately those dark ages seem to be improving, and with the advent of antibiotics not so many children go through the hell experience that I did.

'Sound Therapy worked very well for me, having a history of chronic ear problems — including nerve deafness, that I was told was irreversible. I had been told I should be wearing hearing aids, which I did try briefly but found it was a disaster, because all I kept getting was a roar that was worse than not hearing. The problem was it was amplifying the general noise around me and bringing it in.

Improved 'Listening to Sound Therapy had the effect of
hearing dramatically improving my hearing — so much, that I could make conversation and understand what was going on when I was in crowds of people, which was an ability that I had lost over the past few years. Initially, the hearing problems were caused by continuing abscesses in my ears from a very early age, that went on till I was in my mid-teens. By then, I had lots of problems with
Industrial schooling because I could not hear. Leading on from that,
deafness I amplified the problem with industrial deafness, working in very noisy areas amongst machinery and hammering;

and later on, with the advent of hammer drills, that was another compounding disaster. The first time I was told I had nerve deafness would have been twenty-five years ago. I was told it was an incurable condition that would gradually get worse. The reverse has in fact happened, because since using Sound Therapy, my hearing is vastly improved. I can now hear people when they speak from quite a distance away. I'm still sensitive to some high-pitched sounds, they still annoy me, but no where near to the level that they did previously — and its improving all the time because I continuously use the Sound Therapy. I started to notice improvements after only a few weeks, but the improvement *Tinnitus* is ongoing. It has also virtually got rid of my tinnitus. (Ringing in the ears.)

'I have had some connection with some of the other forms of Sound Therapy where you have to sit in a confined space for an extended period of time. It takes too much time out of your life, and it's very expensive. I have looked at some of the methods that other people use with temple bells and chimes, and I found these do give a momentary improvement but it doesn't seem to last more than a couple of days with me.

'I chose the Joudry Sound Therapy because I like the ease of use, the portability. I can drive around in the car using it, I can have conversations with people with the therapy still working, and I can wear it to bed. I sleep better, I'm more relaxed and I have more energy.

'I went into healing work probably because of suffering from a very early age. Suffering lots of pain, suffering the frustration, and feeling that nothing could help me because doctors kept saying, "he may grow out of it, but it's not something we can really help at this stage." After you hear that from numerous doctors you start to lose a little bit of faith that anything will help, so when you find things that do work successfully you want to retain that benefit — and you also get to a stage where you like to spread the word amongst other people that maybe they can be helped too.

'Sound Therapy is relevant for everyone who's got ears I would think; because with the improvements that I have had, if you've got any sort of hearing, regardless of how minimal, there is always room for improvement. It is very

74% of learning difficulties — hearing problem

important, in particular, for kids with learning difficulties. Seventy-four percent, I think, of the children with learning difficulties have a hearing problem — and as such, Sound Therapy may be able to help them considerably.

'I am sixty-five years old, but I am meeting other people with hearing problems who are in their teens and twenties. Probably from the time they are leaving school, people are getting into situations where they are causing hearing damage.

'My first love is helping children that have got problems, because they still have their whole life in front of them. But with older people, improving their quality of life is a vastly important area too.'

The day the earth stopped moving
Jeanette McKay, educational specialist
– Perth – 2004

Immune problems

'I just have the one child, a boy. From a very young age he had problems with his immunity. He kept on getting ill, with numerous ear infections. When he started school his development appeared to be more or less on track and he coped reasonably well although there were signs that his

Motor skills

co-ordination and his fine and gross motor skills were not as good as they should be. The problems became obvious once he started having to show his skills in reading and writing.

'He had taken a very long time to walk and he didn't crawl for very long. With my background in remedial education, I had a feeling, from these early experiences, that we were in for trouble ahead.

'I believe his nervous system, the centre of integration for sensory information, was stressed. The nervous system is developed through the stimulation of the senses and this in turn stimulates the development of the neural pathways,

Heavy metal exposure

allowing learning to take place. Somehow this wiring and feedback mechanism was not working the way it should. I believe this was partly due to my own ill health when he was in utero, and probably included heavy metal exposure from toxins in my system. In addition the picture was complicated by a very difficult delivery. Added to this was the stress and trauma of moving countries. Our family moved from the UK to Australia when he was ten months old and that was very traumatic for him. He didn't like change at all and he found it extremely threatening. I think all these factors added up to a state of overload on a young, sensitive and already stressed nervous system. *Food* Additionally he probably had some sensitivity to wheat *sensitivities* and dairy products.

'All this had a huge effect on the family. He would only sleep for very short periods, so basically we were getting up to him five or six times every night. He was not always a very happy child. I had to carry him around for a long time until he walked at nineteen months.

'It was a huge problem for the family. It affected my *Up 5 or 6* work, it affected the dynamics of the family and our health. *times a night* My husband's and my health suffered because we were putting in so much effort caring for this child who just wasn't coping. It is true to say that when a child is unhappy the whole family is unhappy.

'We tried different schools for him, in an effort to find *Not coping* the solution to his problems, but this did not work. He *with school* came home one day, when he was in the third grade, at a very caring school, saying that he "felt dumb and stupid". I knew that he was in fact a very bright child, but he just couldn't cope at school. He could see that the other children were achieving and that he couldn't, with the result that he believed he was dumb and stupid. I took him out of school and home-schooled him for just over a year. After three or four months I saw many changes including a great improvement in his self-esteem.

'I tried kinesiology, I tried looking at his diet and I tried occupational therapy as well as speech therapy. With all the therapies I did see changes for the better. We used homeopathy and it was very successful in strengthening his immune system to the point where he seldom had to have antibiotics. We basically tried everything we felt could be beneficial, but I always knew there was something else missing.

'I knew this after we had followed the suggestions of a *High IQ* clinical psychologist. She was a wonderful woman and was *with gaps in* able to identify that he had a typical learning difficulties *processing* pattern where there is a high IQ but there are these gaps in the processing of information. She recommended a reading program for him, which we administered over three months. As a result he went from not scoring at all on the reading scales, to scoring above his chronological age after those three months. It then appeared that he could read, and we thought that we could sit back and enjoy the learning process from that point. But of course this was not the case, and he lost everything that he had apparently learnt within 6 months. He was back to square one again with his reading.

Sensory integration   'I began to realise from that point that there is so much more to learning than simply reading off the page. I began to look a lot more closely at sensory integration work, and that is when I looked around for a really good occupational therapist. I found someone who really understood the process of sensory integration and she did excellent work with him. This laid a strong foundation for his ability to learn. As part of this process I started looking more closely at auditory processing and how it impacted on listening, comprehension and reading. I knew that was where the reading process had come unstuck for him, the fact that he could not process the sounds of the words. He could hear, there was nothing wrong with the functional aspect of his ears. His ears as well as his eyes had been checked and everything was apparently working well. I realised that he just could not get the information from the hearing mechanism to the brain, which was the auditory processing aspect. It wasn't until he was nearly twelve years of age that he started Sound Therapy.

'What happened was a friend showed me a brochure advertising the Tomatis method and it struck me as being terribly expensive, I recall that it was nearly $2000 for the program at that time and someone came over to Perth to do the therapy. I believe all therapies should be affordable and reasonably priced so that everyone can access them and I felt that all the answers to our problems are mostly found within a local area. As a result I literally threw the brochure in the bin. A bit later another friend gave me a book to read by Paul Madaule, "When Listening Comes Alive" which I read and I knew straight away that it was Sound Therapy and the Tomatis method that my son needed to enable him to read. I realised then that no matter what the cost or the distance, it was terribly important that he should be able to read and that this really did have the answers we were looking for. I was prepared to pay the price, (I worked out that it cost $7000 in total including accommodation and airfares,) to go across to Canberra, where the Tomatis therapist was at the time. He had the therapy over two 10-day sessions. The changes that resulted from the therapy made every dollar I spent very worthwhile.

'I had to do the therapy with my son. If I hadn't felt the changes in myself, I would not have understood the subtleties of what was changing for him and his sensory system. I was very, very pleased that I had that opportunity because within three hours of listening to the music I was able to remember and hold three lines of text in my head for the first time in my life.

I felt the changes in myself

'I had never had that ability before, despite having completed a degree in English and History, which is very heavy memory work. I have always known that I've had to work extra hard to achieve what I did. The feeling of being able to hold those lines in my head was absolutely phenomenal. After the next three hours of treatment I could remember those lines forever, and that feeling was totally amazing. I began to realise the extent of my own dyslexia at that point. I began to realise something very significant was going to be happening for my son too, although I couldn't see it.

Memory

'The therapy also changed my vestibular system to the point where I felt as though the earth was stable for the first time in my life. I had always had a lot of car-sickness and other balance problems. This made everything in the way of learning much more difficult. When you have this condition all the time you don't realise it's a problem. Looking back on it now, I realise that it affected the way I walked as well because the whole world would move all the time. It was as if the ground was moving, as if I was walking on a waterbed or something unstable. I didn't know that other people didn't experience this. Looking back I had little clues in the sense that some things would be more difficult for me, such as being in a car and having to watch the road all the time even as a passenger and if anyone took a very sharp turn or changed directions quickly while driving, it would really throw me out and make me feel ill. I realised that I obviously must have a significant problem with my vestibular system.

The world was stable

It was like walking on a water bed

Changed my ability to see 'After sound therapy, when that sense of constant motion stopped, I straight away felt more confident because I felt more secure in my own body. It was the most amazing feeling. It also changed my vision and I believe part of that was the vestibular system settling down, resulting in a change to my peripheral vision. For example after my first trip to Canberra for the sound therapy, we were driving on a section of the road into Perth which we had been driving down for ten years and I said to my husband, "Gosh they have been busy here, what has been going on with all these roadwork's?" I could see earth works set back a fair bit from the road. He looked at me as though I was totally mad and said, "Have you never seen those before?" and I said "No" and he said, "Those have been there for ten years!" Up until that point I had not been able to see what was on the side of the road. My vision also changed in the sense that I had better depth perception so instead of seeing everything as flat, I could see in 3D — depth was added to my world.

'Of course this made me extremely excited. It really changed everything for me and I knew from my experience and the benefits I saw for my son that I would need to somehow make the therapy available to the children and families I worked with in my clinic.

'The first change in my son was that he became a lot happier and within a month of him doing the Sound Therapy I was able to present him cautiously with a reading program. By then he was very resistant to doing any more remedial work, he had been "therapied out". So every few days I would show him a couple of words and go through the sounds with him. I would just spend ten or fifteen minutes working with a purely phonics based reading program. After a month, one day he said to me,

I can read that word now! "Mum I can read that word now." and I said, "How? What do you mean?" and he said, "I can just see it." What he was doing was not only "seeing" the word, he was able to hear the sound in his head and connect the sound with the letters on the page and that was the beginning of his true reading.

'His progress with schoolwork then moved ahead extremely quickly because the Sound Therapy had provided him with the auditory processing awareness that he needed.

His senses were ready to do the reading and then I could teach him reading and spelling skills and once he was given that information he picked it up very quickly and retained it. The other thing I noticed was that his writing started to stay on the line and the letters were also more uniformly written. That also showed me his vestibular system had settled down.

Writing on the line

'He never totally caught up with his age level. He has always been a little bit behind. I feel if we had given him Sound Therapy a lot sooner he would have caught up. He has always needed that extra little bit of support with his schoolwork but overall the progress he has made has been absolutely phenomenal.

'It was about three or four months later that I came across the portable method of sound therapy. I was determined to find something that was easily accessible for the many children I was seeing in my clinic for specialist educational work. When I started to look around I came across Sound Therapy, the one that you and your mother developed. When I heard about it I just knew that it was correct and I followed it up straight away. I was absolutely thrilled that there was a self-help kit people can go away and work with on their own. I was also excited for myself because I left Canberra after having Sound Therapy, knowing that I actually needed a lot more of the therapy but I had no means of accessing it. Here was a way of getting hold of it and using it for the rest of my life if I wanted to, which was wonderful.

I needed more

'For me the longer-term listening just consolidated what had already changed. I found it was very helpful in the times when I was under a lot of stress, when I was studying and very busy at work.

'Families in my practice, who I introduce to Sound Therapy, I find mostly have their children use it when they are sleeping or travelling in the car. At the moment there is one little girl who is using it when she is asleep and getting huge benefits. Her parents couldn't believe the changes in her ability to read following just one 3 hour session of listening.

Use during sleep to overcome resistance

'For myself I use Sound Therapy mostly for my studying, I have recently completed an advanced diploma in Herbal Medicine. It required many hours of study, and the Sound Therapy was very helpful for keeping me focussed. I'm not good with numbers and I find working out my accounts quite stressful. I have found Sound Therapy invaluable for taking the stress out of this task. Sound Therapy is the thing that has really got me through those difficult times in life. I still use it at night if I can't sleep. I have found it to be very good for insomnia. I have about thirty families who have used the Sound Therapy and from the feedback I have received they find it helpful in many different ways. They just love the fact that all the children can access the tapes and they, the parents, can use it themselves. Very often when I talk to the parents about their child and how they will benefit from using Sound Therapy, I can see their eyes light up as they realise the benefits for themselves as well.

Health and wellbeing

'Sound Therapy is definitely a very important part of the whole picture for health and wellbeing and not just for anyone with learning difficulties. I would say it's an essential part of maintaining our health in modern day living and I would highly recommend Sound Therapy to be used by every family. The health of the ears is absolutely critical to the health of all the senses and the whole body. The more I work with people to maintain the health of their nervous system I have realised how much hearing impacts on every sense. The sense of hearing and the vestibular sense actually impact on the vision, tactile sense and sense of the body in space. The health of the ear has an impact on our whole sense of wellbeing and therefore our emotional and body chemistry health as well. I think it's absolutely wonderful that we have this great Sound Therapy self-help kit, available at such an affordable price. This is a therapy that is so natural, with no side effects. I tell people that the only time the therapy won't work is if they don't use it! So thank you very much, I think you and your mother have given the world a great gift.

Less family conflict

Pamela Winter – Perth – 2004

'I've got five children and three of them at the moment are using Sound Therapy. I would like all five to use it eventually.

'Christopher is nine and I really got the Sound Therapy with him in mind. Christopher is a very busy child with an extremely busy mind. At the same time, he can be quite an angry person. He can get quite frustrated with himself and quite restless. I wouldn't call him hyperactive, but his head is spinning all the time and he needs us to stimulate him a lot.

Restlessness

'His reading was behind for his age and also his spelling. So first of all I looked into his language and I now have him with a speech pathologist here in Perth. We are taking him right back to all his phonics and going through spelling and all the rules and everything else.

Reading and spelling

'Sound Therapy, we found, is helping him with memory, and with sleep. Because another thing — Christopher was fairly restless and would have headaches, he would wake up with a headache and was restless at night. Now he sleeps really well, he wakes up very bright and happy, no headaches since we have been using the Sound Therapy. His reading is starting to flow more through going to the speech pathologist and helping him constantly at home; its just really a triangle of help. I am noticing his anger is subsiding, he's projecting a much more positive manner. He seems to be able to think more clearly and he's a more relaxed person.

Headaches

'When I have to give him directions I am finding now that he doesn't get so flustered and he's able to retain more. Now when he is reading a book, he's not only retaining the word from page to page he's retaining it from day to day.

Retaining information

'The speech pathologist was very keen to know about Sound Therapy because she noticed a big change in Christopher's ability.

'Aaron, who is seven, is more of an outgoing child. He can be dominant in the way he approaches things and has quite an "I know better" type of attitude, so he's harder to teach. He also loses his temper extremely quickly, which I believe is often due to fear. He's afraid to start school and afraid to do things but he puts on this front of bravado.

Temper

'I found with Aaron that the Sound Therapy makes him calmer. When I am telling him that what he's done is not acceptable, Aaron is apologising and taking responsibility.

Apologising

'He got very angry about listening to the tapes at first. He would throw it out of his ears and tell me he was not going to listen to it and that he hates it and he doesn't like

Resistance to listening

241

the noise! But now he really likes it, even when I say "you have got to put them on", there's no argument — nothing. I said to him last night, "Do you like it?" And he said yes, he does.

'I must admit that with Aaron I had to treat him a bit differently, it's: "You're wearing them!" I know this is awful and it goes right against what you say in your book about not pressuring them, but with Aaron he will fight whatever I do, so I have to say "now this is something I know is good for you and we are going to put it in place." I know it sounds a bit harsh doesn't it? But it worked.

Stuttering   'Matthew is six years old and he has a slight stutter, which is the main reason why I wanted to use the Sound Therapy on him. Plus he does have a few sound language problems where he's not using the sounds correctly. He doesn't sound very clear when he's talking.

'Now he didn't like the funny screeching sound on the tapes. He said it was frightening, and I really wanted to get the story tapes but financially I couldn't, so I put him on the music, you know the Basic Kit. It was just one week before the stutter was nearly gone and definitely in under two weeks it wasn't there at all! I found that quite incredible for a child who was always going "I, I, I," when he was speaking — to not a word did he stutter or stammer on. He was also *New words* speaking to me and bringing long words into conversations, and in context. Now he must have had those all in his head anyway, but he couldn't bring them down. Matthew's teacher says she has noticed improvement in what he can get done and his writing and language ability

'I think he's also understanding more and I have noticed this with Christopher too, they are both listening to me, much, much better than before.

Hearing better   'Christopher is the one I had a hearing test done on because we did wonder whether he had a hearing problem. But he has no hearing problems at all; he actually came up really well on his tests. It used to take me ages to get his attention but that's not an issue now.

Tinnitus   'But Christopher does have tinnitus as well. This is something that I thought, at his age, "where did that come from?" He has told us for the last year that he has a high-pitched machine noise in his ears all the time. Since Sound

242

Therapy, he reckons that there are times where it gets a lot less and he can only barely hear it.

'I had amazing results too. I am just realising, through the Sound Therapy, where your children's problems come from. I have different problems like Christopher, but you overcome them as an adult, and you kind of use alternatives so that they don't get noticed. Memory is an issue for me, but that's changing. If I am reading a book, I am actually absorbing from one paragraph to the next instead of having to re-read. *Memory for reading*

'I have noticed my social skills improving. I have never liked being in crowds, where you have to speak to a lot of people. I am finding that that's improving. My sleep pattern really changed too. Now I am getting up early and feeling really refreshed from my sleep instead of feeling groggy. *Sleep*

'My husband has also noticed big changes. He's on a computer all day, and then all evening because he's working two jobs at the moment. So he's really exhausted, but he notices a big difference in his energy levels. He uses the Sound Therapy all day while he is on the computer. He's noticed a difference in his own speech, because he has to stand up and speak in front of people and that is something that makes him quite nervous. But he has noticed he is coping with it really well. He is able to retain things and remember things and bring them out at the right moment.

'He has to fly out sometimes, he went to Canada not long ago, and everybody else had terrible jet lag but Jim didn't. That was another thing we were quite shocked about. He didn't put that down to Sound Therapy, he just said "I don't know why I feel so good — the others felt terrible." And I said to him "you know what — I have been reading in the book that that's one of the things that it would help." He was really thrilled with that, so now I always make sure he wears the Sound Therapy when flying. *Jet lag*

'I feel with Christopher and Aaron and myself that issues are coming up and we're dealing with them differently. So you get certain emotional issues surfacing and instead of squashing them back down and getting on with it because you don't understand them, I'm finding that you have a clearer idea of where they are coming from and you can deal with them.

Resolving
conflict

'I feel that being in an argument — if either one of the children is having an issue, or say I'm with my husband and we are talking about an emotional issue and its getting heated — I find that I don't have to join in with that energy. I don't feel intimidated or upset about it. I can understand where the person is coming from. So we can really flow through it and come out the other end without it escalating the way it used to. I feel that that's a huge step for anybody.

'I know my husband, through Sound Therapy, has a greater ability to look at things through a calmer perspective. For me you know — that's just the best thing of all. If we can all communicate and we can all feel good about ourselves and then you know nothing else matters. It's been wonderful.

Watching
television

'They don't watch much television, but if they watch with the Sound Therapy on I don't get the really drawn, grumpy behaviour afterwards. The other thing is, I love it if they are wearing it during reading and during homework because you get different results. I find they concentrate a lot better and reading is more flowing.

'We have re-evaluated vaccination too. I started to vaccinate — Andrew and Michael were both vaccinated. Christopher and Aaron were too in their early stages, and Andrew and Michael had the older vaccinations, and then it came to Matthew, my fifth, who had a very bad reaction to them. He had a very scary reaction on the second one. But I wasn't getting any help from the doctors because they don't want to say that it's the immunisation. I went to a specialist, because as a Mum you know that there is something really wrong. So I researched it as much as I could, and since then I have not vaccinated any of them.

'If I could go back I would have none of my children vaccinated. I am actually fighting my parents with it because they believe you should be vaccinated. It's a real problem, because no one is being advised of the dangers.'

We feel like we've got a little girl
Pietro and Shaylene Garofalo
– Western Australia – 2004

'Khiara is a child who really sort of sticks to herself. She is friendly towards people but then she likes to sit in a corner and do nothing, and is quite happy to sit there all day and just rock.

'She plays with her hands a lot, like she's got her hands in the basin and is washing them; brushes her hair with whatever she's got in her hand, when she's got nothing sometimes she just uses her hand. She doesn't really play with toys or anything like that. *Repetitive behaviour*

'The only diagnosis we've had is "intellectually disabled". That's all they have given us. *Intellectual disability*

'She does go to day care and kindy. And we've had her seeing an occupational therapist and a speech therapist on a regular basis. It didn't help though, not at all, absolutely zero results from that.

'Obviously her condition has caused a lot of stress for the family, a lot of frustration. We are always looking for alternative therapies, something else that works, and we have tried virtually anything and everything that comes up.

'When we started Sound Therapy, within literally two days we noticed some results. Within two weeks we noticed a lot of results — it was huge! We had Khiara on probably ten hours a day every day, and still do. The changes have been she is now pushing toys — as in cars — along the ground. That's something she never ever did. She started putting blocks into a box. We've got a toy box where Mum and our young son, Kaleb, just throw everything into a box at the end of the day, and Khiara is now sitting down and picking up those blocks and throwing them in. We couldn't get her to do anything like that before. There is a lot more communication; she is very affectionate now, especially with me. She comes up and is always giving me hugs and kisses, and we hadn't seen anything like that for at least two and a half years. She is now four. *Expressing affection*

'She did used to do things like that years ago, but she stopped. Now she does it all the time. We don't know what caused her to regress. She has had a lot of ear infections; we actually think it was vaccinations — there has been a lot of controversy about that.

'We sort of had to go back to our notes to see what was happening, and that's how we put together that every time Khiara was vaccinated she sort of dropped back.

'And it wasn't 'til — well she hasn't had her last one — so it took us that long to put it together, and I think that was because we were in such a huge panic with what was happening to her. We could see her regressing and everyone kept telling us "she's alright, she is fine"; and we are going, "she's not!" And being new parents it really sort of you under that much more pressure. But we are pretty convinced that vaccination has been the cause of it. So we haven't vaccinated our little boy, and we won't.

Seizures 'She used to have a lot of urine infections, which caused her to have seizures; but then their records virtually show that they weren't seizures, because while she was actually having seizures they were doing tests and nothing showed, and still nothing does. According to all the tests they have done, you know, MRI scans, EEG's, absent blood tests, nothing shows up at all.

Vaccination 'Her first vaccination was within the first couple of weeks and we did notice her shaking a little bit after that, almost straight away. But like I said, it was a matter of us going back and looking on our records before we switched on to what was going on.

'It is because we have always been against it, and being new parents they really make you feel like you're going to kill your child if you don't do it. They push you and push you, and in the end its like, "I've got to do it", cause if something happens, you know you'll never forgive yourself. I should have gone with my first instinct. It's something you learn in life isn't it?

'But we are seeing amazing changes with her since Sound Therapy. There is a lot more communication — a *Vocal sounds* lot more vocal sounds coming out of her. Within a few days of starting, she woke up at 2 or 3 in the morning and she was actually scaling sounds from low to high pitch, and didn't just do it once, she did it a few times. You could see that she was sort of impressed by what she was hearing, too! *Verbalising* What else did she do? She can actually say "drink" now, not clearly, but she says "ink" which indicates she wants a drink and she can say "up". Khiara has never said a word since she was probably three months when she could say "Mum". That disappeared again and she hasn't said a word again until the last couple of weeks.

'She has been on Sound Therapy for four weeks now and after just two weeks she managed to say "drink" — or "ink" — and "up".

'She has also virtually stopped grinding her teeth, which she was doing all the time. She's not rocking as much, she's got a habit of rocking from side to side, and she would sit there and do that all day. Now she will entertain herself with something else, she will go and play with blocks or something, not like any other normal child would do — but she does pick them up and smack them together and she is definitely progressing in that respect. She's a lot pushier than she was. If she wants something now, she will grab at you and pull, whereas before she would probably sit there and maybe whinge for a while and then just let it go.

Grinding teeth

Rocking

'Before, when she was in any sort of pain — for example ear infections — it would be really hard for us. We wouldn't know until it was literally time to admit her to hospital. Whereas now, if she stubs her toe or anything, she hollers and lets us know that she is feeling the pain.

Expressing pain

'She is grabbing things and pulling them, as in taking CDs off our rack. She is getting into trouble, she knows she is getting into trouble now and is quite cheeky and tends to keep doing it. She kind of looks at you and smiles and keeps doing it, which we reckon is great!

'Her balance has improved. She had a lot of problems with walking, always falling over, always hurting herself. She couldn't judge steps, so for a step that was an inch high, she would probably lift her leg as high as she could to get over it, whereas now she is sort of taking it is as a normal child would. Again, we think that is just excellent. So as you can see we have had a lot of changes here.

Balance

'Her general co-ordination has just improved so much. She was the sort of child who would lose her balance and fall over just standing there. Now she can stand for ages. I guess that's why she never pulled on us, or that sort of thing, because it was a hassle for her 'cause she was falling over all the time. Now she sits better, she stands better, she walks better.

Co-ordination

'She actually had a hearing test yesterday and they said they have seen enough improvement now not to worry about any more testing. We have been testing her hearing

Hearing

for two and a half years. But after yesterday, they are saying they don't want to see us ever again!

Picture books 'She is pointing at pictures in books a lot now, she never did anything even close to that before, so we are really happy about that. She actually brings a book over and throws it in your lap.

'She has started walking on tiptoe quite a few times, which she has never been able to do because obviously she hasn't been able to balance.

'We haven't done anything else with Khiara since she's been on Sound Therapy, because we decided we want to sit back and watch and see what happens ourselves. This is all stuff she just spontaneously does.

'She has started opening cupboard doors, reaching for things and throwing them all over the floor, that's something new. Ear infections have dropped off, dramatically. With the weather in the last month, Khiara would normally have been continuously with an ear infection at this time of year, and she's only had one very mild one, so we are saying Sound Therapy did that.

Ear infections

Ride on toys 'What else? Oh she rides around in the little push car. You know those little four-door, red and yellow things that you just use your feet push? She's doing that quite well — moving around all over the house and turning herself in the hallway, doing little three-point turns.

'Before, you could sit her on one and she could push backwards — that was all she would ever understand. Now she goes backwards, forwards, sideways — she is really good at it actually!

Eating 'She will eat finger foods now. We can give her a biscuit now; whereas before she would put it in her mouth but wouldn't really do anything with it, now she is actually eating it.

'We've got a machine that we have been trying to teach Khiara to use. its called a "techtalk" and it's got a picture and it makes a sound. You actually program your voice into it and you push the button and it will play the word. You know, you could say, "drink please". We had been trying to get Khiara to use that for probably two months. Now that she is on Sound Therapy, she has actually reversed the role a little bit — now she is grabbing our finger when she wants a drink and sticking it on the "techtalk", to say "drink please." We think that's pretty cool!

'She has always had really bad, deep grey bags under her eyes and they have virtually disappeared. She definitely looks brighter in the face. Before, she would walk into a room and maybe focus on one thing, whereas now she will actually look around and really check out what's there. She *Observation* is playing with her brother a lot more; she used to hate having him near her, but recently they have actually spent hours together sitting down playing with things. He is nineteen months. I wouldn't say she's even at his level yet, but she's definitely getting there.

'The hand washing and hair brushing have died down *Hand washing* a great deal, she's not doing that anywhere near as much *and hair* as she was. We figure she was just stimulating herself. She *brushing* seems to find things to do most of the time now. She *movements* dances to music, now, instead of rocking — she actually does little boppy movements. If we are playing The Wiggles or something like that, she will race up to the TV and do *Dancing* a little bop.

'Unfortunately a lot of people that we come across are very sceptical about anything in the way of natural therapy.

'We did it because we are desperate for answers, we are really looking for a cure. We probably won't get one, but we want to improve her quality of life as much as we can. I don't know if it's a little bit of guilt because we vaccinated her. I find it hard to believe that Khiara is going to be the *We were* way they said she would be for the rest of her life. I refuse *told to* to take that as gospel if you like. They said that she would *institutionalise* never have any quality of life. We were actually told at one *her* stage to institutionalise Khiara — that we would be better off. We have been through hell from day one.

'When Khiara was having seizures, at nine months old, we took her to an Osteopath and he stopped them almost instantaneously. She was teething at the time, she had a few urine infections and we think that caused the seizures. We also took her off of Phenobarbitone, which she had been prescribed for her seizures. We weaned her off that straight away after seeing the Osteopath.

'She used to throw up a lot too. She was on Phenobarbitone from a couple of weeks of age to about nine months. They wouldn't tell us about the effects of the drug — we had to go and do our own research and we learned that it actually seizes up the body. They didn't tell us that and still today they refuse to admit it, but it is actually written in their books! We noticed Khiara was starting to seize up on the right side of the body. We kept bringing it up and everyone just ignored us. We actually think that had something to do with slowing Khiara down, on top of everything else.

'We intend continuing to use Sound Therapy long-term with Khiara, because I would not want to stop or slow down when we have had these sorts of results.

'As I said, I don't think Sound Therapy is a cure but we definitely are really, really happy with the results. What we have got out of Khiara so far, we actually feel like we have got a little girl. She follows me up the hallway now, if I walk into another room. I hear footsteps and I turn around expecting to see her brother, and there is Khiara!'

You can see a light going on
Sharon and Jack – Sydney – 2001

Late language development

'I went and saw a paediatrician when Jack was very little and they couldn't find anything wrong. Jack wasn't talking, not until he was three. Then someone suggested that I go and do hearing tests; so I did that, and someone suggested a behavioural optometrist. I went and saw her, and she did a lot of testing on Jack and the first thing she said to me was, "How alternative are you?" I said "if it works, I'll do anything." She then gave me a list of people to go and see. One of them was a clinic where they did Sound Therapy, so that's how we started with Sound Therapy when he was about six.

'At six he was still a little delayed, verbally. He'd had a lot of speech therapy up until then, but the reading is what was keeping him back more than anything. That's when I noticed it was a real problem — it wasn't just speech. The speech therapist tried to teach him to read, but she got really frustrated with him. So we left there and I started looking into other things.

Right-left integration

'There was no definite diagnosis as to what was causing the problem. They just said it was an integration problem, between the left and right hemispheres of the brain. The only really noticeable effect was on his reading. That's what I really wanted to fix. But it wasn't until I started getting into other things, that I began noticing little things about him that could also be related to the integration problem. He had trouble with remembering nursery rhymes and things like that. That's about it, there was nothing major. Everyone we went and saw said he was such a bright little boy, that you didn't notice that there was anything else.

'He has a sister who is three years older, and they say that the reason he didn't talk until he was three is because she used to talk for him. It wasn't until she went to school that he started verbalising.

'Once he started Sound Therapy it sort of made things clearer for him. He was more patient and he enjoyed it. It made a lot of difference, he could recognise signs better and it was after that that we were able to start reading therapy with a tutor. We do Lindamood and spelling with a tutor now. But before doing Sound Therapy, it didn't matter how much you sat down and tried with him, the words just weren't sticking. They were letters and he knew his alphabet — but put them together and it might as well have been a foreign language. It just meant nothing once they were grouped together. But after Sound Therapy, we could actually start moving on. We did a special diet process and had supplements and that sort of thing. We went to a chiropractor and did work with kinesiology as well. Altogether, it really did help. *Patience*

'We've had tests done with the tutor and they show that his reading and his comprehension have improved by two years over about eight months, so he is now reading at the normal level for his age. *Improved reading age*

'I found that at the clinic we were attending they required us to do a lot of expensive tests. The Sound Therapy was offered only on a short-term basis and I felt he needed more, so I decided in the end to obtain the portable Sound Therapy program which Jack could use at home.

'The difference that Sound Therapy made is that you can see it's like a little light going on, and he concentrates better. Now that he's using Sound Therapy at home, he concentrates more on his homework; you don't have to keep drawing his attention back. Even if the TV's on, he'll *Concentration on homework* sit and do his homework. He loves using Sound Therapy and he uses it to relax at night. He says he thinks it really helps. He listens in the car too, going from place to place. He has it on to do his homework and watching TV. Eating dinner too, because we just put it in the pouch so he carries it around everywhere, and he wears it to bed. He just leaves them on, whatever he's doing — unless he's going to run around outside, then he'll take them off. Otherwise he has them in for hours if you let him. He'll even use them instead of a meditation tape that I sometimes play for him at bedtime.

'There's so much worth giving a go, and you have to find which one's right for your child. But Sound Therapy is just easy; they don't have to take anything. It's a soft way of going about it. They enjoy it and it really helps with homework. Homework is a really hard thing, that's why there's a lot of blues at home when a child's doing homework and it's just not working well. If you can give them an aid like that, it really helps them; it makes it easier for everybody.

'After seeing what happened with Jack and the difference it really can make, I decided to do kinesiology myself, mainly so I can muscle test. When he was on this strict diet he could only have a handful of things. I used to take *Muscle testing* him down the supermarket and I would muscle test for *for diet* everything. He'd hold it in his hand and I would muscle test whether it was good for him or not, and that's how I worked out what he could eat. It's easy, once you know how, it makes such a difference; it's not like reading a label all the time, you just put it in his hand and muscle test. When he was holding chocolate or junk food he'd just go limp. Same with immunisation, when they tested the little vials they had, Jack went like a rag doll; there was just no muscle testing happening at all. We think some of his integration problems might have to do with the immunisation. The muscle testing proved that there was nothing, his brain just totally shut down.

'I decided to get the Sound Therapy tapes to use at home because I thought it's a really good way of just keeping that edge; not having to go back and do the whole series again, but keeping up to date with it so he was working well.

'What I've noticed with other children and the difficulties today, is the more they try and put children in a box, the more there are that aren't fitting into it. There's a lot of kids with problems, and unless you know the problems they just look like kids. I can pick up some of the things, and either the parents don't know or don't want to do anything about it. The teachers just scream, "Ritalin" straight away. And that seems to be an easy fix these days; the parents don't want to go into all this, "what else could it be". It seems that with any type of learning disability, they just give Ritalin. Straight away they start saying, "Oh look, the kid won't concentrate — Ritalin." There are a lot of reasons why the child can't concentrate, and there's so many other ways they can go about it which are much less invasive, and without side effects.

'I think what is causing children to have trouble concentrating is the chemicals in everything; we can't breathe without ingesting chemicals. Our food, everything. We're just piling it into them and their systems aren't meant to cope with that. Plus, we expect too much, we want little geniuses all the time. We're not happy with a mediocre learner or a slow learner. So, the pressure's always on the kids and that makes it worse. The more I got Jack to read, the more his brain would just shut down — "snap" — like that.

Chemicals upset concentration

'To find the answer to that, we had to go through a lot of therapies to get him to come back on track. I think more parents should have a go, especially with simple things like this. It makes such a difference. It can always help, and it can't hurt. You don't know what your child's capable of, but rather than pushing them, an easy way is to do something like this.'

Gratified Grandmother
Theresa – Brisbane – 2001

'My granddaughter, Clara, had slow development. We think perhaps she went to school a little bit too early, initially. And then she actually struggled like mad, so we changed schools, sent her to a grammar school. And I gave her your tapes and she uses them every night. She just loved it for herself. She put them on and would just go to sleep with them. So she got her hours up pretty quickly.

Studying improved

253

You could see the change, it was terrific, she really came through and her studying improved out of sight.

'Clara was very frustrated with herself. She struggled with school, struggled with her friendships. Probably nothing that may not have come good in the end, who knows. It was just so good to sort it out at that time.

'She started using the Sound Therapy tapes when she was about six. I supposed she used them for two or three months at least, but she got a lot of hours out of it, because she used to fall asleep with them. They stopped *Nightmares* the nightmares, that was the one that she came through with. She got a good solid sleep with them, so therefore she wanted to use it. But now she's fine as far as her schoolwork goes, her reading. She's reading books. I've had her up in *Reading books* Sydney this week and she's devouring books, so it's really good.

Bladder 'When she was young she had a lot of bladder infections. *infections* She had a reduced immune system I'm sure. Why, I don't know; whether it was her mum smoked a bit when she was pregnant, I always put it down to that, but maybe not. It's very hard to tell, with each individual child.

'I think it helped her academically. I think maybe it quietened her down enough so that she could actually get a hold of what she was doing, whereas before she was skimming over the top because everything was going through so fast. Now you wouldn't know that — she's very different. I'm just so thrilled with her this weekend; she's just had a ball. She seems to be very well-adjusted, but I worried about her for so long. I could tell the difference. I'm not sure if her Mum could, but sometimes when you're close to a person, you don't see the wood for the trees anyway.

'I think it was just a general improvement. And once a general improvement comes through, everyone's satisfied and they all sit back and don't worry anymore. But I know at the time — yes, during 5, 6, 7 — she had lots of ups and downs. Recurring bladder infections that really flattened her out entirely. And tests, but nothing could be *Kidney disease* proved. See, we had a lot of kidney diseases in our family. My husband's mum and sister both died from it. And it's hereditary in the female side, so we were all a bit frantic about that. That all seemed to sort itself out too.

'Initially I thought she might have had a deafness problem, and that might have been causing it, but I don't think it was. It might have just been a developmental problem; some children are slower to learn than others. Of course, you often get ear problems with learning problems. If you can't hear, how can you learn?

'When we did the first lot, we could certainly see that we had achieved benefits. She used it mostly during sleep. She'd put it on at night, that seemed to be the easiest thing. When she went to bed she would put it on and she liked the music. And when she stayed with me, you'd go in at 12 o'clock and it would still be going, you'd turn it off. I had the first and second lot, the Basic kit and the Full Spectrum, and she went through most of those.

'Actually, when I first used it myself I did one tape and I found it really cleared your ears out, like you've had a good syringe. That's what it feels like anyway, because I do build up a lot of wax sometimes. I put it on for a couple of days and I felt as though the old ears were very crisp and clear.

Cleared out the ears

'I took them overseas with me and that was wonderful. I fly an awful lot around Australia and you find it's a waste of time, but if you stick your headsets on and away you go you're really not wasting the time at all. Also, for overseas flights you just get off feeling so good, I've never done that before! I always get off and go to bed for a week. But you don't seem to have to do that if you use your Sound Therapy on the plane.

Jet lag

'I guess you've got nothing to lose have you? If you feel like you've got a problem there. The advantages of doing it far outweigh the advantages of not doing it. I mean I'm not an expert on it by any means, I just know how it affects me. I know that I improved out of sight myself. But it was even more delighted with how Clara improved. And you find that if the children are stroppy and you put it on, if they stick with it a little while, they calm right down. Obviously it does have a big effect on children. I think it's a marvellous thing really. I wish I had known about it years ago.'

Sound Therapy helps counteract violence in Columbia

The following report was sent in by Miguel Olmos, Director of the Pallana Centre for the Development of Intelligence, which is dedicated to helping victims of crime and violence in Columbia. I was very moved by the commitment of these workers, and grateful that our program can be of help even in situations where the lives of children have been devastated by war.

Report on the use of Sound Therapy at the Pallana centre – Columbia – 2003

By Miguel Olmos Sanchez and Astrid Martinez Acosta

The world knows the situation in Columbia, a violent country torn by war. The effects of this impact drastically on our families, educators, children and adolescents.

Low cost treatment We thank Sound Therapy International for their assistance to the PALLANA Centre for the Development of Intelligence by making it possible to offer this treatment at a very low cost. It moves us greatly to see the improvement in understanding and love that this process has brought into the community.

We have begun offering Sound Therapy treatment at the centre, and we have been satisfied that our children and mature students have achieved the objectives that we have intended. The Sound Therapy has given people who have been victims of violence a new opportunity to revive their hopes and conquer their fears. The children have developed better concentration capacity, are able to learn more quickly, and their knowledge is increased so much that they are always asking to learn more.

Effects of violence Regrettably, ours is a country in the midst of war and violence and for this reason the needs of the community are big. One of the aims of our centre is to be able to multiply our knowledge to share with other people who practice similar professional ethics. The children who we work with have been mistreated, or violated; many have permanently lost their families, or lost parts of their body. We apply every possible therapeutic support in our centre to prepare our children so that they can leave these difficulties behind and find new options in life.

256

We work with the international project Risciliencia, *I have,*
(Resilience) based on four principles: I have, I am, I know *I am,*
and I can. In our centres we find that one of the most *I know,*
valuable things we can offer children is to be able to balance *I can*
their brain with music.

In the last two years we have worked with forty children
and adults. Today we report on four cases:

First case

Name: Julian Andrés Rojas Batista Age: 11 Years.
Grade: 4 of Primary.

Neurological Diagnosis:

Difficulty of attention, school apathy and manipulative *Apathy*
behaviours to avoid investing his own effort.

Psychological Diagnosis:

- Alteration in basic devices of learning, restlessness,
  dispersed attention, syllabic reading, confused grammar,
  difficulty in solving problems.
- Difficulties regarding identity, recognition of self inside
  the family and educational group. Difficulty feeling
  connected with the surrounding world and with other
  people.
- Tendency to be reserved, to close up inside himself.
- Experiences a disconnection between practical and
  conceptual thought.

Treatment: Psychological Support and Sound Therapy.

Duration: 3 Months

Sessions: 3 Per week of Sound Therapy.

Results:

- Better results at sensory-perceptive level.
- He works with greater interest and responsibility.
- His understanding of written expression has
  improved.
- Significant achievements in concentration level and
  attention.
- The difficulty in appropriate affective relating
  has improved as he achieved greater security and
  motivation.

- Considerable changes to co-ordination level and balance.
- Integration in the school group.
- Positive results in conduct and deportment.

Second Case

Name: Ivan Javier Ariza

History: Bilateral Blindness, hipoxia from firearm wound, guerilla fighter takes him to the courthouse where she acts as Judge. Visual difficulty.

Psychological Diagnosis:

Speech and language problems — Presents aphasia, characterised by difficulty in nomination, analysis, mathematical processes, comprehension of reading, writing ability and habituation for neurological sequencing, accident to vocal chords hinders speaking ability.

Treatment: Duration: 3 weekly sessions of 1 hour.
- 1 hour: occupational therapy.
- 1 hour: Counselling
- 1 Hour: Sound Therapy.

Results:
- Significant changes at level of thought processes manifested in his communication.
- Better visual fixation and field amplification.
- Improvement in integration patterns of large and small motor skills.
- Better level in memory and concentration.

Third case

Name: María Paula Landinez   Age: 10 Years

Diagnosis:

ADHD
- Neurological Diagnosis: Hyperactivity with dispersed attention.
- Pedagogic Diagnosis: Lower than average academic performance, repetition of grades.

Treatment:
- Psychological Support, Sound Therapy, Occupational Therapy.
- Duration: 3 Months.

Results: Considerably diminished activity; longer attention span, better academic performance.

The treatment began during one month without Sound Therapy. After having begun Sound Therapy, for a duration of a month and half; revised assessment in the centre and the school reported: Improvement every day, with a proportion of 35%.

Fourth Case
Names: Juan Carlos Bustamante - Juan Manuel Heredia   Age: 10 and 11 years.

Diagnosis: Psychological diagnosis: Separation from parents and loss of all possessions in the town of Santander due to guerrilla fighter units.

Trauma — Disassociation

Pedagogic diagnosis: the children seemed unable to listen, unable to understand, and spent their time tossing balls.

Treatment: Sound Therapy. Duration: 3 months

Results:

Behaviour: They are now observed to be connected with the environment. They respond to what they are asked. They share a little more with their friends. They still remain isolated a lot of the time.

Academic results: They improve their thought processes and interest in their work.

Observations: If we say that initially the children were functioning at only 10% of their capacity, they have ascended now to 70%. The improvement was observed as something miraculous. We are convinced of the effectiveness of this therapy.

Chapter 9

WHAT'S THIS ON MY PLATE?

WHAT AM I GUNNA DO, DOC? HE'S DEVELOPED AN INTOLERANCE FOR PIES, CHIPS AND PIZZAS!

Living naturally

Anthony was a bubbly energetic baby, but he had a lot of colds and ear infections which seemed to be triggered especially by vaccinations. He grew into an active, happy toddler, but he couldn't concentrate. He rarely slept through the night, and when he was four his mother found out he had ADHD. In the next few years they battled mood swings, truancy, learning difficulties and vandalism. She joined the ADHD support group when Anthony was eight, and finally had friends who understood what she was going through, and that it wasn't just because of her parenting. She dismissed the idea of following a special diet because she had tried eliminating foods and it made no difference. Besides she didn't want to spend all her time in the kitchen cooking up funny recipes. However when she heard some other mums' experiences she decided to give the full elimination diet a go and find out for sure. She did this with the support of a doctor and a nutritionist who understood the process, so she had plenty of advice when she ran into hitches. What she discovered was that Anthony was intolerant of salicylates found in certain fruits and vegetables, and his dad was intolerant of amines found in cheese, chocolate, and some fermented foods. When she followed a simple but delicious menu, provided by her dietician, which was free of these ingredients, Anthony was so much easier to manage, the family never looked back. She also learned that her chronic dermatitis was caused by sodium lauryl sulfate, a harsh detergent used in most skin care products, and when she switched to a friendlier brand of skin care, the problem went away.

There's nothing like Mum's cooking

Feeding the family is one of Mum's most important roles, and one of the things for which mums are remembered, loved and idealised. Nothing is ever as good as Mum's cooking! But for many mothers, cooking is a drag, and today many avoid it by using the vast array of convenience foods now available. Food has become a complex issue today with hundreds of diets on offer, and the debate about food sensitivities and whether diet can help with learning disabilities can be quite confusing. Parents feel they have little say about what their children eat since TV advertising, the school canteen, peer pressure and other people's parties play such a big role.

I hope this chapter will give you the information and conviction to know how changing diet might help your children, and some useful tips on implementing those changes. Taking cooking back into your own hands may be the most loving and effective way to help your children and show them your love. Using food effectively to make your family healthier and more together can be one of the most rewarding and important aspects of parenting. Dads can help too!

I will also address the issue of medication, to what extent it should be used, the advantages, the pitfalls and where it might fit in your scheme of rehabilitation. And then I will look at other environmental impacts on our children such as ultrasound and vaccination.

Food is full of dangerous chemicals today

Our Western diet has changed dramatically since the 1950s. Many foods contain chemical additives, which lengthen their shelf-life and make them look and feel more appealing. They have added sugar and salt to increase their addictiveness and saleability. Animals are fed growth hormones, antibiotics and chemicals throughout their lives, plus they are given food grown with chemicals. Fruits and vegetables are treated with artificial fertilizers, sprayed with pesticides, irradiated, picked unripe, transported long distances, and grown hydroponically in only water and chemicals, no soil.

Nutrition

The concept that we get all our nutritional needs from a balanced diet is no longer valid. For one thing, very few Westerners today eat a balanced diet. It is almost impossible to stay away from unhealthy additives in food. It is very difficult to obtain foods which contain the mineral concentration that they should have. Also our body's need for nutrients increases due to the toxic environment we live in. Toxic chemicals are found in our food, water, air, plastics, packaging, cars, mattresses, furniture, clothing, renovation materials, paint, grouting, leather treatment, cleaning agents, shampoos, cosmetics, bubble bath, toothpaste, insecticides — everything.[1]

We don't get enough nutrition from our polluted food

What children eat today is horrifying

Many children drink up to three soft drinks per day. There are up to sixteen spoonfuls of sugar in each soft drink. These children will have major changes in their blood sugar levels within twelve hours. Breakfast might be sugar-coated cereal or a granola bar, which is no better; or pancakes or waffles covered with syrup (unbalanced carbohydrates and more sugar.) Lunch often goes uneaten, except for dessert. It may be processed cheese and white bread, and there are no real nutrients in that. Most children with learning problems do not eat fruit and vegetables. So even if we could get all our nutrients from a balanced diet, who today actually eats one?

Children eat too much junk

Our bodies have to work harder and harder to deal with the toxic load we are burdened with. The liver needs a full complement of nutrients in order to detoxify the body of chemicals. No wonder we need more nutrients today than we did fifty years ago.

Those with sensitivities may be exhibiting the 'canary principle'. They are the first to go down, but we should all heed the warning that our environment is becoming unsafe to live in.

This is the philosophy of environmental medicine, a new and rapidly growing field in response to the

Our environment is making us sick

proliferation and increase of environmentally related diseases, which include ADHD, autism, asthma, arthritis, cancer and diabetes.

Environmental medicine is a highly complex field, examining the impact not only of chemical toxins added to food, air and water, but also the cumulative effect of these on the immune system in combination with viruses and immune-compromising diseases such as giardia, glandular fever, tick bites, et cetera.

Many people are only alerted to this important field of health care when they realise that someone in their family has developed food sensitivities. Food sensitivities are likely to run in families; whether due to genetics or shared chemical exposure, is still to be seen.

Children with ADHD often have younger brothers with stomach problems.

Chemical toxins can cause ADHD

Eve Hillary, author of the horrifying and enlightening book, *Children of a Toxic Harvest,* details how her son was born with ADHD after he was heavily exposed to Diazonon, due to her dipping sheep while she was eight months pregnant with him. After multiple chemical exposures on their farm, she came down with chronic fatigue at the same time her son emerged, bouncing with hyperactivity.[2] This dreadful combination is all too common in today's chemically saturated world. It was only after ten years of struggle — going from practitioner to practitioner, marriage breakdown and health nightmare — that Eve found some answers. When she finally found an environmental doctor who understood the problem, she could start identifying foods and chemicals which were triggering their over-taxed systems — and begin using supplements to help the liver to detoxify.

Colloidal (liquid) minerals help us get rid of toxins

Unless the liver can process and eliminate the chemicals, they stay in the body, Eve explains. For each chemical the liver must process, it needs a corresponding enzyme. It can only make that enzyme if it can find the right trace minerals, and if these aren't in the body, it can't be done. Therefore, colloidal minerals, a liquid-based, highly bio-available form of over sixty essential trace minerals were her saving grace. Minerals are essential for life, health and the ongoing performance of the body's myriad complex interactions. Since they are no longer in our soils, they are no longer in our food, so it is essential for everyone today to supplement these minerals to sustain optimum health.

Beginning to supplement your child's diet with colloidal minerals and a high quality chewable multi-vitamin and mineral supplement is an easy first step you can take, whether or not you go on to apply the other ideas in this chapter.

Giving your child supplements is easy

Medical journalist Phillip Day has written extensively on the increasing environmental threats to our health today and the importance of supplementation to combat these dangers.[3]

Indicators that diet may help

Food intolerance is commonly associated with ADHD. Children with sleeping difficulties and allergic-type food reactions have been found to respond well to diet. If there is a family history of eczema, or any recognised response to foods, it is likely that diet will help.

Kids with ADHD can often be helped by diet

Which countries are looking into diet

American researchers into ADHD have lost interest in diet and are now focussing on other things. However, recent research from Britain suggests that lack of manageability may be aggravated by food sensitivity.

There is more interest in diet in Australia and the UK than in the US

Most information now being published in the United States by researchers, doctors, and therefore, ADHD support groups, dismisses dietary control as irrelevant. This is unfortunate, since for those motivated parents diet is a highly effective, significant means of removing the causes of many problems. Sue Dengate has shared the benefits of dietary change with practical, personally-based insight and detail in her book, *Different Kids*. In her experience working with other mothers in a support group, she found that most children do best on a combination of medication and dietary management.

Support for dietary management is actually growing in the UK and Australia. For more detail on how the diet field was mistakenly dismissed by some researchers, see Sue Dengate's book. One doctor she quotes had previously dismissed diet for a particular family. Later he stayed with the family as a friend, and wrote, 'the child's response to foods became much plainer to me in my living room than it had in the clinic.'[4] Of course it is impossible in a short clinic visit to observe a child's behaviour and reactions as accurately as the mother can at home.

Diet is too hard

If diet has failed you before, read on
It can be a daunting idea to change the diet of not just your child but, by necessity, your whole family. You may have tried it before and found it didn't work. You may have decided that medication or other treatments are easier. But please don't despair. The information which follows may give you a new appreciation of the role which diet plays in learning and general well-being for your child, and in your own sense of balance, fitness and happiness, as well. Here, I hope to debunk a few diet myths that may have been detrimentally affecting your life for decades.

Changing your diet is easier than living with an impossible child
In order to determine which foods may be causing a reaction, you will need to undertake an elimination diet, which will enable you to observe the effects of each food one at a time. The hardest part of doing the elimination diet (according to Sue Dengate, who has perfected the method with her own children), is deciding to start. Certainly it is hard to change your eating habits, and those of your children. However, as those who have succeeded can point out, it is far easier to change your eating habits than to live with a constantly demanding and unmanageable child. The advantages of using diet are that there are no side effects and the benefits last twenty-four hours a day, not just until the medication wears off.

Find a dietician who believes in the Elimination Diet
To undertake the complete elimination diet it is important to have the supervision and support of a doctor and a dietician experienced in this field. Co-operation between parent and child is essential, as there are many challenges which it will be too hard for the mother to cope with on her own. Contact your local ADHD support group for referrals. I also highly recommend reading Sue Dengate's book, *Different Kids,* as a reference guide and motivational tool.

Reward children for sticking to the diet
Getting children to stick to their diet is always a challenge, and Sue Dengate in her book gives many useful tips on how to do this — such as small rewards, regular acknowledgement, and starting out with discussion and a co-operative approach. She also gives some useful guides for replacement foods, and some tried and true basic recipes to

get you started. If diet seems to have failed in your family, please read her book before making a final conclusion.

One of your biggest enemies in changing to healthier eating, is television. During children's programming, children are bombarded with ads for junk food, which of course makes compliance to their diet more difficult. Limit TV to educational programs or favourite programs, as part of a reward system. When you watch TV as a family, point out to your children how the ads are manipulating them into wanting to buy things. This will give them back a sense of control, so it's you and them against the advertisers — instead of the advertisers and your kids against you.

Get savvy about junk food adds on TV

Getting children to eat

One way to encourage children to eat their meal is to have a structure. Everyone is required to sit at the table and make interesting conversation. A great routine to improve family communication and make mealtime more interesting, is to ask each person in the family to state what was their high and low for the day. For example a high might be, 'Suzy said she is still my friend' or, 'I got a star for my maths homework' or, 'going swimming'. A low might be, 'I got ratty after lunch when I ate too much chocolate' or, 'the teacher roused on me for not doing my homework' or, 'the kids in the playground picked on me for no reason.' Adults might share a high such as, 'I had fun playing with Tim (the toddler) this afternoon' or, 'I enjoyed my yoga class' or 'I got all the washing done' or, 'I got a promotion at work.' A low might be, 'I felt really tired 'cause the baby woke up five times last night' or, 'the car broke down.' Make sure everyone has a turn. Its OK to have a little conversation or to draw people out more about their 'high' and 'low' as long as you get back to the process and everyone gets their turn.

Dinner time is family time — what was your 'high' and 'low' today?

Once your child experiences the benefit of being balanced, healthy, able to concentrate, achieve at school and make friends, he will probably ask you to help him stick to his diet.

Kids like discipline

Your child appreciates you providing the discipline he cannot provide for himself. My mother was permissive in many ways and decided to let us, as children, eat all

Kids need us to set limits

the sweets and chocolate we wanted so that we wouldn't feel deprived. Then she went through a period of being very concerned about our health, and banned us from having sweets because they were bad for us. At one level, I welcomed this limit because I wanted to be healthy and I knew this rule was coming from her wanting the best for us. However, adult friends thought it too severe and used to sneak us chocolate when she wasn't looking. I didn't have the assertiveness to say 'no', but secretly wished they wouldn't. When my mother found out, she removed the ban and said we could have all the sweets we wanted again. I was secretly disappointed, but unable to express this at such a young age, so I went along with the peer pressure from my sister and friends. I would have preferred responsible adult limitations to help me look after my health.

Order of sensitivities

Which chemicals are the worst? It is useful to know which substances are the most frequent culprits in sensitivities. A study by Anne Swain, et al, in 1985 found the most common sensitivity was to salicylates; followed by preservatives, artificial colours, amines and Monosodium Glutamate (MSG).

Additives to watch out for
Artificial colours and flavours

Read all labels Studies show that the highest number of children react to food colourings and preservatives. If these provoke such a great reaction in so many children, wouldn't it be wiser if we all avoided them? They are likely to be detrimental to your family's health whether there is a specific reaction or not, so it is a good idea to start by cutting them out.

One example is a yellow food colouring, tartrazine, found in sweet mustard pickle. In carefully controlled, double-blind placebo studies, this substance was found to produce increased irritability, restlessness and sleep disturbances in some children with ADHD.[5] The natural colour, annatto (code 160b) can also cause reactions in some children.

Some parents find that when they remove colours and preservatives, the child starts sleeping through the night *Tinned pears* immediately.

are safer than Rather than giving up one colour of cordial and *cordial* deciding the other colours are probably OK, why not use

Sue Dengate's trick of making a safe drink out of tinned pear pulp and water.

However, cutting out additives may not be enough. When a child has a sensitivity reaction to additives it is likely that the child will also react to some food substances. One study found that 80% of children who reacted to additives were also sensitive to foods like chocolate and tomato sauce.[6]

282 or calcium propionate

282 is one of the worst culprits. This is a mould inhibitor used in bread. Though it must be labelled, be aware that labelling is not always accurate. Quantities may be increased in the summer months when grain is more likely to go off. It is used in most bread packed in plastic because the bread is sliced and placed straight in the packet while still warm and is prone to mould. Sue Dengate reports how she was caught out when a previously safe brand of bread started using this ingredient, but she was not aware of it for some months. They were using up old packaging which did not accurately report the ingredients. Then, in the summer months, they increased the quantity. She could not understand why her child was reacting!

Bread wrapped in plastic may be a hazard

On another occasion she was buying a bread labelled, 'All natural, no preservatives.' But noticed her daughter was showing many symptoms related to 282, which had been previously overcome with diet. She rang the bakery and the flour mills many times over several weeks, before discovering that during the summer months only, they added an extra ingredient which was not listed on the packaging. This was a whey powder which produces calcium propionate as a by product. Although the amount was only half that used in preserved bread, it was enough to affect her highly sensitive child. This shows that you just can't be too careful! As soon as they stopped using the bread, her child made noticeable improvement at school.

MSG Monosodium glutamate

MSG is a flavour enhancer which occurs naturally in most foods. Those with high levels include cheeses, mushrooms, tomatoes, stock cubes, sauces, and meat and yeast extracts. Pure MSG is also used as an additive to enhance flavour, particularly in Chinese restaurants. Many children need to avoid the additive, and some may need to avoid the naturally occurring substance too.

Are there carcinogens in your bathroom?

Is this bathroom safe? Be aware that many ingredients used in personal care products, skin care products, and standard bathroom and cleaning products, may contain harmful chemicals. Perfume is the item most likely to produce a reaction in large numbers of sensitive people. Most commercial bathroom products contain sodium lauryl sulfate or sodium lauryth sulfate, and propylene glycol. These chemicals denature protein, so they are not suitable for use by humans. In fact, sodium lauryl sulfate is widely used in trials to intentionally produce a skin reaction. There is evidence that these chemicals often cause skin reactions; and also that they accumulate in the organs, affecting the liver, kidneys and possibly eyesight, in the long term. Many ingredients in commercial personal care products are known carcinogens, but companies do not remove them because of the cost of safer alternatives. Even brands which claim to be 'all natural' may contain these harmful chemicals.

Convert your bathroom to safe products The good news is, there is one company which was formed for the express purpose of making bathrooms safe, and which provides effective and affordable alternatives for health conscious families. That is, Neways International. Neways has a commitment, backed up by fifteen years of research and successful product development, to provide safe products, free of known carcinogens, for family use. Their shower gel, shampoos, bubble bath, moisturisers, et cetera, can be used with confidence that your bathroom is a safe place for your children. They also have a full range of cosmetics and high quality skin care. An excellent resource book based on scientific research on the dangers of day to day chemicals in the home is, *Unreasonable Risk: How to avoid cancer from cosmetics and personal care products* by Samuel Epstein M.D. founder and chairman of the Cancer Prevention Coalition and co-author of the *Safe Shoppers, Bible*.[7] A quick easy reference booklet for families called *Cancer-Causing Chemicals* can help you avoid toxic products in your weekly shopping. Look in the back of this book for more details on this booklet and how to obtain safe bathroom products.

Dr Epstein explains in his book:

'Cosmetic and personal care industries worldwide are, for all intents and purposes, unregulated by government and essentially self-regulating....While nearly all nations require ingredient labelling, this is uninformative and tokenistic at best. The soup of complex chemical names of labelled ingredients, with few common names, is meaningless to consumers. The majority of toxicologists, public health and cancer prevention experts also have trouble deciphering these labels in the absence of any accompanying warning on the carcinogenic or other hazards of the named ingredients.' [8]

It is very difficult therefore to choose safe products off the shelf by reading the labels yourself. As just one example, the ubiquitous Sodium lauryl sulfate can be hidden under another name, as it can be made from a derivative of coconut oil. It is safer, therefore, to go with a well-informed and trusted company which has been investigated by the likes of Dr Epstein.

In a 1997 address to the US Congress, Senator Edward M Kennedy said:

'The 1997 FDA reform bill exempting cosmetics from state regulation is utterly irresponsible. The cosmetic industry has borrowed a page from the playbook of the tobacco industry, by putting profits ahead of public health.... Our message today is that cosmetics can be dangerous to your health. Yet this greedy industry wants to prevent the American people from learning that truth.' Also Ref 7

Australian chemical safety regulations are often found to be of a lower standard than those in the US.

Foods to watch out for

Many ADHD children are fussy eaters suffering from a condition dubbed 'appetite disturbance' by the original ADHD diet proponent, Dr Serfontein. Noticeable thirst is sometimes part of ADHD.

Not all vegetables are safe for ADHD kids

Salicylates

Eating a diet high in vegetables is great, as a general rule. It is always important for one's health to eat freshly

271

prepared vegetables, rather than highly processed fast foods. However, if your child is sensitive to salicylates you will have to choose which vegetables are suitable.

Salicylates are found in high concentrations in the following foods: broccoli, eggplant, tomato paste, button mushrooms, avocado, olives, salami, stone fruits, berries, grapes and fruit juices. Be aware that products containing fruit, such as fruit-flavoured yoghurt, also contain salicylates.

The vegetables which are lower in salicylates tend to be the old fashioned ones your grandmother used to cook, such as peas, beans, lettuce, brussels sprouts, cabbage, celery, carrots, peeled potatos, pumpkin, sweet potato, asparagus, beetroot and parsnip. Add to that list, chives, chokos, leeks, lentils, mungbean sprouts, parsley, shallots, swedes and garlic. The only fruits which are low in salicylates are peeled ripe pears and pears canned in syrup. The traditional meat-and-three-veg diet can work well if you are sensitive to salicylates. For more information on salicylates see, *Friendly Food* by Dr Anne Swain, et al, Murdoch books Sydney 1991. It is very difficult to eliminate salicylates on a vegetarian diet. Note, also, that it is important for vegetarians to be aware of getting enough regular protein. See the section below on controlling insulin. What may appear to be hypoglycaemic symptoms may in fact be triggered by salicylate intolerance.

Amines

Fermentation can be a problem.

Amines are produced by fermentation, or protein breakdown. Therefore fresh protein foods like meat, fresh seafood and eggs are low in amines; but if the food is overcooked, processed or aged amines may occur. A large amount of amines occur in cheese, chocolate, wines, beer, yeast extracts and fish products. Some fresh fruits — bananas, paw paw, avocado and tomatoes — also contain amines.

Wheat

Reactions to wheat are becoming more common among adults and children. Some people do better on rye or spelt (now readily available in health food stores), but the apparent wheat reaction may also be linked to excess carbohydrates (see 'Controlling Insulin', below.) My older sister, who exhibited very mild autistic tendencies, was a difficult child to manage, and had started life as a colicky baby. Desperate and sleep deprived, my parents had tried everything possible before a doctor recommended that my mother, who was still breastfeeding, should give up wheat. The colic stopped immediately and my sister began sleeping through the night.

Sugar

Sugar has been under suspicion for years as a major cause of ADHD. However, research evidence is suggesting that a reaction to sweet foods is more likely to be a result of the natural chemicals or salicylates, rather than the sugar.[9] Many parents are convinced their children react to sugar, but have not investigated carefully enough. Symptoms assumed to be hypoglycaemic reactions may in fact be food intolerances. This is not to say that children should be allowed to go overboard with sugar. Children who eat a lot of sweet, sugary foods may tend to snack constantly between meals, and are probably high on too much insulin due to not having their protein and carbohydrate intake properly balanced. Their blood sugar is actually out of balance from too much unmatched carbohydrate. (See 'Controlling Insulin', below). Restrict them to snacks combining low-fat protein, good carbohydrates (such as fruit or carrots) and a few almonds for suitable fats, as recommended in the Zone diet below. You may well then see that the out of control, hypoglycaemic behaviour will probably stop.

Sugar hides in surprising places

Even if sugar doesn't specifically affect your child's behaviour, its consumption is way out of control in today's addictive, fast food diet. The greatest quantities of sugar are hidden in foods we don't suspect, so choosing more natural, home-prepared foods is a great way to cut down on unwanted sugar. Our carbohydrates should be taken in a healthier form. When children eat too much sugar it ruins their taste and enjoyment of fruits and vegetables, but this will quickly return if you cut out sugar and artificial sweeteners. Other artificial sweeteners such as saccharine and aspartame are being questioned as having potential health risks. Most children today are so used to sweet drinks that they refuse to drink water. However, thirst is on your side. Remove sweet drinks from the house, get a water

273

filter, and teach them the health benefits of drinking water. Model what you say and they will learn from you.

It is important to learn to read labels. Potatoes should not be frozen. The additives they use to make them reconstitute to their right texture are harmful. Dextrose, in frozen potato products, is actually a sweetener. Sugar is added to almost all commercial foods to make them more palatable. Beware of 'low fat' foods. Many of them have added sugar to make them tastier.

Milk

Milk could have all sorts of nasties in it

Apparent reactions to milk may be due to the flavours or other additives, as in the case of flavoured milk. Milk may be found to contain the following carcinogenic toxins: DDT, Dieldrin, Heptachlor, Hexachlorobenzine, antibiotics and recombinant Bovine Growth Hormone.[10] It may be advisable to seek out a source of organic milk if your family uses milk. There is a curious finding that certain delinquents have been observed to drink enormous quantities of milk each day. It is unknown whether this is due to a psychological need for the mother, a habit developed from a history of poor nutrition, or an addiction related to a food intolerance. There is often a tendency for learning-disabled children to have food cravings, to crave the foods they are reactive to, and to obsessively want to eat huge quantities of just one food.

Do it early and get it right!

Working mothers and mothers who have ADHD themselves are less likely to notice the connection between food and learning difficulties.

Food can affect you just like a drug

Sue Dengate's message in her excellent and comprehensive book on diet and ADHD is 'never underestimate the power of food chemicals .' Despite a high level of awareness, having four kids in her family with ADHD and the fact that she always took a great interest in diet and worked with diet control from the early days, she did not identify her daughter's reaction to salicylates for six years because she was put off the scent by unsupportive professionals. Her advice is to do the food elimination diet, do it early and do it right.

Many families try various diets without full

understanding or professional support, and conclude that they don't work. However, when these same families try the diet again under proper supervision and with correct information, they get a different result. It is often the case that medication helps the teacher, but diet helps more at home.

One mum wanted to stop the diet after a week because she didn't think it was helping, until her youngest son told her that it was the first week his brother hadn't hit him after school. Sue Dengate believes that both diet and medication together may be necessary, in some cases, to deal with all symptoms.

'Clutching at straws'

Doctors who are more committed to a drug treatment model sometimes say that using diet to control ADHD is 'clutching at straws'. This is inaccurate, since there is plenty of evidence that this approach can work if done correctly. However, selecting just one food which you may suspect and eliminating that is certainly 'clutching at straws'. Chances are that you will miss some instances of the food by this method, and you may not be addressing the most important foods or environmental factors. This is not to say that for some families just cutting out the most known offenders won't work. This may be quite sufficient in many cases, and is more likely to be successful if combined with a diet which correctly balances protein, carbohydrate and fats, so that hormone levels remain steady. Some of the most obvious foods to cut out are artificial additives, tomato sauce, cordial, fruit juice, chocolate, vegemite and honey.

When you change your diet, be organised

Researchers have found that mothers often fail to make the link between diet and behaviour. This does not mean it isn't there, it may just be hidden by delayed reactions or the complexity of eliminating certain substances consistently.

The 'few foods' diet

If you are going to do the thorough elimination diet, you need to start from a base of likely non-reactive foods. The 'few foods' diet is used as the base from which reactions can be tested. It consists of two meats, usually lamb and turkey; two carbohydrates, perhaps rice and potato; two

Start with only the safest foods

275

fruits, often banana and pear; and a range of root and green vegetables, bottled water, sunflower oil and milk-free margarine, such as Nuttelex.

Hypoglycaemia

It is easy to diagnose hypoglycaemia. If the child is shaky and irritable when hungry, with sudden mood changes, and calms down when fed, that is enough of a diagnosis. A glucose tolerance test is not needed.

Always give protein with a snack

The solution is quite simple — make sure the child never gets hungry. Eliminate refined carbohydrates, soft drinks, candy, pies and cakes. Have the child eat several small meals a day. Have protein for breakfast, not sugary cereals. Children do not have to have conventional breakfast foods. They could have leftovers from the night before. The child should have a snack every two hours. Nut butter sandwiches without added sugar, 'trail mix' with nuts seeds and dried fruit are good. These foods will break down slowly, and this helps to keep the blood sugar levels stable.

If the child is informed, and helped to see the results, most children make sensible food choices. They will want to choose well, once they realise how certain foods affect them.

Controlling Insulin with food

Balance protein and carbohydrates to avoid excess insulin

One of the most important discoveries about diet to be made in the last fifteen years was by Dr Barry Sears, author of the bestselling book, The Zone, and several sequels.[11] Dr Sears' approach to eating is based on balancing hormone functions in the body by reactivating the pancreas. His information shows how errors made in public knowledge about food explain, in part, the tremendous increase in the last two decades in heart disease and diabetes, in spite of the western world's war on fat. The big error has been in overloading ourselves with carbohydrates! The Zone diet aims for balance, and is quite a different approach to something like the Atkins diet, which allows the eating of large quantities of saturated fats.

Carbohydrates stimulate insulin production. The role of insulin is to take excess carbohydrates and lock them into fatty tissue where they stay until the right dietary conditions allow the body to burn up that fat. The right dietary conditions occur when the hormone, glucagon, is produced in sufficient quantities to control insulin levels. This happens when we have a balance of low-fat protein and carbohydrate. Protein stimulates glucagon, carbohydrate stimulates insulin. To have the two balanced we need the right proportions of low-fat protein and carbohydrate at every meal. However, at least 75% of the carbohydrate should be in the form of fresh fruit and vegetables because they enter the blood stream much more slowly than grains and starches.

Good fat helps you to burn fat

The third essential element of the diet is to consume a small amount of 'good fat' with each meal. Dr Sears explains that you must consume fat to burn fat. Good fats are found in avocados, almonds, pistachios, macadamia nuts, olive oil and flax-seed oil. When you learn to keep your insulin level balanced, you are in what Dr Sears calls 'The Zone' — meaning you are mentally alert, energised, focussed and ready for anything. It is easy, in a short space of time, to achieve and maintain this state using the simple steps set out in his books, *The Zone* and *Mastering the Zone*. An easy rule of thumb for preparing meals is to eat a protein portion which will fit on the palm of your hand, and twice that portion of carbohydrate (in the form of fruit and vegetables), plus a spoonful of good fat. This easy measure system applies to any person, old or young, fat or thin. The protein portion, however, should be increased for highly active people, pregnant or nursing mothers and children. Most important, the diet must be made up of mainly fresh food with lots of fresh vegetables and quality low-fat protein, such as fish, which contains important fatty acids. The great advantages of this diet are: you lose weight, you are never hungry, you achieve high energy and what Dr Sears calls 'Super Health', and it prevents heart disease, diabetes, cancer and some of the symptoms of ADHD. It is advisable to read one of Dr Sears' books if you plan to follow the diet, to ensure that you do it correctly. It will give you a solid foundation of understanding on which to base food preparation for your family, whether or not any of you have food intolerances.

Dr Conners and a co-worker undertook a study in 1983 to test the effect of different types of breakfast on ADHD kids. Hyperactive children were found to perform

The right balance helps ADHD kids

277

much better on a breakfast which combined protein (such as eggs) with carbohydrate, than on a pure carbohydrate breakfast. This gives confirmation that the 'Zone' approach could help children with ADHD.[12]

Supplements

The nervous system needs to be nourished with sensory stimulation, oxygen and high quality nutrition in order to function optimally. While the 'Zone' diet takes care of the macro-nutrients, the micro-nutrients may still be deficient. This is why I, along with most naturopaths and environmental doctors, believe supplementation is so important in today's world.

The support of a properly balanced diet can be greatly enhanced with good quality nutritional supplements. Even if your child eats well, today's polluted environment means we requires greater nutrients to allow the body to detoxify from the chemicals which build up in the system. One of the biggest causes of disease today is a lack of the essential trace minerals which are responsible for thousands of important bodily functions. There are sixty minerals which the body needs in varying quantities to support optimum immunity, digestion, respiration, lymphatic drainage, and sensory integration. These are best accessed in the form of a colloidal mineral supplement which is derived from plant matter and comes in a liquid form that is easily absorbed by the body. It should also contain fulvic acid to make it easy for the body to utilise. In addition, a growing child needs high levels of antioxidants and the right mix of vitamins. The antioxidants will be more effective if they use extracts of natural substances which have a high concentration of antioxidants. These include ginko biloba, grape seed, pine bark and curcuminoids. For the best results, it is important to find products which contain all of these ingredients. A high quality, chewable children's multivitamin tablet will provide the right proportions.

Calcium may work as an antidote to hyperactive food reactions, and can also work on the 'lethargic and withdrawn' reaction to food intolerance. It can be useful to take a daily calcium supplement or one which combines calcium, magnesium, phosphorus and potassium, along with vitamin D3 for better absorption.

Some mothers have found that red meat and lecithin help to calm ADHD children by supplying important amino acids. Eggs also contain the full complement of essential amino acids.

It can beneficial to use high a quality fish oil capsule which contains the right balance of necessary oils; but be sure it is known to be free of the toxins which may appear in fresh ocean fish. Good quality products will contain omega 3 marine triglycerides, linolenic, oleic and linoleic acids, which are derived from a combination of: natural fish oil, evening primrose oil, safflower oil and linseed oil.

Sometimes individuals discover one particular mineral or amino acid that is helpful in some cases of ADHD. However, one should not lose sight of the fact that a balance of all essential nutrients is what the body needs. If these come from appropriate, natural sources, the body will only use what it needs so there is no danger of oversupply. To read an example of the effect of quality supplements on a child with ADHD, see Liz Rayner's story in Chapter 8. Feel free to contact Sound Therapy International or one of our distributors for the latest information on supplements suitable for children.

An intolerance is not an allergy

There is a distinct medical difference between a food allergy and a food intolerance, and it is important to understand this distinction when talking to doctors. Doctors hate mothers talking about 'food allergies' when what they really mean is 'intolerances'. An allergy can be a very serious condition, even life-threatening. It occurs in individuals who are genetically predisposed to develop certain antibodies, which are called Immunoglobulin E (IgE). The environmental allergen — the food substance, pollen or dust mite — reacts with the body's own IgE antibodies and produces histamine, or other such substances. These cause the sometimes severe reactions associated with allergy, ranging from difficulty breathing to severe shock. Allergic reactions to food are generally immediate, and vary from swelling, itching, burning sensations in the mouth and throat, to vomiting, cramps or diarrhoea. Children may have a reaction to a substance that causes a skin rash, which only becomes apparent after the offending substance has been removed. The foods most commonly associated with

He's not allergic, just intolerant

allergies include eggs, peanuts, milk, wheat and fish. Most children grow out of their allergies by the age of five, but occasionally they are sustained through adulthood.

Food intolerance is different in that it does not involve an immune reaction but occurs when people have a reaction to food chemicals as though they are drugs. This is called a pharmacological reaction. These reactions are often delayed and therefore harder to notice. The reactions are also related to the size of the dose and may differ considerably in different circumstances. Food intolerances do tend to run in families but each member may display different symptoms to the same foods.

Reaction time

Sometimes a food reaction builds up slowly Reaction might happen the next day and result in the child being irritable all day. Or it may take longer and be much harder to observe. Many parents are fooled by thinking a reaction is obvious and easy to recognise. Don't fall into the trap of suspecting that the last food eaten is the cause of the reaction.

Sue Dengate explains that there are three types of reactions.
• Type A occurs within one to two hours and symptoms last for one or two hours.
• Type B occurs within five to eight hours and the symptoms last for about a day.
• Type C builds up slowly over a few days and the symptoms can take several days to disappear.

This is why, without following the full elimination diet procedure, you cannot be sure that you have correctly judged reactions.

Benefits

Removing the triggers means the real child can be revealed, sometimes for the first time. Parents are frequently amazed at how quickly their child begins to catch up when the irritants are removed. Eve Hillary reports, in *Children of a Toxic Harvest* how her son, who had been completely unable to stop, think, concentrate or study, suddenly started getting B+ grades once given the nutritional support and supplements he needed. Liz Rayner, who used Sound Therapy with the recommended natural supplements, reports, 'My son is less aggressive, calmer, less fidgety, able to concentrate better and more centered.' See her full story in Chapter 8. Children often are amazed at what it feels like to be calm and focussed. They say, 'I didn't know what normal felt like until I was on the diet.'

Coping tricks

Healthy parties. Some support groups organise a circle of healthy parties where they serve sandwiches, fruit and homemade birthday cake. The emphasis on games rather than foods. Prizes are trinkets rather than sweets. There will be less of the wild and excitable behaviour which usually occurs at parties, but kids have a great time.

Get your support group to hold healthy birthday parties

Unfortunately, birthday cake with brightly coloured icing is often served at birthday parties. To give your child an option, send him with a piece of safe birthday cake from home, to eat when the cake is served. Keep a cake in the freezer, in slices, for the purpose. That way he can have a treat, still enjoy the party and not feel deprived.

No more Ritalin

One mother, Mary Ann Block, questioned the medical profession's diagnosis of her child, and decided to become fully informed on the issues herself. She even went so far as to study medicine herself, qualifying as an osteopathic doctor. In the United States osteopathy is a fully recognised branch of medicine, but with its own unique holistic philosophy based on the work of Arnold Stillman.

After a series of medical mishaps beginning with urinary tract infections, brought on initially by pesticide spraying, Mary Ann's daughter was diagnosed with mononucleosis. Her daughter, Michelle, was given an array of drugs by a procession of doctors and her condition got worse and worse, leaving her with a compromised immune system. This was when her mother started being her own medical detective. After doing much of her own research, she took her daughter to an osteopathic physician who welcomed the mother's involvement in managing the case. Using nutritional therapy she was finally able to begin strengthening, instead of weakening, Michelle's immune system, and bring her health back into balance.[13] At medical school, Mary Ann learned how doctors' education is based almost solely around drug therapy and why, therefore, their

Some doctors only know about drugs

response to each of her daughter's symptoms had been to give her more drugs.[14]

Dr Mary Ann Block has written a well-researched book called *No More Ritalin*. Her concise, straightforward style is refreshing to read, and as a self-publisher she has no fear of telling her truth. Once in medical practice, she became very concerned about the way the treatment of ADHD has grown into an industry in which thousands of children are being medicated for long periods of their lives. [15]

Are drugs the answer?

Go for drugs after you have tried everything else

It makes sense, whenever possible, to use appropriate supplements and diet as a preventative treatment rather than making drugs your first port of call. Isn't it better to remove the cause than give your child a substance with questionable long-term effects? It is sad that having allowed our world to become affected by so many toxins, we then give more dangerous substances to our children because they are sick!

If you are reading this book then you are searching for better solutions. However, medication may be a useful and necessary part of the program for some parents, for part of the time. Do not think if you use drugs as part of your solution that you have given up, or that all the other modalities discussed in this book are not still important and relevant to pursue.

What kids don't like about taking drugs

Drugs make kids tired and skinny

Canadian researchers did a follow-up study in 1986 of ADHD boys in their early twenties to find out how they felt about their condition and their treatment. What the boys said they would have liked more of was: individual counselling, tutoring and remedial education. The most important need expressed by ADHD kids, and that which made the biggest difference to them, was having someone who believed in them.

'I don't feel like myself'

One of the ways kids describe the way stimulant drugs make them feel is, 'I don't feel like myself.' One boy explained that all the time he felt as if someone was standing behind him. Kids may say they feel 'different,' but it is 'easier to concentrate'. They also dislike the effect on appetite, the tiredness, and feel embarrassed about needing to take pills.

Excess antibiotics

We all have candida in our systems. Candida is a yeast which grows in the intestines and is not a problem in normal quantities. However, a child who has been on repeated courses of antibiotics may have excessive growth of candida because other good bacteria in the intestinal tract have been killed off. When children take antibiotics it is important to also give them live yoghurt, or a supplement of *lactobacillus acidophilus*, available from health food stores. A well-informed doctor will always prescribe this along with antibiotics. Candida thrives and multiplies when we eat too much refined carbohydrates — sugar again! So lots of sugar and lots of antibiotics will lead to too much candida.

Your kid needs yoghurt to cope with antibiotics

Eighty to ninety percent of ear infections will heal entirely on their own without antibiotics. In fact, some studies show that giving a child antibiotics will result in the child taking longer to get over the infection and having more frequent recurrences, and that children will recover just as well without antibiotics.[16] A healthy immune system supported by good diet, lots of love and avoiding toxins, provides better protection. Yet often doctors at a consultation will say, 'well, we'll prescribe an antibiotic, just to be sure.' Most patients today expect this, but it is time we re-thought the automatic use of drugs in so many circumstances.

Antibiotics don't always speed up the healing

The autonomic nervous system

This is the part of the nervous system which controls our unconscious body functions such as breathing, heart rate, adrenaline, blood sugar levels, and digestion. The autonomic nervous system can be enhanced in many ways including diet, drugs or physical therapies such as osteopathy, the Alexander Technique and Sound Therapy. Osteopaths have found that up to 50% of children with learning difficulties respond favourably to osteopathic manipulation. This type of gentle physical intervention may make dietary changes more effective.

Gentle body work can help your child

Covering up the symptoms

Dr Block makes an important point about the dangers of drug therapy. Because drugs are in most cases wholly geared towards treating the symptoms, by suppressing the

It is important to treat the cause of the problem

283

symptoms in this way we make it less likely that we will ever identify and treat the underlying cause of the problem.[17]

It may be that narrowing the diet helps to narrow the field of negative triggers for a child, like an island getting smaller and smaller, but does it, on its own, help to increase the resilience of those kids to a wider range of substances? To do that, it is necessary to supplement, to detoxify and to eat a correctly balanced diet which brings insulin levels into balance.

The 'quick fix' may take longer in the long run

It is understandable that many parents opt to give their children medication, because this does appear to provide a quick fix. The many stresses of caring for learning-disabled children mean parents are often desperately in need of a break. However, environmental medicine suggests that this may be only a short-term solution and that the long-term effect on the health of the next generation could be much more serious. Our children need to be able to provide their offspring with healthy immune systems, but today's drug reliant approach means that our immunity is suffering, and this problem may be compounded in future generations.

Drug companies have all the power

Dr Block's observations, from her own inside experience, are that drug companies have enormous power over medical practice. They heavily influence the curriculum in the medical schools, what the doctors are taught in their continuing education, and the content and focus of medical journals and medical research.[18]

Sadly, parent support groups are often influenced by drug companies — who give them funds and use them as fronts to lobby for laws more favourable for the pharmaceutical industry. This does not only happen in America. Drug companies are globalised corporations which exert enormous power over governments, and frequently put their profits ahead of the public good.[19] For further reading on this topic, see Dr Mary Ann Block or Phillip Day.[20]

If the oil light comes on, you have to fix the car

Why does the body produce symptoms? To tell us there is a problem which needs to be addressed! If we suppress the symptom it is as though the oil light on the dash board came on and we smashed the dash to stop the light coming on. Suppressing the symptoms prevents us from finding out what is causing them. There is a world of difference between suppressing the symptoms and treating them.

Suppose you stepped on a nail and it became embedded in your foot and caused an infection. The doctor inspects the foot, examines the redness and swelling, tests for the type of infection and prescribes an antibiotic to treat that type of infection. He tells you to stay off the foot until it is healed, but does nothing about removing the nail. When the infection keeps recurring because of the nail in your foot, he just prescribes stronger and stronger medication. Eventually, because this doesn't work, he puts you on long-term antibiotic treatment and pronounces that you are handicapped with a chronic infection which means you cannot walk on your foot. Block uses this story to illustrate what we are doing to children with ADHD.

Remove the nail before dressing the wound

Upper or downer

On watching a hyperactive child, one would assume that they need a 'downer' to calm them down. In fact the drugs given to ADHD children are 'uppers'. Ritalin is a form of speed. The reason ADHD kids are given speed is because it helps them to concentrate.[21] In short-term drug use there is noticeable improvement in about 80% of cases.[22]

Speed helps kids to concentrate

What is alarming is the rate of increase at which medication is being given to our children. The rate of medication has doubled every two years since 1971.[23] In a survey of public schools in Baltimore County, 5.6% of all students (10% of all males) were receiving stimulant medication.[24] 'If drugs get results, what's the problem?' Block asks. The problem is that only 20% improved over eight years (according to one study). After eight years 80% showed no improvement.[25]

More and more kids are on medication

Though there is a philosophy that kids will outgrow the symptoms by puberty, other evidence suggests that this is not the case. If you do not address the underlying cause, says Block, you will be left with a problem which has to be treated for a lifetime.[26] Drugs are not normally aimed at the cause but merely at relieving the symptoms.

Drugs may just cover up the symptoms

Are the drugs dangerous?

This is a highly controversial question which elicits quite different answers depending on who is undertaking and interpreting the research. Ultimately the decision is usually made by the parents, based on their overall philosophy of health. It is important, though, to be informed of potential side effects, as it is to be aware of alternative, drug-free forms of treatment.

What are the potential side effects?
Ritalin
Short term
Loss of appetite, decreased growth, tics, visual disturbances, nervousness, insomnia, depression, social withdrawal, irritability, abdominal pain, increased heart rate and psychotic-like symptoms.[27]

Long term
Studies are being conducted right now on our children. We don't know! The inserts with the drugs make it clear that the companies making them do not know the long-term safety or efficacy of the drug.

Other drugs
Dextroamphetamine (Dexedrine)
Was a favourite in the past but is used less frequently now.

It was used as a diet pill in the sixties due to its side effects as an appetite suppressant. However it proved to have too high a potential for abuse to continue with such use. Odd that a drug deemed too dangerous for adults to take on a regular basis is considered suitable for children! It has been found to have side effects similar to Ritalin.[28]

Pemoline (Cylert)
Was used until it was observed that continued use creates the potential for liver damage. Also has multiple side effects.[29]

Protecting your baby from toxic and dangerous interventions
Mothers who took thalidomide did not know until their babies were born that the drug would cause birth defects. The last generation of people who took to smoking cigarettes did not know what a serious health hazard they would prove to be. The first generation of scientists and radiologists working with X-rays did not know they could cause cancer. All the workers who installed asbestos in the 1950s, 60s and 70s did not know they were setting

themselves up for mesothelioma and asbestos lung cancer. Likewise, mothers today do not know the implications for their children's future health, when undertaking procedures such as ultrasound and vaccinations. There is sufficient evidence that these procedures may be harmful, to warrant every parent undertaking careful investigation before deciding if they will expose their children to these procedures. A few hours of research beforehand could save years of remedial therapy and thousands of dollars. It is my hope that many parents will read the following sections in time to make their own informed decisions.

Ultrasound

Ultrasound technology is based upon ultra high-frequency sound waves, which bombard the child in the womb at an extremely high rate of speed. (These waves are in a completely different range, using 3 to 10 million Hertz, rather than 0 to 20 thousand Hertz as used in Sound Therapy.) This allows an image of the baby to be seen on a video screen. According to the World Health Organization and a U.S. Department of Health and Human Services Report, 'It is not clear at this time whether ultrasound foetal monitoring is beneficial to the mother or foetus in terms of pregnancy outcome... If there is no generally acknowledged benefit to the monitoring, there is no reason to expose patients to increased cost and risk. The question of benefit has not yet been resolved... and the potential for delayed effects has been virtually ignored.' Numerous studies point to possible damaging effects of ultrasound on the foetus.[1] (Former Endnotes 30, 31,32)

Reading this information, one cannot but ask whether the increasing use of ultrasound is responsible in part for the increase in learning difficulties today.

The vexed question of vaccination

Vaccination is a complex and emotionally fraught question which all parents must address. A number of parents today are reaching the conclusion that vaccination has caused serious damage to their children. Numerous environmental doctors have also taken a stand against vaccination and have brought into question the theory of immunization and whether in fact vaccination strengthens or weakens our immunity.

My mistake was not arming myself with information sooner. My parents were developing an interest in natural health and stopped vaccinating their children in my early childhood, so I received fewer vaccinations than most.

However, I failed to fully investigate the reasons and pass on the knowledge of the other side of the argument to my foster daughter in time. Her active, healthy boy returned from his first round of vaccination with respiratory disturbances and fretful behaviour which had not been there previously. After the second round of vaccinations at eighteen months, his symptoms worsened. As he became a toddler, behavioural abnormalities showed up which were finally diagnosed as ADHD. His mother then informed herself, found supportive professionals and did not vaccinate her second child, who shows none of these behavioural disorders.

A network of concerned parents and professionals have dedicated themselves to making information about independent research on vaccination available to the public. The Australian Vaccination Network (AVN)[31] is an association which presents the latest knowledge and research into the effects of vaccinations, and alternatives and remedial therapies to deal with the after-effects. Information about AVN can be found on the internet. You can visit their website www.org.avn.au to learn more about the AVN and their resources. Their magazine, 'Informed Choice,' is an excellent resource for parents and practitioners wishing to keep informed on issues of environmental health. AVN provides support for parents wishing to know their legal rights in relation to vaccination. Enforced vaccination is not legally mandated in Australia.

Since this is a complex issue with many proponents on each side, you will need to do your own research in order to make the right decision for you. To learn about the alternative view, which is not presented by most doctors or the mainstream media, a very informative website on vaccination, which includes easy to understand scientific articles[32] and many resource books and videos, is www.vaccination.inoz.com . There you can order the video, 'Vaccination: The Hidden Truth'. [33] This is a highly informative exploration of the alternative view on vaccination, with interviews by over twelve doctors, researchers and parents who have in-depth knowledge of the issue. Parents who like to make their own decisions will want to see this video before forming their own conclusions.

How to rectify the damage

This information about the potentially damaging effects of chemical toxins, ultrasound and vaccination, will inevitably bring grief, remorse and anger to parents who find out too late what they might have avoided. However, it is better to be informed than not. On the encouraging side, the reports in Chapter 8 detail the positive changes which can be achieved in healing children with supportive therapies.

It is never too late for a child, or even an adult, to improve. Nature and the human body are incredibly resilient, always striving to heal, always recreating cells, always processing and clearing out foreign matter which the immune system rejects. Given half a chance, remarkable healing happens. So please be heartened by the new knowledge you have, by the fact that you have choices every day as to which chemicals, foods and other stimuli your family will be exposed to. Use this information to exercise those choices and help to create a toxin-free, naturally nurturing environment for your loved ones.

PRACTICAL ACTION TIPS

How to create a natural, healthy home

✪ Cut out all artificial additives such as food colourings, preservatives and artificial sweeteners.

✪ Eliminate the triggers from your child's diet and environment and see if it makes life easier.

✪ Get qualified support to do the elimination diet properly.

✪ Avoid using toxins in the home such as insect sprays, perfumes and commercial air fresheners.

✪ Use natural aromatherapy for fragrance (as long as none of your family reacts to it.)

✪ Find a group of parents who want to have healthy birthday parties.

✪ Keep healthy treats in the freezer so your child can have a substitute and avoid temptation.

✪ Use good quality supplements to ensure your children get all the nutrients they need.

✪ Learn recipes which do not include foods your family has intolerances to.

✪ Buy bathroom products which are free of toxic chemicals.

✪ Investigate carefully before you vaccinate or use ultrasound.

✪ If you decide to use drugs for a time, also thoroughly explore alternative treatments so that you can avoid overuse of the drugs.

References

1   Hilary, E. *Children of a Toxic Harvest.* Melbourne: Lothian, 1997.

    Crumpler, Diana. *Chemical Crisis.* Newham, Australia: Scribe Publications, 1994.

2   Hilary, *Ibid.*

3   Day, P. *Cancer: Why We're Still Dying to Know the Truth,* and *Health Wars.* UK: Credence 2001 http://www.credence.org/

4   Dengate, Sue. *Different Kids. Growing up with Attention Deficit Disorder.* Sydney: Random House. 1994, 178.

5   Rowe, K.S. 1988, Rowe, K.S. and K.L. 1994, cited in Dengate *Ibid.* 182.

6   Dengate, *Ibid.* 182.

7   Epstein, S. *Unreasonable Risk: How to Avoid Cancer From Cosmetic and Personal Care Products: The Neways story,* Chicago: Environmental Toxicology, PO Box 11170, Chicago Illinois 60611, USA, 2001.

8   *Ibid.*

9   Swain, et al. *Friendly Food,* cited in Dengate, *Ibid.*

10 Epstein, *Ibid.*

11 Sears, B. *The Zone.* Harper Collins 1995, and *Mastering the Zone.* New York: Harper Collins. 1997. http://www.drsears.com

12 Conners, C.K. *Feeding the Brain,* New York: Plenum Press, 1989; and Conners, C.K. *Food additives and hyperactive children.* New York: Plenum Press, 1980, cited in Dengate, *Ibid.*

13 Block, M.A. *No More Ritalin.* New York: Kensington Books,1996, 11.

14 *Ibid.*

15 *Ibid.* 14.

16 *Ibid.* 126.

17 *Ibid.* 24.

18 *Ibid.* 25.

19 *Ibid.* 25.

20 Block, *Ibid,* Day, *Ibid.*

21 Block, *Ibid.* 26.

22 *Ibid.* 27.

23 Jacobvitz, D, et al. 'Treatment of attentional and hyperactivity problems in children with sympathomimetic drugs: A comprehensive review article,' *Journal of the American Academy of Child and Adolescent Psychiatry,* Vol. 29, No. 5, (Sept. 1990).

24 Block, *Ibid.* 27.

[25] *Ibid.* 28.

[26] *Ibid.*

[27] *Ibid.* 31.

Dulcan, M. 'Using stimulants to treat behavioural disorders of Children and Adolescents' *Journal of Child and Adolescent Psychopharmacology,* Vol 1, No. 1, (1990) 7-19.

Arky, R. Physicians' Desk Reference. New Jersey 1996. 412-413, 674-675, 848-849, 856-857, 919-923, 1526-1527, 2474-2476, cited in Block, *Ibid.* 31.

[28] Block, *Ibid.* 32-33.

Vinson, D. 'Therapy for attention deficit hyperactivity disorder;' *Archives of Family Medicine,* Vol 3, May 1994, pp. 445-451.

Bellak, L. 'Attention deficit hyperactivity disorder in adults,' *Clinical Therapeutics,* Vol. 14, No. 2, (1992) 138-147.

[29] Block, *Ibid.* 33.

[30] Matthews, R. 'Ultrasound Scans Linked to Brain Damage in Babies', *Journal of Epidemiology* (Dec 9, 2001) 12:618 http://educate-yourself.org/cn/2001/ultrasoundandbraindamage19dec01.shtml

Uhlig, R. 'Ultrasound Scans May Harm Unborn Babies', *New Scientist,* Issue 1476 (10 June 1999).

Christopher, J.R. *Every Woman's Herbal.* Quoting from: *The People's Doctor,* Vol.7, No. 11. 3. cited on http://educate-yourself.org/cn/2001/ultrasoundandbraindamage19dec01.shtml

[31] Australian Vaccination Network www.org.avn.au

[32] Hancock, B. 'Vaccination, A Fatal Error' www.vaccination.inoz.com

Scheibner, Viera, Ph. D *Behavioural Problems in Childhood: The link to vaccination,* on www.vaccination.inoz.com

Scheibner, V. 'Shaken Baby Syndrome' www.vaccination.inoz.com

Scheibner, V. Interview at Blackheath, transcribed by Rafaele Joudry. 2002.

[33] 'Vaccination: The Hidden Truth, Should we shoot first and ask questions later?' www.vaccination.inoz.com

Chapter 10

RESEARCH

The brain and Sound Therapy

Brain research

There is a class of doctor who is driven by a deep curiosity and passion to understand and remedy the mysteries of human disease. These doctors relate to their patients not as 'cases', numbers or specimens, but as full human beings in need of deep understanding and compassion as well as medical treatment. These doctors become leaders, pioneers and sometimes scapegoats of those who follow conventional treatment paths for fear of disapproval. They leave a legacy of a major shift in thinking, and a new leap of understanding of our humanity. They leave a body of work which instructs and inspires generations to come. Into this class of doctors I would put Sigmund Freud, Carl Jung, Alfred Tomatis, Oliver Sacks and Harold Levinson.

Some doctors are true pioneers

Dr Tomatis was the first specialist to identify the crucial role of the ear in learning difficulties. His conviction was based on his clinical observation of the spectrum of ear-related problems affecting his clientele. He was then able to treat and remedy a wide spectrum of language, communication and learning issues, by treating the ear. His

Dr Tomatis made discoveries about the ear that were before his time

approach was experimental, ground-breaking and personal. It was supported by theories from his own perspective on the world, which of course aroused a range of criticisms from his colleagues. His efforts to prove his discoveries with controlled studies produced a range of results, some positive, some not. In some circles he lost credibility, while a solid band of supporters remained, who admired the wholism of his approach and were impressed with the transformations sometimes brought about by his treatment. His method did not become mainstream, perhaps because the world was not ready to understand the profundity of what he had discovered. Just as Galileo and Copernicus were persecuted for saying the world is round, Tomatis made claims that science did not yet have the ability to fully prove or understand. However, his body of work has remained very alive in theory and practice, and many other specialists have since made discoveries which help to reveal the deeper truths behind Dr Tomatis' claims. In this chapter I will explore some of those discoveries and the research that supports the Tomatis principles.

The Cerebellar-Vestibular connection

Dr Levinson confirmed the role of the ear

The neurologist Dr Harold Levinson specialised in the treatment of dyslexia (which was then the general term for learning difficulties) for many years, and reached some surprising conclusions about the role of the ear in learning disorders. After several years of clinical practice he developed a model to explain the role of the cerebellum and the vestibular system in learning difficulties. Levinson found information about the cerebellum which explained the far-reaching effects of the inner ear or vestibular system.

Is it the ear or the brain?

The evidence should come before the theory

From his clinical observations as a neurologist, Levinson was certain that dyslexia was caused by an inner ear disorder. The scientific community refused to entertain this possibility, convinced as it was that it was a cerebral disorder. Levinson verified his observations through independent testing. He then found a theory to explain his observations. This is the more scientific approach. It is dangerous to become attached to a theory and then seek evidence to support it. It is more scientific to collect evidence and then develop a theory to explain the evidence. As Levinson says, 'If the clinical facts do not fit the theory, the theory is wrong!'[1]

When Levinson began working with learning-disabled children he accepted a post where he was required to follow the accepted psychiatric model which held that dyslexia was a psychiatric disorder. After examining 1000 kids over several years, he found that the symptoms he was observing simply did not fit the psychiatric model he was expected to use to explain them. This required acute and incisive observation, for at first glance, certainly, the symptoms of dyslexia appeared to be the symptoms typically considered psychiatric: emotional and behaviour disorders, phobias, obsessions, mood disturbances and even the so-called psychosomatic symptoms such as bed-wetting, muscle tics, headaches, dizziness, nausea, vomiting, and abdominal pain. Certainly these symptoms were considered to fall within the realm of psychiatric practice. However, being a true scientific thinker, Levinson realised that since the evidence he was seeing did not clinically and statistically fit the theory, the theory must be in error. To be able to detach from a theory in which one has been trained and steeped over many years requires a truly bold and independent mind, and a dedicated scientist.

The associated symptoms lead Dr Levinson to the ear

The prevailing theory to explain dyslexia at that time was that dyslexia was due to a disturbance in the cerebral cortex — the thinking, speaking brain, the seat of intelligence. Kerr and Morgan first recognised and described 'word blindness' in 1896. At that time it was believed that dyslexia was an abnormality in the functioning of the left hemisphere, the primary site for language. However, this theory was obviously flawed because of evidence that many highly intelligent people had dyslexia, hence indicating that nothing was seriously wrong with the thinking brain. Many neurologists then assumed that the problem was caused not by cerebral damage but by a developmental delay in the thinking brain. However this theory fell far short of explaining the observable clinical facts. Sometimes, we can't see the forest for the trees, and those investigators, convinced the problem was in the cortex, did not look any further than the cortex. In fact the problem, Levinson believes, is in another area of the brain which secondarily causes the delay in cerebral processing.

Dyslexia is not a disorder of the thinking brain

295

The cerebellum is integral to sensory integration   Through thousands of case studies, Levinson came to the realisation that in every case of dyslexia, and representing all the myriad of varied symptoms, the unifying factor was inner ear dysfunction. He realised that dyslexia affects every aspect of one's life, auditory and visual processing as well as motor co-ordination and balance, both waking and sleeping. Hence, he says: 'I came to view the inner-ear system as a fine-tuner for the entire sensory input and motor output system.' When one looks deeper to see which brain structures are involved in this ear-related processing, the part which comes to light as fundamental in sensory integration, is the cerebellum. This crucial nub of basic sensory processing could be seen as the 'grand central station', linking the local exchange of the inner ear to the final destination of the cortex.

The cerebellum also integrates auditory and visual signals   The cerebellum is an ancient and fundamental part of the brain's circuitry, playing a key role in the processing of all our sensory information. It is positioned at the back of the skull, next to the brain stem, and its purpose did not yield to scientific investigation as early as parts of the cortex did. For some years, the cerebellum was known to play a role in physical co-ordination, but only more recently have scientists realised that it also works as a clearing-house for auditory and visual signals. Rather like the central operating system of a computer, nothing goes on in the brain without the cerebellum being involved.

A study by Snider and Stowell, at the John Hopkins University in 1942, also showed that the tactile, visual and auditory centres of the cerebellum are linked to the corresponding centres in the cerebral cortex. So, while the cerebellum itself directs no body functions, it operates as monitor and co-ordinator of the brain's other centres, and as mediator between them and the body.[2]

Numerous other scholars of high repute (Leiner and Dow, Rudolfo Llinas of the New York University Medical Centre and Paula Tallal of Rutgers University), concurred with Levinson's hypothesis that the cerebellum plays a significant role in learning and language disabilities.[3]

ENG tests confirmed the presence of inner ear dysfunction   Other studies have corroborated the evidence for the inner ear dysfunction theory. When numerous dyslexic people were tested at four leading hospitals with electronystagmography (ENG), a special physiological inner ear testing method, 90% showed definite evidence of inner ear dysfunction. Dr Viera Scheibner, independent researcher into early infant mortality, explains that neural pathways can be regenerated and are affected by sensory input.

> 'Klein and Rapin (1990) ascertain that the recovery of function after brain damage represents reorganisation of brain circuitry by regenerations and proliferation of surviving neurons, not by cellular division. The younger the person, the faster the recovery of function.
>
> Abnormal sensory input has been shown to alter the structural and functional organisation of an undamaged central nervous system. As an example, when one eye is deprived in early development, not only do the activity-deprived axons have a variable reduction in arbor size and other changes, but also the axons from the non-deprived eye become abnormal. Despite having received normal sensory stimulation, axons of the non-deprived eye have expanded axonal arbors and other changes.'[4]

Scheibner gives further detailed description of the crucial role of the cerebellum in neural development and function.

> 'The cerebellum stands at one of the busiest and most interconnected neural intersections in the human brain. All major components of the human brain – cerebrum, limbic system, basal ganglia, diencephalon, brain stem and spinal cord – send information there and receive neural activity from it.'[5]
>
> 'The cerebellum projects abnormal activity to a great number of brain systems: physioanatomical connections with arousal and attention systems; hippocampal memory systems; the amygdala; serotonergic, noradrenergic and dopaminergic systems; the opiate system; hypothalamic nuclei; speech systems; systems mediating semantic associations; brain stem, thalamic and cortical visual, auditory, and somatosensory pathways; brainstem autonomic systems; the vestibular system; systems mediating classical conditioning operations; motor planning and execution systems; and frontal and parietal cortex, just to name a few.'[6]

Children read with their ears

The ear guides the eye Tomatis says 'children read with their ears.' Levinson has tested and confirmed this theory with his research. 'The inner ear system has been proven to direct and guide our eyes and tracking responses, automatically, during the reading process.'[7]

Dyslexic people have a slower eye-tracking speed. Through experimental methods which he designed himself, Levinson found that dyslexic people had half the blurring speed of non-dyslexic people. This proved to him that there was an eye-tracking defect in dyslexic people.[8]

Definitions

Dyslexia can be severe or mild Dyslexia was traditionally defined as a severe reading disorder. A dyslexic person's reading score had to be two years behind peers with whom they are perfectly matched for IQ, socio-economic, physiological and educational factors. Levinson discovered this definition to be completely wrong and useless. Part of the reason for its being instated was that experts only saw those with severe reading disabilities for they were the only ones referred for help.[9] Because he also looked at less severe cases he began to get a greater understanding of the whole syndrome.

The connection to IQ

IQ and learning difficulties have nothing to do with one another.[10] However, dyslexia or ADHD can occur *LD is not low IQ* in combination with any other disorder, including mental retardation, deafness, cerebral palsy etc. In fact most intellectually disabled people also have a hidden impairment of the inner ear system (cerebellum), so treating their dyslexia may be a significant first step in improving their functioning.

Dyslexia and ADHD need not exist prior to birth. They may be acquired due to inner ear damage or brain damage caused by infections, toxins or trauma, ear infections, allergies, whip lash injuries, et cetera. Though there is evidence of a genetic element in some cases, experts now say that the genetic component is at most, thirty percent. Genetic vulnerability is also profoundly influenced by environmental factors.

Dyslexia or ADHD?

At the time of Dr Levinson's research and his ground-breaking book, *Smart but Feeling Dumb*, (1984), dyslexia was the popular term for most learning difficulties. However, his discovery of inner ear involvement in learning-related disorders is not exclusive to the diagnosis of dyslexia. Now the term dyslexia is much less used and the emergence of a new category, ADHD, has tended to become an umbrella for many types of learning disorders. Levinson recently observed that ninety percent of children diagnosed with ADD/ ADHD have inner-ear-related problems similar to dyslexic people.[11] Levinson therefore concludes that these two disorders originate from the same cause, though the symptoms have been differently defined leading to different diagnoses.

ADHD and dyslexia may originate from the same cause

Dr Levinson used his discoveries to develop a treatment program using medications to help inner ear function. He had remarkable success with this system in helping many dyslexic people to overcome their difficulties. Other researchers preferred non-invasive methods, so while based on the same theory, drug-free sensory integration programs using movement or Sound Therapy are just as successful.[12]

Dyslexia source and symptoms

Levinson has analysed 35,000 dyslexic people —the largest sample ever, he claims. He paid great and detailed attention to all symptoms he observed, whether or not they fitted his original understanding, and eventually wove the symptoms together into a new understanding of dyslexia. His conclusion was the same as Dr Tomatis': that dyslexia is an inner ear dysfunction, which can affect capabilities in any or all of the following areas.[13]

1. Reading
2. Writing
3. Spelling
4. Mathematics
5. Memory
6. Direction
7. Time
8. Speech
9. Hyperactivity, overactivity, impulsiveness

10. Concentration and distractibility
11. ADD/ADHD
12. Phobias and related mental behavioural disorders
13. Balance and co-ordination

Dyslexics are ingenious at coping Dyslexia is sometimes difficult to diagnose because humans are ingenious at creating compensatory mechanisms to deal with a functional inadequacy. Therefore, not only do dyslexic people compensate for a lack in one area, such as reading and writing, by being overly proficient in another, such as speaking, but they will find methods of managing difficult tasks so that it is not even apparent that they are struggling; things like tensing the writing hand to know which way is right, or following the words with the finger to help eye tracking.

A dyslexic person may have difficulties in any combination of the above functions, for each inner ear system is different and difficulties may be very specific. Hence the reading score of a dyslexic person may be normal for their age level, or even superior. What is of importance in tracking the source is that we look at the link to inner ear dysfunction in each of the symptomatic areas.

Reading

Changing position may help reading The dyslexic person reading disorder is due to visual and or phonetic memory instability for letters and words. Reversal or directional disturbances are frequent. 'Was' is mistaken for 'saw', etc. Fixation or eye tracking difficulties are often the cause of this. It is frequent for dyslexic people to experience symptoms when they read which could be seen as psychosomatic; such as headaches, dizziness, nausea, double vision, or words seeming to move around. These symptoms relate to poor cerebellar / vestibular function. Dyslexic people can often be observed using compensatory mechanisms such as tilting the head or the page, blinking, refocussing, or finger pointing in an attempt to realign the body's inner gyroscope. All this occurs because eye tracking is controlled by the vestibular system.

Writing

The ear guides the hand Dyslexic people often have problems with the shape, direction and spacing of letters. Writing is often sloppy, and reversals may be present. Some find mirror writing easier. Some prefer to write only in separated letters, while for others the rhythmic flow of script writing may help. Letters or words may be omitted or repeated, and it is hard for the dyslexic person to pick these errors himself. All this is easy to understand if we think of the cerebellar / inner-ear system as being like a guided missile system which is guiding our hands and fingers in space. Any dysfunction within this system will result in poor co-ordination of the fine motor mechanisms required to write. In some dyslexic people, drawing is also affected, while others may be very skilled artists.

Spelling

Linear sequential processing and poor auditory memory are the reason which many dyslexic people have difficulty with spelling, but again not all. Some are exceptional spellers. Some will be better at spelling words learned later in life, and hence will be accurate on large, complex words but may have residual errors on simple words which were learned incorrectly and got stuck in the memory. These difficulties relate very much to efficient links between the ear and auditory cortex. Our timing, and the speed of our sequencing abilities, are functions again of a smoothly operating vestibular system.

Timing is an ear function

Mathematics

Maths is an area where dyslexic people often perform better than they do in English because maths is more conceptual, rather than linguistic. The problems they do have with maths relate to its linguistic or spatial components, pointing again to the ear. Some children have difficulty with maths because they cannot write their numbers in neat columns, resulting in adding errors. This can be helped by using graph paper to write sums. Some may have trouble remembering equations or theorems while others will have trouble grasping concepts. Recent research at Melbourne University, where the brains of exceptionally talented mathematicians were examined though MRIs, found that both hemispheres of the brain are more involved than usual in mathematical thinking. In addition it was found that, in these people, much greater areas of the brain were active when thinking about maths problems than in the average person.

Special sense is important for maths

Memory

Memory can be auditory or visual

The type of memory problems experienced by dyslexic people is quite unique between individuals. Some may suffer from visual, and others from auditory memory problems. Hence some may have a poor memory for visual letter or word recall, yet have an excellent memory for phonetics. They will remember what they heard but not what they read. Similarly, some will have no trouble remembering addition and subtraction equations but will be unable to memorise multiplication tables. The explanation is that each piece of information is stored and retrieved separately and independently, and different brain processes are used for each type of information. Some people will find it impossible to remember names, others numbers. Some children have great difficulty learning to tell the time or remembering the days of the week or the months. Some may be able to recall facts, but once memorised they have no ability to erase and change the memory if the fact recorded was wrong. Once sensory integration is enhanced and brain connections are stimulated through sensory inputs such as movement or Sound Therapy, memory problems often disappear.

Direction

The inner ear is the body's compass

The inner ear is the compass of the body and is affected by directional disturbances, which may mean the dyslexic person cannot distinguish right and left, east and west; or, in some cases, not even up from down or front and back. In some cases, this translates as being unable to find one's way around and constantly getting lost.

Time

The inner ear is the clock

The inner ear is like the body's clock. It gives us our sense of rhythm and time, so a disturbance might result in the inability to sense time or even to tell the time. This can result in chronic lateness, or extreme earliness, as a compensatory measure. Of course, some of the behaviours mentioned here may be simply bad habits, but the persons themselves, or those close to them will most likely know if this is the case or if it is due to a dyslexia-like disability.

Speech

Children who are late to begin speaking may turn out to be dyslexic. Stuttering — which is frequently linked to dyslexia — as Dr Tomatis has found, is a timing problem, related to the flow of speech and right ear dominance. Sometimes, stuttering is caused by a delay due to difficulty recalling words or thoughts.

Stuttering is a timing problem

Cluttering is a condition related to stuttering, where speech comes out in sudden bursts rather than in a smooth flow. Cluttering is another sign of dyslexia; and so is the development of a slow or rambling habit of speech, or saying words out of sequence. Background noise problem, sometimes called 'cocktail party syndrome', may accompany dyslexia because the inner ear plays a part in sorting and choosing the emphasis of listening. Understanding and using simple grammatical rules may be a problem for dyslexic people, and of course this is reflected in speech patterns.

Hyperactivity, overactivity, impulsiveness

Tomatis has shown that the ear is the modulator for the body's energy levels. Energy disorders, whether they be over or underactivity, are generally related to the inner ear. This problem can begin even in utero, when mothers already know that they have a hyperactive child. When such problems begin later, they may be viewed as psychological in nature; but both developmental and acquired hyperactivity are due to inner ear dysfunction, according to Levinson.[14] The problem can also be acquired later due to exposure to environmental toxins or other trauma.

Hyperactivity may start in utero

Concentration and distractibility

A dyslexic person has to be constantly on hyper-alert with concentration in order to avoid mishaps which the rest of us do not have to worry about. Most people can function in many situations on automatic pilot, whereas for the dyslexic person this is impossible. The extra concentration required can be exhausting, and result in lapses appearing as an inability to concentrate normally.

Dyslexic people can't rely on automatic pilot

If the subject is of great interest then concentration becomes easier. This is true for all of us, but has greater repercussions for the dyslexic person. Someone who may not normally be able to read a book at all can perhaps do so if the book is of great enough interest. There is a physiological basis for this—interest stimulates adrenaline, thereby neurochemically enhancing concentration and mental functioning, while reducing distractibility.

Balance and co-ordination

Balance requires a lot of co-ordination

The ear regulates balance, so of course a disturbance in the inner ear usually results in balance disorders, travel sickness or co-ordination problems. These are specific to different individuals, and some may be well co-ordinated in some activities but not others. Just as they have difficulty co-ordinating visual and auditory inputs, dyslexic people may have trouble co-ordinating multiple motor tasks because this ability relies heavily on cerebellar function.

Ear function is the root cause of learning problems

Theoretical confirmation of Tomatis' ideas

Tomatis found ear function to be at the crux of most learning difficulties. His position is validated and confirmed by Levinson's observations of the key role which the inner ear and vestibular system play in all the common symptoms of dyslexia. Levinson, like Tomatis, solved these problems by treating the ear. Dr Levinson's work, then, gives an objective theoretical validation of Tomatis' thesis. The difference is that Levinson used medication to improve ear function. Tomatis did it with sound.

Research into Sound Therapy for Learning Difficulties

Research has been done in several countries

Since his method was made widely available in the 1970s, fairly extensive research has been carried out at a number of clinics around the world to examine the direct effect of Sound Therapy on a range of learning difficulties and areas of linguistic, psychological and neurological functioning. What follows is a summary of that research.

Canadian Studies

Weiss

At the University of Ottawa, Weiss (1985) examined the impact of Sound Therapy on the vocal quality of three theatre students. The students underwent a program of Tomatis therapy for seven months to test its effect on the long-term average spectra of speech.[15]

All subjects showed a shift of vocal energy to the higher frequencies. Energy decreased in the band from 0 to 800 Hz. and increased in the band from 800 to 1800 Hz. Subjects also reported greater articulatory ease and improvement in accent variation after the treatment.

Vocal energy shifted to the high frequencies

Sandislands

In Lethbridge, Canada, in 1989, Sandislands compared 32 underachieving children with a control group of 40. The treated group showed greater improvements in listening, oral reading and behaviour[16]

Listening and reading improved

Wilson

Wilson et al. (1982) examined the effect of the Tomatis method when used for preschool language-disordered children. The control group was given a program of remedial intervention called the Wilson program, which had previously been shown to be effective. The experimental group received the Tomatis treatment in addition to the Wilson program. Results of the study indicated that the group receiving the Tomatis treatment made several gains, in advance of the control group. Testing for Auditory Closure and Sound Mimicry showed greater improvement in the Tomatis group. The assessment of parents and teachers was that the Tomatis group demonstrated greater ability to express their thoughts and feelings in words.[17]

Improved expression of thoughts and feelings

Gilmor

Gilmor (1982) conducted a survey to measure the performance of children and adolescents on a wide variety of psychological tests before and after receiving Tomatis treatment. The tests measured aspects of intellectual functioning, achievement functioning and general adjustment. The study was undertaken at the Listening Centre in Toronto.

Improved family relations, mood and self-

The tests used included WISC-R verbal and non-verbal sub-tests, WRAT reading, arithmetic, speaking and the Monroe Sherman test. Participants showed significant improvement on all of the tests, with some variation between age groups. In addition, measures of general adjustment showed marked improvement in self-concept, moodiness, anxiety, sensitivity to criticism, social isolation, family relations and somatic complaints. Other measures also showed positive changes in certain specific language and motor skills.[18]

Roy and Roy

Perceptual processing improved J.N. Roy (1980) and R.T. Roy (1980) each completed doctoral theses on the use of the Tomatis method on the same group of five dyslexic boys. The Tomatis treatment was administered at the Child Study Centre in Ottawa. Regular observation and measures were made over a fourteen month period. R.T. Roy found improvements in perceptual processing and academic skills during, and two months after, the treatment program. There were significant gains in many areas. This study differs from others (Gilmor 1982, Wilson et al. 1982), in that no remedial tutoring was given along with the Tomatis treatment. J.N. Roy looked for changes in the subjects' cognitive control and spontaneous speech functioning. The main test used was Santo Stefano's *Better cognitive* Cognitive Control Test. The test measures four principles *control* of cognitive control: Focal Attention, Field Articulation, Level-Sharpening and Equivalence Range. Four of the five boys benefited from the program. These showed positive changes in cognitive control functioning and spontaneous speech. Roy concluded that the remediation of audio-vocal control achieved by the Tomatis treatment improves certain prerequisite skills for reading at the academic level.[19]

Rourke and Russel

IQ improvement In 1982, Rourke and Russel conducted a study using both sound stimulation and child and parent counselling to evaluate the usefulness of the Tomatis method for older children with learning disabilities. Thirty children were studied, twenty-one in the experimental group and nine in the control group. A number of testing methods were used including: WISC; Personality Inventory for Children; Wide Range Achievement Test; Seashore Rhythm Test; Auditory Analysis Test and Grooved Pegboard Test.

The treatment group showed a greater improvement in Full Scale IQ and on the majority of specific tests. The experimental and control groups were not identically matched in terms of IQ, or other instruction being received. However, there was a sufficiently greater improvement in the treatment group on most scores to clearly indicate positive results from the Tomatis method.[20]

South African Studies

This is a summary of excerpts from the paper 'Audio-psycho-phonology at Potchefstroom: A review.' by Pieter E. van Jaarsveld and Wynand F. du Plessis, 1988.

Studies on laterality

Van Wyk

Van Wyk (1974) tested the hypothesis that more stutterers than normal speakers failed to develop right ear dominance (the directive ear, or the main controlling ear in the speech-hearing feedback circuit, according to Tomatis). Her method was to apply two different techniques to explore the auditory dominance in a group of twenty stutterers and a group of twenty normal speakers. The two techniques used were: the dichotic stimulation technique of Kimura (using digits), and the audiolaterometric investigation method of Tomatis.

Stutterers more likely to be left-eared

The results indicated no significant differences could be found in the auditory dominance of the normal speakers and the stutterers through using the dichotic stimulation technique. The audio-laterometric results, however, identified significant differences between the two groups: stutterers showed a significantly greater left-ear dominance, or non-specific ear preference, while a significantly greater number of fluent speakers showed a significantly greater right-ear dominance. Van Wyk[21]speculated, therefore, that the two techniques measured different aspects of auditory laterality. This study provides interesting evidence to support Tomatis' premise that left-ear dominance leads to stuttering. This is despite the fact that Van Wyk failed to implement Tomatis' controlling technique — that is observing the amount of mobility of the left or right facial muscles during the speech act — which provides a further indication of a right or left speech-hearing preference.

Although Van Wyk took various precautions to control contaminating effects, several factors necessitate a cautious interpretation of the results. One was the small sample sizes, and another was the use of solicited subjects instead of a randomised groups design.

Badenhorst

Badenhorst (1975) undertook a more in-depth investigation of the nature and measurement of auditory laterality, also using the techniques of Kimura and Tomatis. In this study Badenhorst paid special attention to Tomatis' physical observation technique for determining right or left speech-hearing preference. Badenhorst hypothesised that left-handers experience difficulty in realising their inner potential. The primary aim of the study was thus to determine differences between the Rorschach responses of two groups of subjects. Group A consisted of completely right lateralised (right-handed) female subjects (age 19-21) with a strong right speech-hearing preference, while group B was composed of female students of the same age with reasonably general right lateral preference, but with a left speech-hearing preference — in other words they were right-handed but left-eared.

Left ear dominance = more prone to frustration

Three independent raters concluded that the right speech-hearing subjects displayed a superior capacity to relate spontaneously and appropriately to emotional stimuli. They also displayed a more extroverted orientation, were more responsive and in control of their emotional responses; were less prone or subject to anxiety, tension, frustration and aggression. These findings were in line with the predictions of the Tomatis theory regarding laterality.

Regarding the secondary aim, the comparison between the two techniques of Tomatis and Kimura for ascertaining auditory laterality, Badenhorst's findings shed more light on the findings of Van Wyk (1974). Badenhorst concluded that 'closed selectivity' (i.e. the inability to distinguish between neighbouring frequencies) and audiometric deviations, as identified by the Listening Test of Tomatis, had to be taken into account when interpreting the results achieved by means of dichotic stimulation.

In conclusion, Badenhorst's results demonstrated a significant relationship between audiometric and audio-laterometric results, confirming the view of Tomatis[22] that handedness and in particular ear preference are an indicator of communication abilities.

Studies on Stuttering
Van Jaarsveld

Some interesting and enlightening studies of Tomatis' therapy on stuttering were carried out by Van Jaarsveld[23] (1973, 1974). Van Jaarsveld devised a long-term study to measure the effect of auditory training with Tomatis' Electronic Ear on a group of forty-three stutterers. The subjects were re-tested one year or more after treatment to confirm its long-term effects. The ages of the subjects ranged from 14 to 53 years. For each subject, questionnaires were also completed by a close family member and a close friend who were well acquainted with the client's speech ability both before and after auditory training.

All the clients experienced reduced stuttering and more fluent speech after the initial treatment. This improvement was significant in 82.5% of the participants. The results revealed that the adult group improved significantly more than the adolescent or the middle-aged groups. The participants reported significant progress after the concentrated Sound Therapy program, as compared to long-term speech therapy received previously. However, only 54% of the participants maintained a high level of improvement for one year or more after treatment. No comparative study has been done to see if improvements could be maintained over the long term, with ongoing listening, now possible with the portable method.

More fluent speech for stutterers

Once again, certain methodological limitations of this study make it difficult to isolate the specific contribution of the auditory training technique. The complete Sound Therapy program was not applied, and a comparable control group was not available. Also, the use of a questionnaire as the only measuring tool seems somewhat limited. On the other hand, the inclusion of independent observer ratings certainly provides some objectivity. It is commendable that the ratings were based on observations of the clients' speech behaviour in 'real-life' situations. Observations of real-life situations are acknowledged as the highest form of evidence in a court of law. Van Jaarsveld's second study[24] provided an in-depth analysis of the Tomatis approach to the treatment of stuttering. The aim of this study was to examine the effect of auditory training on the speech behaviour of adult stutterers. The experimental group consisted of thirty young adults. The results indicated a generally positive outcome as follows:

a) The severity of stuttering, as measured by the Lanyon SS Scale, was significantly less after auditory training.

b) Participants performed significantly better with regard to the number of speech dis-fluencies in a representative speech and reading sample.

c) A significantly faster rate of speech and oral reading was registered at post-treatment.

d) The participants' attitude towards stuttering improved significantly.

e) The audiometric results supported Tomatis' observations that stutterers have a relative hearing loss in the frequency range of the speech area, especially for the right ear, and that acuity improves after re-education.

f) A spectral analysis also supports Tomatis' observation, indicating a significant gain in energy in the vocal output after training.

Sound Therapy leads to improved hearing and speech The general conclusion drawn by Van Jaarsveld was that auditory training led to improved hearing and speech. The results of this study would have been more convincing if a comparative outcome study had been possible. However, the methodological challenges of procuring a comparable non-solicited group of adult stutterers, and an acceptable alternative treatment technique which meets all the controls and criteria spelled out by Kazdin (1986), seemed insurmountable at that stage.

Studies on Anxiety and Depression
Peché

More social directness Peché [25] undertook an evaluation of the effect of Sound Therapy on ten anxious female students, but no control group was used. Measurements including clinical observations and test results, led Peché to the general conclusion that, the participants developed more social directness and objectivity regarding their problems. There was a significant decline in neurotic and hypochondriac behaviour patterns. Peché reached the conclusion that psychic blocks may be eliminated by Sound Therapy treatment, and that it can therefore be regarded as a valuable aid to psychotherapy.

Botes

Botes[26] conducted a study which examined in-depth many functional behaviours of three clients with neurotic depression (dyschymic disorder). The results after Sound Therapy treatment indicated higher retest scores on the S.A. Wechsler Intelligence Scale, reduced depression on the Beck Depression Inventory, improved interpersonal relations and improved self-control and self-concept on the TAT and Rorschach.

Reduced depression

Du Plessis

Du Plessis undertook an exploratory study on anxiety and Sound Therapy. This study is commendable due to several methodological features which overcame the pitfalls of previous studies: the use of an experienced therapist during the experimental period; assignment of clients to an experimental and a control group; the inclusion of a no-treatment control group; a 14 month follow-up; virtually no subject attrition; and the use of an extended range of specific outcome measures. Du Plessis assessed a population of 424 first-year female students — by means of the IPAT Anxiety Scale, the Reactions to Everyday Situations (RES) test, a biographical questionnaire, and the Personal, Home, Social and Formal Relations Questionnaire (PHSF) — in order to identify an anxious and a non-anxious group, each consisting of forty subjects.

Twenty solicited subjects from the anxious group were then assigned to an experimental and a control group of 10 subjects each. The experimental group received a Sound Therapy anxiety reduction program consisting of sixty half-hour sessions of filtered music, and also regular therapeutic interviews. When the subjects were re-tested following treatment, the anxiety level of the experimental group had decreased significantly, whereas no change was found in the control group. Scores on the Purpose in Life test had increased significantly in the experimental group, yet decreased in the control group. In both groups, scores on the S.A. Wechsler Intelligence Test showed a significant increase in performance and total scores, but only the experimental group achieved a significant increase in verbal IQ. Finally, the experimental group manifested a significant increase on a measure of self-actualisation. This group had enhanced their level of mental health, were utilising their

Reduced anxiety

time more constructively and were functioning more in keeping with their inner needs and motives.

Du Plessis then applied the same stimulation program to a sample of 14 students from the non-anxious group, with very similar results. However, practicalities prevented him from checking the results with a control group.

Increased self-actualisation

A follow-up study of the anxious experimental and control groups 14.3 months after the initial testing, showed that the anxious experimental group (consisting of ten subjects) had maintained its reduced anxiety. A significant increase in the level of self-actualisation was maintained in the experimental group, but not in the control group. A follow-up evaluation of the non-anxious experimental group (of 13 subjects) also indicated a significant increase in the level of self-actualisation.[27]

Studies on mentally retarded people

Profound mental retardation

De Bruto (1983) conducted a carefully controlled study to investigate the effect of Sound Therapy on a group of profoundly retarded children. An additional aim was to inquire into intervention as a contaminating factor. Thirty inmates of Witrand Care and Rehabilitation Centre were selected. Their ages ranged from 4 to 14 years, and they had been previously diagnosed as profoundly mentally retarded but with the ability to sit and walk. They were randomly assigned to three groups which received:

a) Sound Therapy plus a sensory motor stimulation program (group A);

b) Music stimulation (but without the Sound Therapy effect) plus the same sensory motor stimulation program (group B);

c) No treatment (group C).

Results were measured with psychological tests including Bailey Scales of Infant Development and a measure of responsiveness. The results indicated that both experimental groups increased in mental age, but the increase in group A, the Sound Therapy stimulation group, was significantly higher than that in group B. No change was found in group C.

Increased responsiveness

Whereas no significant differences in terms of responsiveness in group A and B were observed prior to the stimulation program, a statistically significant reduction of self-directed response, together with significant increase in object-directed responses, occurred after Sound Therapy treatment.

Studies using Joudry Tapes
Sound Therapy Australia Survey

Results of survey of Sound Therapy Australia customers over four years 1991 — 1994

Methodology
Sound Therapy Australia sent out questionnaires to all customers over a four-year period. Questions asked for a subjective assessment of changes to a list of conditions which commonly respond to Sound Therapy. During the first two years of the survey, the conditions listed were: tinnitus, hearing loss, energy, stress, sleep, communication and dizziness. In 1993 the number of tapes sold for use by children increased, and so conditions related to learning difficulties in children were added. These were: autism, dyslexia, speech problems, learning difficulties and behaviour problems, and communication difficulties related to Down Syndrome.

In addition to a 'yes' / 'no' answer on specific conditions, The questionnaire allowed for additional comments, and some listeners reported improvement in conditions not included in the list. The number of responses to these additional conditions is much smaller, possibly because they were not solicited. The additional conditions have been added to the list for the tabulation of results. These additional conditions are: headaches, jet lag, well-being and depression.

Results
The total number of responses received over four years was 388. The Table below shows the sample size responding to each question and the percentage who reported positive results. If a condition was not relevant to the person they were instructed to write 'not applicable', and these responses have not been included. Where the listener had failed to follow the program as directed, their results were not included.

Results of Sound Therapy Australia Survey 1991-1994		
Condition	Reported improvement	Sample size
Tinnitus – overall benefits	84%	187
Tinnitus – reduction in noise level	45%	187
Tinnitus - symptoms completely gone	7%	187
Hearing Loss	56%	123
Energy	84%	122
Stress	86%	80
Sleep	75%	127
Communication	78%	71
Dizziness	70%	30
Autism	50%	4
Dyslexia	100%	2
Speech Problems	64%	14
Learning Difficulties	85%	14
Downs syndrome	100%	1
Headaches	100%	1
Jet lag	100%	1
Well being	80%	15
Depression	100%	6

Results of Sound Therapy Australia Survey 1991 -1994

Discussion

The weakness of the survey is that responding was voluntary and subjective. The rate of return on questionnaires sent out was approximately 33%. Lack of response could be attributed to not having followed the listening program consistently, to dissatisfaction with results or to simply not getting around to returning the questionnaire. In several instances, verbal reports describing positive results were received by telephone, but the person had not returned their form; so there is reason to believe that both positive and negative responses have gone unreported.

Given the limitations of a survey, the results appear to indicate significant positive change for the conditions listed.[28]

A high rate of positive changes

Bell

Estelle Bell undertook a case study of the effect of the Joudry Sound Therapy tapes on a Year 2 child, named Timothy. Timothy had been assessed as having delayed speech and gross motor abilities. His academic performance had been poor. On initial contact with Timothy, Bell noticed that a significant language disorder and mild speech delays caused difficulties with peer acceptance. He rarely attempted, and never completed, classroom tasks, but instead constantly roamed around making loud, inappropriate noises and growling and whistling. He had an unusual gait and posture and spoke out of the left side of his mouth. Timothy had been administered Tryptanol because of his behaviour and activity level.

Timothy was introduced to the Sound Therapy program, which he listened to in class and at home over a three-week period. Assessment of Timothy's progress was made by Bell, by his class teacher, his special Education Supervising Teacher, his peers and his mother. All observers noted improvements in Timothy's behaviour, language and conceptual skills, articulation, concentration and social relationships. He began taking an interest in the meaning of words, and reasoning about perceptions. His posture and way of speaking became more symmetrical and he became less clumsy. His expressive composition, drawings and handwriting improved dramatically, and he began to read. He ceased much of his anti-social behaviour and vocal noises, and began expressing more affection and appropriate emotions.[29]

Learning, affection and appropriate responses

Rintel and Rintel

Elizabeth Rintel and Derek Rintel conducted a study in Brisbane in 1995, using the Joudry Sound Therapy tapes on children in a remedial learning program. An experimental and a control group were used, each consisting of seven children. The experimental group (E group) received the Joudry Sound Therapy listening program, and the control group (C group) listened to the same music without the Sound Therapy recording method. Due to time limitations the children received only 32 hours of treatment, which is less than the recommended minimum of 100 hours. The study can therefore be said to only partially demonstrate the effectiveness of the program.

Five normed tests were administrated to the children. These were:

1) Test of Auditory discrimination (TAD); Golman-Friste-Woodcock (AGS 1970) revised 1976 using a standard audio cassette.
2) Neale Analysis of Reading Revised (Neale 1987)
3) Neale Analysis of Reading (Neale Comprehension)
4) Westwood Spelling (1970)
5) Schonell Spelling Test

Parent and teacher observations were recorded on: Distractibility, Overactive behaviour, Reading improvement, Left/right confusion and Misinterpretation of questions.

Better auditory processing and reduced ear infections
The general trend on most of the indices of standard tests and parent and teacher observations was that the experimental group showed more rapid advances than the control group, who received classical music alone. Of significance, the experimental group showed improved auditory processing and a reduction of ear infections. They advanced faster in reading age. Their interest in writing appeared to improve and parents noticed an improvement in laterality.[30]

Sanches and Acosta

Psychological improvements after violent events
Sanches and Acosta, 2004, Columbia. Over a two year period, forty children underwent a range of treatments including Sound Therapy, occupational therapy and counselling. The children had undergone devastating events where they had been mistreated, violated, and many had permanently lost their families, or lost parts of their body. Assessments were done before and after treatment by a psychologist, an occupational therapist and an educational specialist. Improvements were substantial in psychological, neurological and academic areas and were estimated at between 35% and 60% for each child. The evaluating specialists attributed many of these improvements to Sound Therapy.[31]

The rewards of research

Those researchers who have taken the time to study the effects of Sound Therapy have been pivotal in helping this remarkable modality to become more widely used and known. They have chosen to pursue a particular interest, followed their own sense of logic and inspiration, and been rewarded by seeing results easily achieved which have many repercussions for learning and development. Because the ear — and its related organs and brain pathways — is so complex and so integral to our functioning, it is hard to tabulate, measure and prove the effects of treating it. Those who attempt this process always meet with serendipitous surprises, and often become passionate advocates of therapy for the ear and the beauty it reveals to our consciousness.

A complex field renders serendipitous surprises

Ongoing research

We are continuing to collect data on the success of Sound Therapy and your input is invaluable in this regard. We have received hundreds of reports from our listeners over the years and we value all the feedback we get. Each story is unique and may be of benefit to share with another listener. We are always delighted to receive your letters telling your story in your own way. In addition, we are beginning to collect information in a more organised way, using our client feedback forms. If you have not previously sent in a full client history on your family members or clients, we ask you to complete one using the feedback forms which we send out with all our Sound Therapy kits. If you do not have a form, please contact our office or your local Sound Therapy distributor.

Record your own story

Nurturing the ear

My Sound Therapy journey has been one of realising the connectedness of all things; the role of hearing and balance in our sense of space, in true listening, attention, and awareness of others, awareness of self; and of our impact on the world and our fellow human beings.

The ear connects us to the world

Today, the world is all about communication. In the exponential growth of this medium, let us not forget the importance of our internal communication ability. The impact of pristine functioning of our biological listening and communication system, has far-reaching implications for our race, for civilization, and for the planet.

317

The impact of sound upon our children, then, should never be underestimated — for 'Vocal food,' as Tomatis says, 'is as necessary to our human development as the milk we take in.' [32]

References

1 Levinson, H. N. *Smart but Feeling Dumb*. New York: Warner, 1984. 138.

2 Cited in Levinson, *Ibid*. 122

3 Levinson, *Ibid*. 123.

4 Scheibner, V. *Behavioural Problems in Childhood: The link to vaccination*. Blackheath, NSW: Scheibner, 2000. 5. www.vaccination.inoz.com

5 Scheibner, *Ibid*. 9.

6 *Ibid*.

7 Levinson, *Ibid*. 119.

8 *Ibid*.

9 *Ibid*, 125.

10 *Ibid*, 127.

11 *Ibid*, 162.

12 Young, E. 'Controversial dyslexia treatment "works"'. NewScientist.com news service 16:59, 05 (Nov. 2002). http://www.newscientist.com/news/news.jsp?id=ns99993012

Nicholson, R.I., Fawcett, A.J., Berry, I.L., Jenkins, I.H., Dean, P. and Brooks, D.J. 'Association of abnormal cerebellar activation with motor learning difficulties in dyslexic adults'. *Lancet* 353, 9165: (1999) 1662-1667. http://www.shef.ac.uk/psychology/publications/individual/fawcett.html

13 Levinson, *Ibid*, 136-137.

14 *Ibid*, 157.

15 Weiss, W. 'Long Term Spectra of Continuous Speech', Ottawa: Dept of Theatre, University of Ottawa, 1985

16 Sandislands, M, 'The Tomatis Listening Training Program: A Quasi Experimental Field Evaluation,' *International Journal of Special Education*, 1989

17 Wilson, B.C., Iacoviello, J.M., Metlay W., Risucci D., Rosati, R. & Palmaccio, T., 'Tomatis Project Final Report', Toronto: The Listening Centre, 1992.

18 Gilmor, T.M. 'Results of a Survey of Children's Performance on a Variety of Psychological Tests Before and After Completing the Tomatis Program'. Rexdale, Ontario: MDS Health Group Ltd, 1082.

19 Roy, J.N. 'Cognitive Control Functioning and Spontaneous Speech: Intensive Case Studies of Audio-Psycho-Phonological Remedial Training with Five Dyslexic Boys,' unpublished PhD Thesis, University of Ottawa, 1980, cited in Stutt, H.A. 'The Tomatis Method: A Review of Current Research'. Montreal: McGill University, 1983.

Roy, R.T. 'Perceptual Processing Abilities and Academic Skills: Intensive Case Studies of Audio-Psycho-Phonological Remedial Training with Five Dyslexic Boys,' unpublished PhD Thesis, University of Ottawa, 1980, cited in Stutt, H. A, 'The Tomatis Method: A Review of Current Research'. Montreal: McGill University, 1983.

20 Rourke B.P. and Russel, D.L. 'The Tomatis Method Applied to Older Children: An Evaluation', 1982, cited in Stutt, H. A, *The Tomatis Method: A Review of Current Research*. Montreal: McGill University, 1983.

21 Jaarsveld, Van, P.E. and du Plessis, W.F. 'Audio-psycho-phonology at Potchefstroom: A review'. Potchefstroom University of Higher Education, 1988.

22 *Ibid.*

23 *Ibid.*

24 *Ibid.*

25 *Ibid.*

26 *Ibid.*

27 *Ibid.*

28 Joudry, R. *Sound Therapy Manual for Practitioners*. Sydney: Sound Therapy International. 2000.

29 Bell, E. 'An Ethnographic Report and Evaluation of the Implementation of Audio-Psycho-Phonology (Sound Therapy) in the Support of Timothy,' Griffith University Thesis, 1991. Reprinted in: *Background Reading Material for Sound Therapy Practitioner Training Certificate Course*. Sydney: Sound Therapy International, 2001.

30 Rintel, E and D. 'Sound Therapy for the Learning Disabled Child: The Effect of High Frequency Filtered Music on Listening and Learning Ability'. Brisbane: 1994.

31 Sanchez, M.O. and Acosta, A.M. *Four Case Studies on the effect of Sound Therapy on subjects of the Resilience program*. Columbia: Paper for Sound Therapy International for Certificate Course, 2004.

32 Tomatis, A. A. *The Ear and Language*. Phoenix: Moulin, 1996. 58.

Chapter 11

CONCLUSION

The integrated brain

So, dear reader, parent, practitioner, lover of children. We have seen how the child's complex auditory neurology, formed through the incredible interaction of cellular growth on the DNA pattern, is nourished by the vibratory essence of the mother's voice in the womb.

We have heard how the development of listening in the baby's early years, lays the foundation in place for all our later learning. We have seen how the development of right auditory laterality is paramount in brain organisation and successful language ability.

We have heard the explanation of how linguistic skills can be enhanced at any stage of the child's life through the input of Sound Therapy, how the right sort of music stimulates ear function, auditory cortical pathways, and the integration of the auditory sense with the other senses.

Learning is built on listening

We have explored the act of learning, how it happens with ease and joy, and what are the key elements to its developing organically, as it was intended.

We have gone into the feel and balance of all our physical senses, how they are so intertwined, and the role they play in brain development. We have felt our way through the tactile, proprioceptive and vestibular senses, as

Therapy done through the senses gets the brain working together

321

well as the neurological aspects of vision; the interactions of each of these with the auditory sense. We have discovered how sensory therapies can work through any of our senses to improve cerebellar integration.

Then we examined all the usual labels for different types of learning and developmental difficulties. We discovered their believed causes, symptoms, prognosis, tips for managing them and their potential response to sensory integration therapies, including Sound Therapy.

It helps get Next we tuned in to follow the stories told by numerous
families families who have experienced the effects of Sound Therapy
together for themselves. We saw the variety of applications and results. We learned of cases where Sound Therapy, along with other sensory integration therapies, has assisted recovery from dyslexia, ADHD, autism, epilepsy, hearing problems, recurrent ear infections; and a range of less defined problems such as anger management, auditory processing problems, spatial and vestibular disorders, and problems with memory and comprehension. We heard how families applied the program and the changes they saw in their children, and noticed in their interactions.

Choose natural Then we had a taste of the world of allergies, food
food and avoid intolerances and how to provide a delicious, healthy non-
hazards toxic diet for sensitive children. We questioned the validity of drug use over the short and long term; its multiple pros and cons in conjunction with sensory integration therapies. And we probed the potential hazards of ultrasound and vaccination, as against their supposed benefits.

Finally, we recapped some interesting research which substantiates the philosophy and approach put forward in this book regarding the fields of Sound Therapy and sensory integration therapies.

Three models for learning difficulties

Let us recap, now, the different models for looking at learning difficulties which we discussed in Chapter 1. There is the Behavioural view, which advocates behaviour management, better teacher training and stricter parenting. There is the Mechanistic view, which sees learning difficulties as genetic and inevitable, and which advocates treatment with drugs to make the situation more manageable. Then there is the Organic/Integrative approach, which has been explored in detail in this book. This is the approach which seeks to work with nature to support the innate ability of the nervous system to heal itself, by providing the right environment and input through the senses — the portals designed by nature to influence the body. Below is a table which gives more detail on the different implications of each of these paradigms or philosophies.

Pros and cons of the Behavioural view

The behavioural stance is so called because its strategy for change pivots around managing behaviour. On the positive side, this is the view which has lead to intensive teacher review processes, where all teachers' performances are objectively measured by the grades of their students. It has lead to the proliferation of classes on parenting and the reinstatement of reward and points systems for behaviour management. It advocates remedial instruction for children with learning difficulties, where an attentive, well-trained tutor works with an individual student to find ways of making the information meaningful and accessible to his capabilities. Many positive changes in education, from which everyone benefits, have occurred through efforts to make learning easier for the learning disabled.

On the negative side, this view leads to report cards which say things like 'would do well if he only tried harder', or 'Needs to change her attitude.' It can lead to more and more repetitive hours of study which don't do much good, because the child is not capable of concentrating or remembering. It can be used to blame the parents for the child's behaviour and to deny the existence of biological learning and behaviour difficulties. Because this view advocates changes to curriculum, it can lead to a watered down, lowest-common-denominator curriculum, which is actually designed for slow learners.

Pros and cons of the Mechanistic view

The Mechanistic position is rather cut and dried, with one solution fitting one problem, but without much regard for the complex mysteries of nature. The positives of this view are that it isolates the exact brain chemical needed for better performance, and provides that chemical directly in the form of a pill. Unmanageable children instantly become placid and reasonable. Parents are given a break and children are able to concentrate and learn.

323

Three Views of Learning Difficulties - Part I

Three views of learning difficulties – Part I

Question	1. Behavioural	2. Mechanistic	3. Organic/ Integrative
Deficit: **What's missing?**	Desire / discipline	Neurotransmitters	Sensory integration
Input needed	Input study time	Input Speed / Ritalin	Input sensory activation
Cause: **At what level is the problem caused?**	Education	Genetics	Organic environment
Responsibility: **Who is causing it?**	Parents, schools	Nature, God	Society, government
Increase / decrease: **Will we see it increasing or decreasing, and why?**	Ought to be decreasing due to better education and parenting	Is increasing due to better medicine (sick people survive which weakens the gene pool)	Is on the rise due to increasing environmental toxins
What happens due to the deficit? / Why is the child not learning?	Child is not learning because he needs a different type of instruction	Child is not learning because the brain malfunctions unless given drugs	Child is not learning because fundamental function is not developed
Belief about system's potential for self-correction: **Why doesn't it fix itself?**	Child is wilful - naughty	Brain is fatally flawed and can only work if given chemicals	Brain / system is self-healing if given the right support
Implication for change	Child has ability to change response – just needs to try harder	Brain function is static. He will always have ADHD	Brain is plastic – constantly improving
			Continued on opposite page

- see opposite Page for part 2

Three views of learning difficulties - Part 2

Three views of learning difficulties - Part 2

Question	1. Behavioural	2. Mechanistic	3. Organic/ Integrative
Favoured point of intervention	'Carrot & stick'	Suppress symptom or behaviour	Support the system to effect self-repair of fundamental malfunction
What makes it work?	Practice builds brain's ability	Chemicals make the brain function	Sensory input builds neural network
System organisation	Repetition will change function	Malfunctions can be isolated and compensated for	Integration is the key to functioning
View of interdependence	Desire determines outcome	You have to isolate the specific problem in order to treat it	No malfunction can be treated in isolation
Treatment	Behaviour management	Drugs	Sensory input
Choice: How will we solve the problem?	Parenting classes – better curriculum	This couple will have no more children	Toxin free, sensory stimulating environment – more activity, less TV
Social implications	Outcome measures – test teacher effectiveness	Eugenics - Genetic manipulation	Clean up the environment
Ultimate social outcome	More and more behaviour / social control. Lowest common denominator rules the curriculum	Environmental causes not addressed, genes get more and more damaged	Change social values to work in harmony with natural ecosystem. Ecological instead of economic rationalism
Whose agenda does this view serve?	Avoids looking at the big picture, focus stays on individual, keeps society short-sighted.	Pharmaceutical interests, genetic researchers	Future generations
When would the problem first appear?	As a result of parenting or teacher influences	Conception	After vaccination or other environmentally induced trauma
Energy investment	Many hours of extra instruction	Taking pills is easy. Quick fix to make child manageable	On-going therapy, some of which is resource intensive
Negative side effects	Added struggle is hard for child	Loss of appetite, possible future depression, drug addiction	None

Blame is removed from the parents, the school and the child, and the behaviour is treated effectively with medication. Since this view sees causation as genetic, genetic counselling is important so that parents can decide to stop having children if they realise their genes are likely to keep reproducing the problem. Genetic research is handsomely supported so that solutions can be found in the future. Medication is easy to deliver, and because it is government subsidised, it is relatively cheap for the families.

The negatives of this paradigm — or philosophy — are the increasing dependence on synthetic substances. The drugs have side effects such as loss of appetite, decreased growth, tics, visual disturbances, nervousness, insomnia, depression, and psychotic-like symptoms. Because they solve the immediate problem, however, the more fundamental cause of poor neurological function is not addressed. Most families fail to seek out other forms of treatment, which could support better neurological integration, because the immediate crisis has been dealt with. The powerful pharmaceutical interests, which promote the use of medication, have a large influence on public knowledge through the media and the medical profession — which they use to denigrate other approaches. While public faith, interest and money are pushed into genetic research, the increasing health threat of environmental pollutants is being ignored.

Pros and cons of the Integrative/Organic view

The organic perspective stems from an appreciation of the intricate relatedness of biological systems which make up our natural environment. The benefit of this approach is that it supports our glorious natural inheritance — to be the best that we can be. By giving the right sensory and organo-chemical inputs, the body is nurtured to develop to its own supreme, natural balance. The level of vitality thus achieved, is higher and more fulfilling than that achieved by other means. The inputs are harmless, and in fact, have numerous unexpected benefits in addition to treating the presenting problem. For instance, in addition to treating learning problems, the spin-offs may be better energy, more nourishing sleep, and enhanced creativity, vitality and longevity.

The only negatives of this approach are presented as being a large investment of time and money into questionable and unproven treatments. In fact, no single treatment will entirely solve the problem. Some will work better than others for particular conditions, and it may take some months or years to fully reap the rewards of sensory integration therapies. The application of these methods does require a fair commitment, and a willingness to accept whatever improvements are achieved as another step in the right direction, rather than expecting the type of sudden and dramatic effects which may be seen with drugs. Conclusions on this should be drawn form experience, however, rather than whatever may be publicised by those who represent the more conservative, pharmaceutically-based interests.

A Sensory conclusion

This has been a great deal of sensory input, to enlighten you and give you a strong and resilient position if you choose to use supportive, life-enhancing therapies.

Make the right decision for you

We have shown you a broad perspective on signs of dysfunction so that you will notice them easily in a child in your care.

You have heard the argument for Sound Therapy, and understand its essential contribution to all sensory integration difficulties, as well as the benefits for enhanced performance of the highly accessible, home- based program.

By now you will have a 'gut feel' for early intervention, and recognise its importance if you are to gain the greatest leverage in treatment.

Catch problems early

Each type of sensory treatment has a certain leverage, depending on the child's particular needs; so it strengthens your stance if you are in a position to know where to access a range of sensory integration treatments.

It is important to weigh up the facts and come to a balanced position on medical/pharmaceutical treatment versus sensory integration, and how each will contribute to better learning and brain development.

Find the right balance

There are instances where you need to be able to 'smell a rat', and undertake your own investigations about the pollutants and invasive procedures which could be causing untold damage to your children.

327

Supporting health versus fighting disease

The philosophy of sensory integration has a different flavour to the standard medical approach, and you will now understand the difference between supporting and nurturing the natural development of the nervous system, versus covering symptoms for immediate manageability.

Sense for the future

Altogether, this input allows you, finally, to mull over and integrate the different angles and come to an intelligent, well-informed conclusion about learning and brain development; and how best to support your child to grow every day in talents, abilities, potential and creative expression, in this beautiful precious world of which we are the keepers.

You are your children's champion

Go forward, holding your love and hopes for your children like a beacon! With you championing them, they will give more to the world of their bold, fine vision, their un-jaded joy, as they sing for us all their songs of hope, happiness and profound, innocent wisdom.

Bibliography

'Dirty Secrets', *New Scientist,* Nov 1996, cited on www.avn.org.au 20/20 SHOW, ABC television, October 27, 1995.

Alexander, F.M. *The Use of the Self.* London:Victor Gollancz,1985.

American Psychiatric Association: *Diagnostic and Statistical Manual of Mental Disorders,* Fourth Edition, Text Revision. Washington, DC, American Psychiatric Association, 2000.

An Introduction to the Alexander Technique: 'The Head Leads and the Body Follows.' DVD, produced by In Such a Way, 1997. http://www.alexandertrust.org.uk/#projects

Arky, R. Physicians' Desk Reference. New Jersey 1996. 412-413, 674-675, 848-849, 856-857, 919-923, 1526-1527, 2474-2476, cited in Block, Ibid. 31.

Australian Vaccination Network www.avn.org.au

Bellak, L. 'Attention deficit hyperactivity disorder in adults,' *Clinical Therapeutics,* Vol. 14, No. 2, (1992) 138-147.

Bellis J. 'Subprofiles of CAPD.' www.angelfire.com/bc/capd/.

Benjamin, M. 'Autism, vaccine link considered', United Press International, 5/6/2003 2:59 PM www.upi.com/view.cfm?StoryID=20030505-123913-6672r

Block, M.A. *No More Ritalin.* New York: Kensington Books, ,1996.

Cameron, Oliver G. 'Interoception: The Inside Story — A Model for Psychosomatic Processes' *Psychosomatic Medicine* 63:697-710 (2001).

Carter, Rita, *Mapping the Mind,* London: Phoenix, 2002.

Centres for Disease Control and Prevention, 2003.

Christopher, J.R. Every Woman's Herbal. Quoting from: *The People's Doctor,* Vol.7, No. 11. 3. cited on http://educate-yourself.org/cn/2001/ultrasoundandbrain damage19dec01.shtml

Clark, Michael, interview conducted for video: 'Sound Therapy: Creating Enhanced Listening Around the World,' Sound Therapy International, 2003

Clements, Michele. 'Observations on certain aspects of neonatal behavior in response to auditory stimuli'. Paper presented to the 5th Internat. Congress of Psychosomatic Obstetrics and Gynecology, Rome, (1977).

Conners C.K. *Food additives and hyperactive children.* New York: Plenum Press, 1980, cited in Dengate, ibid.

Conners, C.K. *Feeding the Brain,* New York: Plenum Press, 1989.

Cosford, R. *The Mind of a Child* - conference summary, www.acnem.org/journal/19-1_april_2000/mind_of_a_child_conference.htm

Crumpler, Diana. *Chemical Crisis.* Newham, Australia: Scribe Publications, 1994.

Dart, R. 'The attainment of poise' *Sth. African Medical Journal.*, pp. 74-91, cited in Fjordbo, G. D., 'On the Development of Habit - from the viewpoint of the Alexander Technique and early neuromotor patterns of development.' Private Publication. Thesis submitted to the study-council for the Audiologopedic Studies at the University of Copenhagen, 1993.

Day, P. Cancer: *Why We're Still Dying to Know the Truth*, and *Health Wars.* UK: Credence 2001 http://www.credence.org/

Deliege and Sloboda, 1996, cited in Whitwell, Giselle. 'The Importance of Prenatal Sound and Music'. http://www.birthpsychology.com/lifebefore/sound1.html, 2004, found on http://www.birthpsychology.com/index.html

De Mause, L. *Foundations of psychohistory.* New York: Creative Roots, (1982), cited in Whitwell, ibid.

Dengate, Sue. *Different Kids. Growing up with Attention Deficit Disorder.* Sydney: Random House. 1994.

Dominique Oyston www.dominiqueoyston.com

Dr Russell Barkley. *Attention Deficit and Hyperactivity Disorder: A Handbook of Diagnosis and Treatment,* New York : Guilford Press, 1998. (cited in Dengate, ibid.)

Dulcan, M. 'Using stimulants to treat behavioural disorders of Children and Adolescents' *Journal of Child and Adolescent Psychopharmacology,* Vol 1, No. 1, (1990) 7-19.

Elia J, Ambrosini P. J., Rapoport J. L. 'Treatment of attention-deficit-hyperactivity disorder.' *NEJM* 1999; 340:780-788.

Epstein, S. *Unreasonable Risk: How to Avoid Cancer From Cosmetic and Personal Care Products: The Neways story,* Chicago: Environmental Toxicology, PO Box 11170, Chicago Illinois 60611, USA, 2001.

Federico, Gabreil F. 'Music Aids Development in the Womb', page http://www.birthpsychology.com/lifebefore/sound5.html , 2004, site address: http://www.birthpsychology.com/index.html

Fox, Mem. *Reading Magic.* Australia: Pan Macmillan, 2001.

Friere, P. *Pedagogy of the Oppressed,* Harmondsworth: Penguin, 1972.

Fridman, Ruth. 'The Maternal Womb: The First Musical School for the Baby' http://www.birthpsychology.com/lifebefore/sound2.html 2004, found on http://www.birthpsychology.com/index.html

Garlick, D. *The Lost Sixth Sense.* Sydney:The University of New South Wales, 1993.

Gilmour, P. 'Overview of the Tomatis Method,' in *About the Tomatis Method,* ed. Gilmour, et al. 18-21.

Gilmour, Timothy M. 'School Listening Training Programs.' in *About the Tomatis Method,* edited by Gilmour, T. M., Madaule, P. and Thompson, B. Toronto: The Listening Centre Press, 1989.

Goldman L. *Healthy From the Start.* Pew Environmental Health Commission. 1999.

Goldman L.R, and Koduru S.H. 'Chemicals in the environment and developmental toxicity to children: A public health and policy perspective.' *Environ Health Research;* 2000 108 (Suppl 3): 443-448.

Goldman L. S., Genel M., Bezman R.J. and Slanetz P.J. 'Diagnosis and treatment of attention-deficit/hyperactivity disorder in children and adolescents.' Council on Scientific Affairs, American Medical Association. *JAMA* 1998; 279:1100-7.

Green, C. and Chee, K. *Understanding ADH.* Sydney: Doubleday, 2001.

Greenfield, Susan. *The Human Brain.* London: Phoenix, 1997.

Hancock B. Cert. 'Vaccination, A Fatal Error' www.vaccination.inoz.com

Hilary, E. *Children of a Toxic Harvest.* Melbourne: Lothian, 1997.

Holt, John, *Freedom and Beyond.* New York: Dutton, 1972.

Holt, John, *How Children Learn.* New York: Dutton, 1970.

Howard, Damien, 'The Ear Troubles Kit,' http://www.eartroubles.com/ 2004.

http://ldam.org website of Learning Difficulties World Wide Inc.

Jaarsveld, P.E. and du Plessis, W.F. *Audio-psycho-phonology at Potchefstroom: A review.* Potchefstroom University of Higher Education, 1988.

Jacobson J.L., Jacobson S.W., Humphrey H.E. 'Effects of in utero exposure to polychlorinated biphenyls and related contaminants on cognitive functioning in young children.' *J Pediatr* 1990; 116:38-45.

Jacobson J.L., Jacobson S.W. 'Intellectual impairment in children exposed to polychlorinated biphenyls in utero.' *NEJM* 1996; 335:783-789.

Jacobvitz, D., et al 'Treatment of attentional and hyperactivity problems in children with sympathomimetic drugs: A comprehensive review article,' *Journal of the American Academy of Child and Adolescent Psychiatry,* Vol. 29, No. 5, (Sept. 1990).

Joseph, R. 'Emotional Trauma & Childhood Amnesia'. *Journal of Consciousness & Emotion,* 4 (2), 151-178, 2003.

Joudry, P. and Joudry, R. *Sound Therapy: Music to Recharge Your Brain.* Sydney: Sound Therapy International, 2000.

Kranowitz, Carol Stock. *The Out of Synch Child.* New York: Penguin.1998.

Lai T.J., Guo Y.L., Yu M.L., Ko H.C., Hsu C.C. 'Cognitive development in Yucheng children.' *Chemosphere* 1994; 29:2405-11.

Landrigan, P. J., and Slutsky, J. 'Are Learning Disabilities Linked to Environmental Toxins?' http://ldam.org/ldinformation/resources/O1-04 LDToxins.html cited on.

LeFever G.B., Dawson K.V., Morrow A.L. 'The extent of drug therapy for Attention Deficit-Hyperactivity Disorder among children in public schools.' *American Journal of Public Health.* 1999; 89:1359-1364.

Levinson, Harold. 'Thirty Five Years and 35,000 Patients Later,' in *The All in One guide to ADD and Hyperactivity,* eds Ali, Elvis et al. New York: Ages Publications, 2001.

Madaule, P. 'Listening Problems and the Young Child,' in *About the Tomatis Method,* edited by Gilmour, T. M., Madaule, P. and Thompson, B. Toronto: The Listening Centre Press, 1989.

Madaule, P. 'Music: An Invitation to Listening, Language and Learning,' in *About the Tomatis Method,* ed. Gilmour, et al.

Madaule, P. 'The Tomatis Method for Singers and Musicians,' in *About the Tomatis Method,* ed Gilmour et al.

Madaule, Paul, 'The Dyslexified World', in *About the Tomatis Method,* edited by Gilmour, T. M., Madaule, P. and Thompson, B. Toronto: The Listening Centre Press, 1989.

Matthews, R. 'Ultrasound Scans Linked to Brain Damage in Babies', *Journal of Epidemiology* (Dec 9, 2001) 12:618 http://educate-yourself.org/cn/2001/ultrasoundandbraindamage19dec01.shtml

Morgan, A.V.M. 'Listening and Learning Disability.' in *About the Tomatis Method,* edited by Gilmour, T. M., Madaule, P. and Thompson, B. Toronto: The Listening Centre Press, 1989.

Murooka et. al. 1976: DeCasper 1983: Rossner 1979. Cited in Whitwell, Giselle. 'The Importance of Prenatal Sound and Music'. http://www.birthpsychology.com/lifebefore/sound1.html , 2004, found on http://www.birthpsychology.com/index.html

National Academy of Sciences. *Toxicity Testing: Needs and Priorities.* Washington, DC: National Academy Press, 1984.

Needleman H.L., et al. 'Deficits in psychological and classroom performance of children with elevated dentine lead levels.' *New England Journal of Medicine.* 1979; 300:689-695.

Nicholson, R.I., et al. 'Association of abnormal cerebelar activation with motor learning difficulties in dyslexic adults.' *Lancet* 353, 9165: (1999) 1662-1667. http://www.shef.ac.uk/psychology/publications/individual/fawcett.html

Ostrander, S. and Schroeder, L. *Superlearning 2000.* New York: Delacorte Press, 1994.

Patandin, S., et al. 'Effects of environmental exposure to polychlorinated biphenyls and dioxins on cognitive abilities in Dutch children at 42 months of age'. *J Pediatr* 1999; 134:33-41.

Patandin, S., Lanting, C.I., Mulder, P.G., Boersma, E.R., Sauer, P.J., Weisglas-Kuperus, N. 'Effects of environmental exposure to polychlorinated biphenyls and dioxins on cognitive abilities in Dutch children at 42 months of age'. *J Pediatr* 1999; 134:33-41.

Pheloung, Barbara. *Help your child to Learn.* 2003, *Overcoming Learning Difficulties.* 1992 and *Help your Class to Learn.* 1997.

'Prevalence of Autism in Brick Township,' New Jersey, 1998: Community Report. *CDC.* April 2000.

Pujol, R., Lavigne-Rebillard, M., and Uziel, A. 'Development of the human cochlea.' *Acta Otolaryngologica,* 7-12. (1991) 482.

Purvis, Karen L. 'Phonological Processing, Not Inhibitory Control, Differentiates ADHD and Reading Disability,' *Journal of the American Academy of Child and Adolescent Psychiatry,* April 2000. http:www.findarticles.com

Rodier, P.M., Ingram, J.L., Tisdale, B., and Croog, V.J. 'Linking etiologies in humans and animal models: studies of autism.' *Reproductive Toxicology* 1997; 11:417-22.

Rodier, P.M., Ingram, J.L., Tisdale, B., Nelson, S., Romano, J. 'Embryological origin for autism: developmental anomalies of the cranial nerve motor nuclei.' *J Comp Neurology* 1996; 370:247-61.

Sacks, Oliver. *The Man Who Mistook His Wife For A Hat.* London: Picador, 1985.

Sanchez, M.O. and Acosta, A.M. 'Four Case Studies on the effect of Sound Therapy on subjects of the Resilience program.' Columbia: Paper for Sound Therapy International for Certificate Course, 2004.

Sasse, Margaret. *Tomorrow's Children.* Australia: GymbaROO, 2002.

Satt, B. J. 'An investigation into the acoustical induction of intra-uterine learning.' Ph.D Dissertation, Californian School of Professional Psychology, Los Angeles, (1984).

Schaffer, M. 'Children and toxic substances: confronting a major public health challenge.' *Environ. Health Perspect* 1998; 102 (Suppl. 2):155-15.6.

Scheibner, V. *Behavioural Problems in Childhood: The link to vaccination,* Blackheath, NSW: Scheibner, 2000. www.vaccination.inoz.com

Scheibner, V. Interview at Blackheath, transcribed by Rafaele Joudry. 2002.

Sears, B. *The Zone.* Harper Collins 1995, and *Mastering the Zone.* New York: Harper Collins. 1995. http://www.drsears.com

Shahidullah, S. and Hepper, P. 'Hearing in the fetus: Prenatal detection of deafness.' *International Journal of Prenatal and Perinatal Studies,* 4 (3 and 4), (1992), 235-240.

Sheil, Mary Lou and Dyson, Dr Marilyn, *SAMONAS Sound Therapy: Rationale and Results,* Private publication, 1996.

Sidlauskas, A. E. 'Language: the Ideas of Dr Alfred Tomatis,' *Revue Internationale D'audio-psycho-phonologie.* No 5 Special–April-May (1974).

Sidlauskas A. E. *The Phenomenon Of Language,* Ottawa: Child Studies Centre, The University of Ottawa.

Silva, P.A., Hughes, P., Williams, S., and Faed, J.M. 'Blood lead, intelligence, reading attainment, and behaviour in eleven year old children in Dunedin, New Zealand.' *J Child Psychol Psychiatry,* 1988; 29:43-52.

Society of Teachers of the Alexander Technique. http://www.stat.org.uk

Spirig, E. 'Dyslexia, Mental Deficiency and the Electronic Ear', IVth International Congress of Audio-Psycho-Phonology, Madrid, May 1974, translated by Jacques J. Waters, Child Study Centre, University of Ottawa.

Stehli, Annabel. *The Sound of a Miracle: A child's triumph over autism.* New York: Doubleday, 1991.

Stewart, P., Reihman, J., Lonky, E., Darvill, T., Pagano, J. 'Prenatal PCB exposure and neonatal behavioral assessment scale (NBAS) performance.' *Neurotoxicol Teratol* 2000; 22:21-9.

Strömland, K., Nordin, V., Miller, M., Akerström, B., Gillberg, C., 'Autism in thalidomide embryopathy: a population study.' *Developmental Medicine and Child Neurology* 1994; 36:351-356.

Szmeja et al. 1979, cited in Whitwell, Giselle. 'The Importance of Prenatal Sound and Music'. http://www.birthpsychology.com/lifebefore/sound1.html, 2004, found on http://www.birthpsychology.com/index.html

Thompson, B. M. 'Listening, the Basic, Basic We've Been Seeking', in *About the Tomatis Method.* edited by Gilmour, T. M., Madaule, P. and Thompson, B. Toronto: The Listening Centre Press, 1989.

Thomson GO, Raab GM, Hepburn WS, Hunter R, Fulton M, Laxen DP. 'Blood-lead levels and children's behavior-results from the Edinburgh Lead Study'. *J Child Psychol Psychiatry* 1989; 30:515-528.

Tomatis, A. A. *The Conscious Ear,* New York: Station Hill Press, 1977.

Tomatis, A. A. *The Ear and Language.* Phoenix: Moulin, 1996.

Uhlig, R. 'Ultrasound Scans May Harm Unborn Babies', *New Scientist,* Issue 1476 (10 June 1999)

'Vaccination: The Hidden Truth, Should we shoot first and ask questions later?' www.vaccination.inoz.com

Vinson, D. 'Therapy for attention deficit hyperactivity disorder;' *Archives of Family Medicine,* Vol 3, May 1994.

Volkow, Nora, et al, 'Is Methylphenidate like cocaine?' *Archives of General Psychiatry,* Vol. 52, (June 1995).

Weeks, B. S. 'The Therapeutic Effect of High Frequency Auditon and its Role in Sacred Music,' in *About the Tomatis Method,* edited by Gilmour, T. M., Madaule, P. and Thompson, B. Toronto: The Listening Centre Press, 1989.

Williams, R.S., Hauser, S.L., Purpura, D.P. DeLong, R., and Swischer, C.N. 1980. 'Autism and mental retardation: Neuropathologic studies performed in four retarded persons with autistic behaviour.' *Arch Neurol;* 37: 749-753.

Young, E. 'Controversial dyslexia treatment "works"'. NewScientist.com news service 16:59,05 (Nov 2002.) http://www.newscientist.com/news/news.jsp?id=ns99993012

Zametkin, A. J. *National Institute of Mental Health.* 1990, cited in Dengate, *Ibid.* 155.

Zentner, M. R. and Kagan, J. 'Infant's perception of consonance and dissonance in music'. *Infant Behavior and Development* 21(3), (1998), 483-492.

Appendix I

Onomatopoeic Words

Babble, bang, bark, bawl, bellow, bicker, blare, blather, bleat, bleep, blubber, bluster, boo, boom, bray, bubble, burp, buzz

Cackle, carol, caterwaul, caw, chatter, cheep, chide, chime, chuckle, clang, clamp, clap, clatter, click, clink, cluck, coo, crack, crackle, crash, creak, croak, crow, crunch, cuss

Dribble, drip, drivel, drone, drool, ding-dong,

Echo, explode

Fizz, flap, flop, flutter

Gasp, gargle, giggle, grate, grind, groan, growl, grumble, grunt, gurgle

Hiss, honk, hoot, howl, huff, hum

Jabber, jibe, jingle, jubilate

Knock

Lisp, low

Moan, mumble, mutter

Nag, natter, neigh

Ooze

Pant, patter, peal, plop, pound, prate, prattle, puff, purr, pop

Quack, quarrel

Rap, rasp, rattle, rejoice, ring, roar, rumble, rustle

Scrape, scratch, scream, screech, shriek, shuffle, sigh, sizzle, slam, slap, slosh, slump, smack, smash, snap, snarl, sneer, sneeze, sniff, snigger, snivel, snore, snort, sob, spit, splash, splutter, squeak, squeal, stamp, strum, stutter, suck, swish

Throb, thump, thunder, tick, tingle, toll, tootle, tremble, trickle, trill, twang, tweet, twitter

Wail, warble, wheeze, whimper, whine, whinny, whir, whisper, whistle, whoop, whoosh

Yap, yell, yodel

Zip

Appendix II

Sibilants for Voice Training with the Sonic Brain Activator

Socialisation
Espresso
Approximation
Succinctly
Suspicious
Susceptible
Assumption
Surreptitiously
Serendipitously
Sea shells
Oceanic
Extreme
Excessive
Sibilant
Suction
Psychedelic
Supercilious
Silly
Sandals
Opossum
Extrasensory perception
Spaghetti
Sandpiper
Brontosaurus
Tyrannosaurus
Psychology
Psychological
Sassafras
Stampede
Esoteric
Essendon
Specific
Necessarily
Necessity
Satisfaction

Stupendously
Fish and chips
Cheshire
Shashuna
Apostrophe
Apostle
Sociability
City to surf
Sans Souci
Sashimi
Sashay
Sanctimonious
Shoeshine

Appendix III

DSM IV diagnostic criteria for ADHD

The following is a modified version of the criteria for diagnosing ADHD contained in the Diagnostic & Statistical Manual for Mental Disorders (DSM-IV-TR) 2000.

The criteria presented here have been simplified somewhat in order to make them more accessible to the general public. These criteria should be used only by trained health care providers to diagnose or treat ADHD. They are listed here for information purposes only.

DSM-IV Criteria for ADHD

I. Either A or B:

A. Six or more of the following symptoms of inattention have been present for at least 6 months to a point that is disruptive and inappropriate for developmental level:

Inattention

1. Often does not give close attention to details or makes careless mistakes in schoolwork, work, or other activities.
2. Often has trouble keeping attention on tasks or play activities.
3. Often does not seem to listen when spoken to directly.
4. Often does not follow instructions and fails to finish schoolwork, chores, or duties in the workplace (not due to oppositional behavior or failure to understand instructions).
5. Often has trouble organizing activities.
6. Often avoids, dislikes, or doesn't want to do things that take a lot of mental effort for a long period of time (such as schoolwork or homework).
7. Often loses things needed for tasks and activities (e.g. toys, school assignments, pencils, books, or tools).
8. Is often easily distracted.
9. Is often forgetful in daily activities.

B. Six or more of the following symptoms of hyperactivity-impulsivity have been present for at least 6 months to an extent that is disruptive and inappropriate for developmental level:

Hyperactivity

1. Often fidgets with hands or feet or squirms in seat.
2. Often gets up from seat when remaining in seat is expected.

339

3. Often runs about or climbs when and where it is not appropriate (adolescents or adults may feel very restless).
4. Often has trouble playing or enjoying leisure activities quietly.
5. Is often "on the go" or often acts as if "driven by a motor".
6. Often talks excessively.

Impulsivity

1. Often blurts out answers before questions have been finished.
2. Often has trouble waiting one's turn.
3. Often interrupts or intrudes on others (e.g., butts into conversations or games).
II. Some symptoms that cause impairment were present before age 7 years.
III. Some impairment from the symptoms is present in two or more settings (e.g. at school/work and at home).
IV. There must be clear evidence of significant impairment in social, school, or work functioning.
V. The symptoms do not happen only during the course of a Pervasive Developmental Disorder, Schizophrenia, or other Psychotic Disorder. The symptoms are not better accounted for by another mental disorder (e.g. Mood Disorder, Anxiety Disorder, Dissociative Disorder, or a Personality Disorder).

Based on these criteria, three types of ADHD are identified:

1. ADHD, *Combined Type*: if both criteria 1A and 1B are met for the past 6 months
2. ADHD, *Predominantly Inattentive Type*: if criterion 1A is met but criterion 1B is not met for the past six months
3. ADHD, *Predominantly Hyperactive-Impulsive Type*: if Criterion 1B is met but Criterion 1A is not met for the past six months.

American Psychiatric Association: *Diagnostic and Statistical Manual of Mental Disorders,* Fourth Edition, Text Revision. Washington, DC, American Psychiatric Association, 2000.

Sound Therapy International

Where to find an Independent Distributor

Australia
Australian Capital Territory

Chris Galvin
ACT
Phone: 02 6259 5583
Mobile: 0407 893 446
Email: cgalvin@webone.com.au

New South Wales
Ken Bailey
Merewether NSW 2291
Phone: 02 4963 2411
Email: kenbailey@hotkey.net.au

Marilyn Bodnar
Naturopath and Bowen Practitioner
Heckenberg NSW 2168
Phone: 02 9825 0078
Mobile: 0410 627 556
Email: mbodnar@optushome.com.au

Catherine Bull
Holistic Remedial Practitioner
Energetic Healer
Sydney, NSW
Mobile: 0408 492 011
Email: catandbull@ozemail.com.au

Dr. Robyn Cosford
Northern Beaches Care Centre
Mona Vale NSW 2103
Phone: 02 9979 9444

Merryl Cobbin
Central Coast & Newcastle NSW 2265
Phone: (02) 4977 1225
Mobile: 0402 489 740
Email: cobbinco@hunterlink.net.au

Lynley Gibson
Reiki Master
St George-Sutherland
Sydney NSW 2218
Phone: 02 9588 2175

Robert Hampton
Servicing Newcastle, Hunter Valley
and Lower North Coast
PO Box 85, East Maitland NSW 2323
Mobile: 0407 244 868
Email: cropdoc@bigpond.com

Marilyn Martin
Reflexologist & Holistic Health
Practitioner
Belfield NSW 2191
Home: 02 9642 5328
Mobile: 0412 244 735
Email: marilynm@netspace.net.au

Anca Ramsden
Pyschologist
North Shore, Sydney 2064
Phone: 02 9418 3695
Mobile: 0414 414 286
Email:
anca@neuro-psychotherapy.com

Narelle Russell

Practitioner of Natural Therapies
Personally experienced improvement
in hearing, memory, coordination and
tinnitus
Far South Coast NSW
Phone: 02 64 936 567
Mobile: 0438 336 567
Email: narelle@acr.net.au

Dr. Viera Scheibner

Author of two books:
Vaccination
Behavioural Problems in Childhood:
The Link to Vaccination
Tel: 02 4787 8203
Fax: 02 4787 8988

Eldin Seif

Physiotherapist & Naturopath
1A Dover Street, Eastwood NSW
2122
Phone: 02 9887 3441
Mobile: 0411 477 902
Email: eldin@ozemail.com.au

Kevin Tibbey

Tea Gardens NSW 2324
Phone: 02 4997 1566
Email: kevin.tibbey@bigpond.com

Rustam Yumash

Mind/Body Therapist
Tweed Heads, NSW 2485
Phone: 07 5599 2220
Fax: 0413181147
Email:
r.yumash@solstice-indmatters.com.au

Victoria

Barbara Adamson

Advanced Bowen Therapist and
Nutritionist
Balwyn VIC 3103
Phone: 03 9817 1949
Fax: 03 9817 5878
Email: adamson7@austarmetro.com.au

Roslyn Boyar

Caulfield South VIC 3162
Phone: 03 9532 9228
Mobile: 0412 344 474
Email: rosboyar@hotmail.com

Peter Glynn

Glen Waverly VIC 3150
Home: 03 9561 7372
Work: 03 9803 7520

Tina Impey

Educational Kinesiologist
Brain Gym Instructor/Consultant
RN Div 1
Flower & Shell Essence Practitioner
Gordon, VIC 3345
Phone: 03 5368 9475
Email: tanji@iinet.net.au

Helen Milbourne

Childrens Remedial Education
Specialist
Albury/Wodonga VIC 3690
Phone: 02 6024 4464

Ian Patterson

Glen Iris VIC 3146
Phone: 03 9885 3906
Mobile: 0407 352 447

Sylvia Dawn Callander

6/606 Nepean Highway,
Bonbeach VIC 3196
Phone: 03 9773 1805

Margaret Yarnton
Natural Therapist
SE Victoria
Phone: 03 5668 1561
Email: myarnton@vic.australis.com.au

Tasmania
Don Morgan
Primary Tasmanian Distributor
81 Tara Drive
Acton Park, TAS 7170
Phone: 03 6248 1567
Email: cogohelp@bigpond.com

Queensland
Ron Bassett
Sunshine Coast QLD 4551
Phone: 0409 711 728
Email: barks@squirrell.com.au

Mary-Ellen Bidner
Phone: 07 46 388483

Jan Burguez
Springhill, Queensland
Phone: 07 3257 3040
Email: J.Burguez@bigpond.com

Lynette Jones
Reflexologist
North Brisbane, QLD
Phone: 07 5497 4521
Mobile: 0401 651 049
Email: lynettej@microed.com.au

Rev. Sarsha Gale Carpenter
Northern NSW and SE QLD
Paradise Point 4216
Home: 07 5529 6197
Mobile: 0414 914 197
Email: sarsha@reversespeech.com

Barbara Gilsenan
Atherton QLD 4883
Phone: 07 4091 5929
Fax: 07 4091 6171

Les Hills
South Queensland
Sunshine Healing Haven
Kalbar QLD 4309
Phone: 07 5463 7050
Email:
sunshinehealinghaven@hotmail.com

Gayle Marcussen
79 – 91 Simmental Drive
Tamborine QLD 4270
Phone: 07 5543 6049/3859 5676
Mobile: 0438 280 173
Email: specialtybooks@iprimus.com.au

Klaus Rennebarth
Hill End QLD 4101
Phone: 07 3844 6988
Email: shiatsuman@bigpond.com

Kay Whitley
Caboolture QLD 4510
Phone: 07 5495 2461

Darryl Smith
72b Amersham St
Kipparing QLD 4021
Phone: 07 3283 8262
Mobile: 0418 732 677
Email: darryl@mydeepblue.com

Kay Ritson
Harmony Centre for Natural
Therapies
PO Box 2180 GAILES QLD 4300
Phone: 07 3818 6766
Email: harmonyk@bigfoot.com

Dr. Thomas Bige
Life Beyond 2000 Health Clinic
Broadbeach QLD 4218
Phone/Fax: 07 5573 3598
Email: drbige@naturesarmy.com

Carol King
(Carol's Centre for Natural Healing)
Albany Creek QLD 4035
Phone: 07 3264 7221
Mobile: 0428 881 626
Email: cmking01@bigpond.net.au

Vivienne Williams
Occupational Therapist
Brisbane QLD
Phone: 07 3278 1078
Mobile: 0405 679 849
Email: sijourneys@uqconnect.net

Western Australia
Hilary Peart
Sound Therapy WA
Perth, Western Australia
Phone: 08 9343 2758
Email:
soundtherapywa@optusnet.com.au

Janet Alexander
Palmyra WA 6157
Phone: 08 9319 1166

Bernice Brown
Lynwood WA 6147
Phone: 08 9350 9545
Email: berniceb@iinet.net.au

Simone Collins
Kensington WA 6151
Mobile: 0411 474 450
Email: organist@iinet.net.au

Jeanette Mackay
Darlington WA 6070
Phone: 08 9299 7416
Email: jeanette@upnaway.com

Clara Rapp
7 Yeldon Tor, Winthrop WA 6150
Phone (w): 08 9262 1190/92
Phone (h): 08 9310 6133
Mobile: 0423 323 707
Email: grapp@iprimus.com.au

Northern Territory
Helen Summers
4/9 Keith Lane, Fannie Bay, Darwin NT
Phone: 08 8981 1399
Mobile: 0412 613 450
Email: helensummers@octa4.net.au

South Australia
Judith Booth
Morpett Vale, SA 5162
Phone: 0412 376 112
Email: jbooth@boothtransport.com

Udita Simon
Glenalta
Phone: 08 8178 0145
Mobile: 0414 216 283
Email: uditasimon@yahoo.com

Linda Schache
Nutritionist and Life Coach
Adelaide
Phone: 08 855 77 668
Email: lindavivien@yahoo.com

New Zealand

Suzanne B Abel
Vision & Learning Consultant
PO Box 17469
Greenlane, New Zealand, 1005
Phone: 021 139 66 49
Email: eyecan@maxnet.co.nz

Louise Cullen
PO Box 1172, Hastings,
New Zealand
Phone: 00 11 64 6 873 5956
Fax: 00 11 64 6 873 5976
Email: louise@inhbco.nz

Val Parker
Fairlie, South Canterbury, New
Zealand
Phone: 0011 643 685 8491

Nans Stolk
Counsellor
135 Brook St, Nelson, New Zealand
Phone: 0011 64 3 546 6212
Email: nanzie@xtra.co.nz

USA

Norma Anders
H & A Enterprise
Long Beach, California 90804 USA
Phone/Fax: 00 11 1 562 597 0424
Email: thekid2@gte.net

Dede Farrell
PO Box 12072, Portland, Oregon
97212
Phone: 00 11 1 503 288 5846
Email: starlady144@qwest.net
Website:
www.soundtherapyoregon.com

Pohara Joy S Heart
Serving Northern California (and
beyond)
Phone: 00 11 1(888) 861-2758
Email: soundtherapyusa@aol.com

Michael Purcell
Feldenkrais Practitioner
Grass Valley CA. 95949
Phone: 0011 1 530 274 1164/9977
Fax: 0011 530 274 1164
Email: mppurcell@aol.com

Tys Dammeyer
Ever Free Company
San Diego Area, California
Phone: 00 11 1 (619) 274-0326
Toll Free: (877) 231 6685 (US only)
Email: tys@everfreeco.com

Indonesia

Joseph Tardjan
Jakarta
Email: protons@rad.net.id

INDEX

Entries in **bold** refer to major references. Entries in *italics* refer to diagrams.

A

Aboriginal children 115
Accelerated learning 107
ADD *see* ADHD
Additives in food 268-270
ADHD / ADD (Attention Deficit and Hyperactivity Disorder) 9, **70-72**, 124-125, 63, **175-183**, 209-210
   adults 179-180
   Alexander Technique for 146-147
   & auditory processing 71-72
   'behavioural view' 16-17, 323, 324-325
   behaviour problems 182-183, 209-210
   & the brain 71
   cause 178
   common behaviours 14-15
   Conduct Disorder (CD) 180-181
   denial 175-176, 178
   diagnosis 176-177
   diet 265-281
   discipline 182-183
   drugs 281-287
   & dyslexia 299
   foods to watch out for 271-274
   gender 176
   gifted children & adults with ADHD 178-179
   'growing out of it' 179
   history 161, 175
   'integrative/organic view' 19-21, 324-325, 326-327
   'mechanistic view' 18-19, 323-326
   medication 18, 19
   Oppositional Defiance Disorder (ODD) 180
   practical action tips 209-210
   recognising ADHD 175
   & schooling 17
   solutions 181-183
   Sonic Brain Activator 91-93
   & Sound Therapy 6-7, 72-73
   symptoms 176
   terminology 175
   treatment 181-182
   toxins 19-21, 263-264
   tutoring 181
   see also Listeners' experiences of Sound Therapy 215-260
   see also Sensory Integration Dysfunction
Adults
   with ADHD 179-180
   with learning disorders 161
Alexander, F.M. 146
Alexander Technique 146-147
Allergies 10
   additives 268-270
   food allergies 271-274
   vs. intolerances 279-280
Amines 272
Annatto 268
Antibiotics 283
Anxiety 124-125
   Sonic Brain Activator 91-93
   Sound Therapy research 310-312
Apraxia 113
Asperger's syndrome 10, 78, 164, **184-185**
   handling children with 211-212
   see also Autism, Autism Spectrum Disorders
Attention Deficit and Hyperactivity Disorder *see* ADHD
Auditory processing 69-70, 137-138
   & ADHD 71-72
   auditory associative deficit 165
   decoding deficit 165
   disorder / dysfunction 9, 133

The Next Step

The great gift of **Patricia and Rafaele Joudry's Sound Therapy** is that it not only informs you about the harmful and healing effects of sound, it gives you an easy and efficient way of applying this knowledge in your own family. The self-help Sound Therapy program is simple to use and easily fits into the routine of most families. Your child can listen after school, at bed time, during quiet activities or when travelling in the car.

Along with the other methods discussed in this book, **Sound Therapy** is a cost effective, convenient way of helping your children to develop good auditory processing and lay down a strong foundation for learning.

✪ The next page contains ordering details for the Sound Therapy tapes and additional resources.

Our range of listening programs is tailored to suit a variety of families. Should you have any further questions, one of our consultants at **Sound Therapy International** will be pleased to speak with you and advise you over the phone. We can help you to decide which program would best suit your family's needs. Or you may prefer to contact one of our independent distributors, listed on the earlier pages.

Sound Therapy International Pty Ltd
92 Maloney St, Rosebery NSW 2018 Australia
Phone (Aust) 1300 55 77 96
Tel: Intl: (+612) 9317 3799
Fax: (Intl +612) (Aust 02) 9317 3499
Email: info@soundtherapyinternational.com
Website: www.soundtherapyinternational.com

Sound Therapy
INTERNATIONAL Pty Ltd

EXPRESS ORDER FORM
for Children's Sound Therapy Programs
First time listener starter packs. To make ordering easy.

THE COMPLETE CHILDRENS PROGRAM

Family Kit	10 hours of music and stories	$589.00
Childrens Nutrients for the Ears	Minerals & vitamins	$76.00
Basic Portable Player	With mini earphones	$119.00
Leather Carry Pouch	**Value $22.00**	$15.00
Nutrition for the Ear Booklet	**Value $6.00**	FREE
Video:VHS__ or DVD __	**Value $19.95**	FREE
3 Progress Consultations by phone	**Value $150.00**	FREE
Listening Helps Learning Booklet		FREE
	Product Value $1,000.00 -- NOW ONLY	**$799.00**
	Express Postage & Handling	$22.00
	Total (Australian $ inc GST)	**$821.00**

THE ECONOMY PROGRAM

Basic Music Kit	6 hours of music	$399.00
Basic Portable Player	With mini earphones	$119.00
Listening Helps Learning Booklet		FREE
	Product total	**$518.00**
	Express Postage & Handling	$16.50
	Total (Australian $ inc GST)	**$534.50**

Shipping for international orders will be charged at actual rates

PLEASE SEND ME:

Complete Program ☐   **Economy Program** ☐ TOTAL $_____

Name:_____

Address:_____

Post code:_____   Email:_____

Phone:(   )_____   Fax:(   )_____

Where did you hear about Sound Therapy?_____

PLEASE DEBIT MY: MASTERCARD ___ BANKCARD ___ VISA CARD ___

CARD NUMBER_____/_____/_____/_____

EXPIRY DATE:____/____ SIGNATURE_____

PLEASE FIND ENCLOSED: CHEQUE ___ MONEY ORDER ___

Independent Distributor

Sound Therapy
INTERNATIONAL Pty Ltd

Sound Therapy International Pty Ltd
92 Maloney St, Rosebery NSW 2018, Australia
Phone (Aust) 1300 55 77 96
Ph: Intl:(+ 612) 9317-3799
Fax: (intl +612) (Aust 02) 9317-3499
Email: info@soundtherapyinternational.com
Website: www.soundtherapyinternational.com

PRICES ARE ACCURATE AT TIME OF PRINTING.SEE WEBSITE FOR UPDATES

ORDER FORM & CATALOGUE FOR CHILDREN'S SOUND THERAPY
See also Express Order Form

BOOKS	Postage due		Price	Qty	Price
Sound Therapy : Music to Recharge your Brain by Patricia Joudry and Rafaele Joudry	$5.50		$24.95		
Triumph over Tinnitus by Rafaele Joudry	$5.50		$21.95		
Why aren't I Learning? By Rafaele Joudry	$5.50		$19.95		
LISTENING PROGRAMS					
Basic Music Kit for adults or children — Six hours of filtered music	$11.00		$399.00		
Family Kit for adults or children ages 3 -12 — Ten hours of filtered music and stories at 8.5% discount	$11.00		$589.00		
Older Childrens Starter Kit for ages 8 to 12 — Five hours of filtered music and stories at 7% discount	$7.50		$299.00		
Younger Childrens Starter Kit for ages 3 to 7 — Two and a half hours of filtered music and stories at 7% discount	$11.00		$149.00		
EQUIPMENT					
Basic portable player (price subject to change)	$7.50		$119.00		
Deluxe portable player (call for current price and availability)	$7.50		POA		
Leather Carry Pouch	$5.50		$22.00		
Sound Therapy Video - VHS ___ or DVD ___	$5.50		$19.95		
Listening Helps Learning Children's Booklet			$2.00		
Cancer Causing Chemicals Booklet			$6.95		
NUTRIENTS FOR THE EARS					
Colloidal Minerals for adults or children	$7.50		$48.25		
Children's Chewable Vitamin & Mineral Tablets	$5.50		$37.15		
Children's Nutrients for the Ears and Brain Includes both of the above at 10% discount	$11.00		$76.00		
Non-Toxic Family Bathroom Pack	$11.00		$99.00		
Express Postage & Handling Sub-total			**Sub-total**		
International orders - shipping will be charged at actual rates	**P&H total--** *(Maximum $30.00 in Aust.)*				

Name:_____ **Total** (Aust.$)

Address:_____

Post code:_____ Email:_____

Phone:( )_____ Fax:( )_____

Where did you hear about Sound Therapy?_____

PLEASE DEBIT MY: MASTERCARD ___ BANKCARD ___ VISA CARD ___

CARD NUMBER_____/_____/_____/_____

EXPIRY DATE:_____/_____ SIGNATURE:_____

PLEASE FIND ENCLOSED: CHEQUE ___ MONEY ORDER ___

Independent Distributor

Sound Therapy International Pty Ltd
92 Maloney St, Rosebery NSW 2018, Australia
Phone (Aust) 1300 55 77 96
Ph: Intl:(+ 612) 9317-3799
Fax: (intl +612) (Aust 02) 9317-3499
Email: info@soundtherapyinternational.com
Website: www.soundtherapyinternational.com

PRICES INCLUDE 10% GST AND ARE ACCURATE AT TIME OF PRINTING. SEE WEBSITE FOR UPDATES